Precalculus Mathematics

MERRILL MATHEMATICS SERIES

ERWIN KLEINFELD, *Editor*

Precalculus Mathematics

F. Lane Hardy

Armstrong State College

CHARLES E. MERRILL BOOKS, INC., COLUMBUS, OHIO

Library of Congress Catalog Card Number: 67-14217

PRINTED IN THE UNITED STATES OF AMERICA

1 2 3 4 5 6 7 8 9 10 11 12 13 14 15-76 75 74 73 72 71 70 69 68 67

Preface

As the title implies, this text has been designed to provide sufficient mathematical background for a student to undertake a standard calculus sequence. The book is not intended to be a remedial work; the student is expected to have some acquaintance with real numbers and with elementary geometry. It is not assumed that the reader knows any trigonometry or coordinate geometry.

Until recently, texts available to meet the needs for which the present one is intended were the traditional algebra-trigonometry texts. Since the admirable work of the School Mathematics Study Group, more modern efforts have appeared. Some of these have produced a wealth of new notation without producing a corresponding increase in understanding of the concepts involved. In fact, it is my opinion that the present trend in elementary mathematics has produced many extremes—reaction to which is now beginning to be felt.* It seems reasonable to believe that there is a middle ground towards which one may aim for the most effective communication with his students. This is what I have tried to do in this text.

Generally, I have tried to adhere to the rule that a topic is not included if it cannot be justified for calculus. Although, strictly speaking, some of the included topics cannot meet this test, they nevertheless have been construed as lending additional practice in ideas which are definitely essential to calculus. Analytic geometry has been included so that a calculus text which does not include this topic may be used. An asterisk (*) has been used to mark those topics which might be considered nonessential for calculus and also to mark some topics which may be left to a calculus course.

Because of the purpose of this text, the guiding theme throughout has been functions and their graphical representation. In Chapter 1, functions and their graphs are introduced in a general setting, and then more special real functions are considered in subsequent chapters.

I wish to express my appreciation to Dr. Walter B. Laffer II, of Armstrong College, and to Professor H. E. Hall, of DeKalb Junior College, both of whom read parts of the manuscript and made valuable suggestions. I also gratefully acknowledge the many helpful discussions with my former colleague Professor B. K. Youse of Emory University. The encouragement received from Professor Erwin Kleinfeld was most beneficial. Special thanks go to Mrs. Magali R. Overman for her excellent typing.

Comments, criticisms, and suggestions are most welcome.

F. Lane Hardy
Savannah, Georgia

---

* See, for example, R. C. Buck, "Goals for Mathematics Instruction," *American Mathematical Monthly*, November, 1965.

Table of Contents

Chapter 2

The Real Numbers **27**

Chapter 3

Real Relations, Functions, and Their Graphs **51**

Chapter 4

Polynomial Functions **89**

Chapter 5

The Trigonometric Functions **129**

For

Knolie, Pole, and Phodal Knut

1

Sets

Of fundamental importance in the study of mathematics is the theory of sets. For the purposes of this book we require only the language of sets and, in this chapter, we set forth the language of sets which will be useful throughout the remainder of this exposition.

1.1 Notation and Terminology

Our concept of set is that of many things conceived as a single object. For example, we think of Mr. and Mrs. Jones, John, and Jane (their children) as the Jones family. (The term "family" is sometimes used as a synonym for "set.") Also, we think of certain individual advisors to the President collectively and call this group the cabinet. Such terms as "family," "team," "group," "duo," etc. suggest the common use of the set concept.

We shall use the words "set" and "collection" interchangeably, and the individuals which comprise a set or collection will be called the *members* of the set. In the examples above, Mrs. Jones is a member of the Jones family, and the Postmaster is a member of the cabinet.

The customary practice of naming or denoting sets by capital letters and members of sets by lower case letters will be followed here. Usually Latin letters will be employed: $A, B, C, \ldots$ will be used for sets and $a, b, c, \ldots$ for members of sets. As a shorthand notation for the phrase "a is a member of the set A," we use the symbolism

$$a \in A$$

—the symbol "$\in$" standing for the phrase "is a member of." In case a is not a member of set A, we write

$$a \notin A.$$

A common method of specifying or describing a set is to tabulate its members or elements. The set that we call the Jones family is described by its members: Mr. and Mrs. Jones, John, Jane. Similarly, we specify the President's cabinet by listing its members: Secretary of State, Secretary of the Treasury, Secretary of Defense, Attorney General, Postmaster General, Secretary of the Interior, Secretary of Agriculture, etc. When this method is used to describe a set, it is common practice to enclose the list of members in brackets. As an example of this, we say that the Jones family is

$$\{\text{Mr. Jones, Mrs. Jones, John, Jane}\}.$$

Generally, if $a, b, c, \ldots$ are members and the only members, of a set A, we write

$$A = \{a, b, c, \ldots\}.$$

We read this: "the set A is the set whose members are $a, b, c, \ldots$"

Quite often it is not practical to list or tabulate all members of a set. This will always be the case when a large number of objects is involved. In such cases an alternative procedure for specifying the set is to use a property which the members of the set share. Rather than list all colleges in the U.S., for example, we describe the set by the property: "is a college in the U.S." In other words, we speak of the set whose members are colleges of the U.S. Symbolically, we express this using the bracket notation as follows:

$$\{x \mid x \text{ is a college in the U.S.}\}.$$

We read this: "the set of all objects, say x, such that x is a college in the U.S." There is obviously nothing special about the use of the letter "x" here, and any other letter of the alphabet would have served just as well. If P stands for any property whatever, we express the fact that an object, say a, has property P by writing $P(a)$. For example, P may be the property: "is a whole number." Then $P(10)$ expresses the fact that 10 is a whole number. We can then, for each such property P, describe a set:

$$\{x \mid P(x)\}$$

i.e., the set of *all* objects, say x, having the property P. If P is the property "is a whole number," then $\{x \mid P(x)\}$ describes the collection of whole numbers.

Example 1-1. The set whose members are 1, 2, 3 is denoted by "$\{1, 2, 3\}$" and also by "$\{y \mid y$ is one of the first three whole numbers$\}$" and also by "$\{x \mid x$ is 1 or x is 2 or x is 3$\}$." The statements "$1 \in \{1, 2, 3\}$" "$2 \in \{1, 2, 3\}$" and "$3 \in \{1, 2, 3\}$" are true, while "$4 \in \{1, 2, 3\}$" is false.

Example 1-2. Suppose that $P(x)$ expresses the fact that x is a number, and that $x^2 = 1$. Then "$\{x \mid P(x)\}$" describes the set $\{1, -1\}$.

DEFINITION. The sets A, B are the *same* or *equal* provided their members are the same. This is expressed by "$A = B$."

From our definition of equal sets, we have that $\{1, 2, 3\}$ is the same set as $\{y \mid y$ is one of the first three whole numbers$\}$ and also that

$$\{1, -1\} = \{x \mid x \text{ is a number and } x^2 = 1\}.$$

It should be emphasized that *a set and its members are distinct from each other.* This, no doubt, is obvious for sets of more than one member, but is equally true for sets of only one member: The set whose only member is 8; i.e. $\{8\}$, is not the same as 8. Generally, $\{a\} \neq a$ for any object a. Sets of only one element are sometimes called *singletons* or *unit sets.*

Consider the sets $A = \{t \mid t$ is a triangle$\}$ and $B = \{r \mid r$ is a right triangle$\}$. It is clear that every member of B is in particular a triangle, and hence, a member of A. Another way of saying this is: "if $x \in B$, then $x \in A$." This relation between the sets A, B may be expressed by saying that "B is a subset of A."

DEFINITION. A set B is said to be a *subset* of set A provided every member of B is a member of A.

If B is a subset of A, this is symbolically expressed by writing "$B \subseteq A$." Thus, we have

$B \subseteq A$ if and only if every member of B is a member of A, or
$B \subseteq A$ if and only if $x \in B$ implies $x \in A$.

From our definition of equality for sets (they have the same members) and our definition of subset, we conclude that

$$(^*)\ A = B \text{ if and only if } A \subseteq B \text{ and } B \subseteq A.$$

Example 1-3. Let $P(x)$ express: "x is a triangle of Euclidean geometry and the sum of the interior angles of x is 180°," and let $Q(y)$ express: "y is a triangle of Euclidean geometry." Then if $A = \{x \mid P(x)\}$ and $B = \{y \mid Q(y)\}$, we have $A = B$. This is easily established by using $(^*)$ above, and observing that $A \subseteq B$ and $B \subseteq A$. It is clear that every member of A is a member of B so that $A \subseteq B$; and also, since in Euclidean geometry *every* triangle has an angle sum of 180°, $B \subseteq A$.

Example 1-4. If we insist that every property P defines a set, we are led to the conclusion that there are sets having no elements. Consider, for example, the property $P(x)$: "x is a triangle of Euclidean geometry having angle sum less then 180°." Then the set $\{x \mid P(x)\}$ has no elements since there are no objects having the property in question. One can think of many properties of this kind. The role of this set which has no elements is analogous to that of the number zero; this analogy will become clearer as we proceed. We call such a set a *null set,* and use the symbol "$\varnothing$" to denote any such set. As an immediate consequence of our definition of subset, we have

$$\varnothing \subseteq X \text{ for all sets } X.$$

This is true because there are *no* elements of $\varnothing$ which are *not* in X. This also shows that there can be only one null set since if $\varnothing_1$, $\varnothing_2$ are both null sets, then $\varnothing_1 \subseteq \varnothing_2$ and $\varnothing_2 \subseteq \varnothing_1$ from the above, and hence by $(^*)$ $\varnothing_1 = \varnothing_2$.

Exercises

1. Use appropriate definitions to justify the truth or falsity of each of the following:
   (a) $\{1, 2, 8\} \subseteq \{x \mid x \text{ is a whole number}\}$.
   (b) $\{w \mid w \text{ is a whole number}\} \subseteq \{1, 2, 8\}$.
   (c) $\{1, 2, 8\} = \{y \mid y \text{ is a whole number}\}$.

2. Let Y be a particular point in a plane, and let

$$A = \{c \mid c \text{ is a circle of radius 4, 6, or 8, and center at } Y\}$$
$$B = \{d \mid d \text{ is a circle of radius 4, 6 or 8}\}.$$

(a) How many members has set A?
(b) How many members has set B?
(c) Which of the statements $A \subseteq B$, $B \subseteq A$, $A = B$ are true?

3. Denote by W the set whose members are letters of the Latin alphabet: $a, b, c, \ldots$ Let V denote the vowels.
(a) Which of the statements below are true?

(i) $V \subseteq W$. (ii) $W \subseteq V$. (iii) $W = V$.

(b) If $Q = \{y \mid y$ is a letter of the word "algebra"$\}$, discuss the following statements:

(i) $Q \subseteq V$. (ii) $Q \subseteq W$. (iii) $Q = \{r, g, l, b, e, a\}$.

4. (a) If $X = \{\varnothing, \{\varnothing\}\}$, discuss the following statements:

(i) $\varnothing \subseteq X$. (ii) $\varnothing \in X$. (iii) $\{\varnothing\} \in X$. (iv) $\{\varnothing\} \subseteq X$.

(b) If $X = \{\varnothing\}$, discuss the statements in (a).
(c) With $X = \varnothing$ discuss the statements in (a).

5. Prove that if W is a set, $W \subseteq W$.

6. (a) If $A = \{1, 2\}$, how many subsets does A have?
(b) If $A = \{1, 2, 3\}$, how many subsets does A have?
(c) Can you guess the number of subsets of a set of 4 elements? Of 5?

7. From the definition of subset, show that $\{a\} \subseteq A$ if, and only if, $a \in A$.

8. Let A, B, C denote sets.
(a) Prove that if $A \subseteq B$ and $B \subseteq C$, then $A \subseteq C$.
(b) Prove that if $A \subseteq B$, $B \subseteq C$ and $C \subseteq A$, then $A = B = C$.

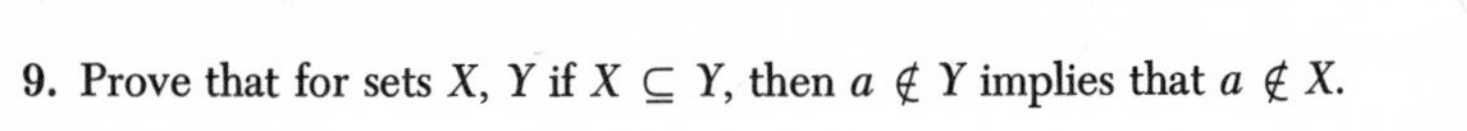

9. Prove that for sets X, Y if $X \subseteq Y$, then $a \notin Y$ implies that $a \notin X$.

1.2 Union, Intersection, Complement

If one starts with sets A, B, there are several ways of describing sets in terms of A and B. The sets so described will sometimes be different from both A and B and thus produce for us new sets. Two such descriptions are embodied in the following definitions.

DEFINITION. Let A, B denote sets.

(a) The *union* of A, B is $\{y \mid y \in A \text{ or } y \in B\}$.
(b) The *intersection* of A, B is $\{q \mid q \in A \text{ and } q \in B\}$.

The word "or" as used in the definition of union is used in its *inclusive* sense; i.e., the statement "$y \in A$ or $y \in B$" is true if and only if either *one* or *both* of the statements "$y \in A$", "$y \in B$" is true. The word "or" will consistently be used in this way.

The notation commonly used for union and intersection is "$\cup$" and "$\cap$" respectively; i.e.,

$$A \cup B = \{t \mid t \in A \text{ or } t \in B\}$$

and

$$A \cap B = \{r \mid r \in A \text{ and } r \in B\}.$$

Example 1-5. For the sets $A = \{1, 2, 3\}$, $B = \{3, 4, 5\}$, we have $1 \in (A \cup B)$ since it is true that $1 \in A$ or $1 \in B$. Similarly, $2 \in (A \cup B)$, $3 \in (A \cup B)$, and $5 \in (A \cup B)$. Quite obviously, the statement "$x \in A$ or $x \in B$" is false if $x \notin A$ and $x \notin B$. We conclude from the definition of union that 1, 2, 3, 4, 5, are the members and the only members of $A \cup B$:

$$A \cup B = \{1, 2, 3\} \cup \{3, 4, 5\} = \{1, 2, 3, 4, 5\}.$$

Now to consider $A \cap B = \{1, 2, 3\} \cap \{3, 4, 5\}$, we note that the statement "$y \in A$ and $y \in B$" is true if and only if $y = 3$. Hence, from the definition of intersection,

$$A \cap B = \{1, 2, 3\} \cap \{3, 4, 5\} = \{3\}.$$

Example 1-6. If $X = \{y \mid y \text{ is an even whole number}\}$
$= \{2, 4, 6, 8, \ldots\}$,

and

$$Y = \{w \mid w \text{ is an odd whole number}\} = \{1, 3, 5, 7, \ldots\},$$

then

$$X \cup Y = \{1, 2, 3, 4, 5, \ldots\} = \{z \mid z \text{ is a whole number}\}.$$

Also

$$X \cap Y = \varnothing.$$

Example 1-7. If W, Z are sets for which the statement "$a \in W$ and $a \in Z$" is false for every object a, then $W \cap Z = \varnothing$ from the definition of intersection. See Example 1-6.

Example 1-8. Suppose that "$a \in A$" is a true statement for some set A and object a. Then the statement "$a \in A$ or $a \in B$" is true for every set B. This shows that if $a \in A$, then $a \in (A \cup B)$ by the definition of union. Therefore, from the definition of subset,

$$A \subseteq (A \cup B) \text{ for all sets } A, B.$$

In a similar manner it follows that

$$B \subseteq (A \cup B) \text{ for all sets } A, B.$$

Example 1-9. Under what conditions does the union of two sets A, B not result in a set different from both A and B? For instance, what can we conclude from "$A \cup B = A$"? We can conclude that $B \subseteq A$. This is true because of our definitions of union, equality, and subset. The definition of subset requires that each element of B be a member of A for $B \subseteq A$ to be true. But if $x \in B$, $x \in (A \cup B)$ by Example 1-8, and since we have $A \cup B = A$, the definition of equality of sets requires that $x \in A$. Thus, if $x \in B$, $x \in A$. Hence, if $A \cup B = A$, $B \subseteq A$. These considerations then show that we obtain a set different from both A and B by taking the union $A \cup B$, only if $B \not\subseteq A$ and $A \not\subseteq B$.

DEFINITION. If X, Y are sets, the *difference* of X, Y is

$$\{p \mid p \in X \text{ and } p \notin Y\}.$$

For the difference of X, Y we adopt the notation $X \sqcap Y$; i.e.,

$$X \sqcap Y = \{p \mid p \in X \text{ and } p \notin Y\}.$$

(We read $X \sqcap Y$: "X less Y".)

To illustrate this definition, let Z be the set of whole numbers and let X be the set of even whole numbers. Then the statement "$x \in Z$ and $x \notin X$" is true if and only if x is a whole number and x is not even; i.e., if and only if x is a whole number and x is an odd whole number. We conclude that $Z \sqcap X$ is the set of odd whole numbers.

It is easy to prove that for all sets X, Y

$$X \cup Y = Y \cup X \quad \text{and} \quad X \cap Y = Y \cap X.$$

(See Exercise 12.) This usually is expressed by saying that the union and intersection of sets are *commutative* operations. This property of the union and intersection is not shared by the difference operation, however. By this we mean that it is *not* true that for all sets X, Y

$$X \sqcap Y = Y \sqcap X.$$

To see this, let $X = \{1, 2, 3\}$ and $Y = \{3, 4, 5\}$. Then by definition of "$\sqcap$"

$$X \sqcap Y = \{1, 2\} \qquad \text{and} \qquad Y \sqcap X = \{4, 5\}.$$

Therefore, $X \sqcap Y \neq Y \sqcap X$.

In particular discussions, the sets under consideration will all be subsets of some set, say U. The set U may be referred to as the ***universal* set** and, in this situation, the following abbreviation is usually adopted: instead of writing $U \sqcap A$ we write A'. This is read "A-complement." Since it is understood that $x \in U$, we have

$$A' = \{x \mid x \notin A\}.$$

It always will be understood in the following that each set A is a subset of some set U whenever we use the notation A'.

Example 1-10. From the definition of A', $x \notin A$ if and only if $x \in A'$. Hence, we may express the difference $X \sqcap A$ as follows:

$$\begin{aligned} X \sqcap A &= \{t \mid t \in X \text{ and } t \notin A\} \\ &= \{t \mid t \in X \text{ and } t \in A'\} \\ &= X \cap A'. \end{aligned}$$

Exercises

10. Describe the following sets by listing their members, if

$$X = \{7, 8, 11, 13, 4\},\ Y = \{2, 4, 8, 17, 9\},\ Z = \{1, 7, 5, 11, 19\}.$$

(a) $X \cup Y$.	(e) $X \cap Z$.	(i) $X \sqcap Z$.
(b) $X \cup Z$.	(f) $Y \cap Z$.	(j) $Z \sqcap X$.
(c) $Y \cup Z$.	(g) $X \sqcap Y$.	(k) $Y \sqcap Z$.
(d) $X \cap Y$.	(h) $Y \sqcap X$.	(l) $Z \sqcap Y$.

11. Prove that for sets S, T

$$(S \cap T) \subseteq S \qquad \text{and} \qquad (S \cap T) \subseteq T.$$

12. For all sets X, Y prove that (a) $X \cap Y = Y \cap X$, and (b) $X \cup Y = Y \cup X$. These are called the *commutative laws* for intersection and union.

13. Prove that for all sets L, M, N
(a) $L \cup (M \cup N) = (L \cup M) \cup N$.
(b) $L \cap (M \cap N) = (L \cap M) \cap N$.
These are called the *associative laws* for "$\cup$" and "$\cap$," and show that we may write $L \cup M \cup N$ and $L \cap M \cap N$ without ambiguity.

14. Prove that for all sets L, M, N

(a) $L \cap (M \cup N) = (L \cap M) \cup (L \cap N)$.

(b) $L \cup (M \cap N) = (L \cup M) \cap (L \cup N)$.

These are called the *distributive laws.* We now shall prove the first of these to illustrate a method of proof commonly used in showing the equality of two sets.

Solution. To prove (a) we use (*) and show that

$$L \cap (M \cup N) \subseteq (L \cap M) \cup (L \cap N)$$

and

$$(L \cap M) \cup (L \cap N) \subseteq L \cap (M \cup N).$$

It then will follow from (*) that statement (a) is true.

From the definition of "$\subseteq$", to show that $L \cap (M \cup N) \subseteq (L \cap M) \cup (L \cap N)$, we must show that if x is a member of $L \cap (M \cup N)$, then x is a member of $(L \cap M) \cup (L \cap N)$. If $x \in L \cap (M \cup N)$, then from the definition of "$\cap$", $x \in L$ and $x \in (M \cup N)$. But $x \in (M \cup N)$ implies, from the definition of "$\cup$" that $x \in M$ or $x \in N$. Therefore, we have that if $x \in L \cap (M \cup N)$, then $x \in L$ and $x \in M$ or $x \in L$ and $x \in N$. The definition of "$\cap$" gives $x \in L \cap M$, if $x \in L$ and $x \in M$; $x \in L \cap N$, if $x \in L$ and $x \in N$. So, if $x \in L \cap (M \cup N)$, then $x \in (L \cap M)$ or $x \in (L \cap N)$. Finally, the definition of "$\cup$" implies that $x \in (L \cap M) \cup (L \cap N)$, if $x \in (L \cap M)$ or $x \in (L \cap N)$. Hence, if $x \in L \cap (M \cup N)$, then $x \in (L \cap M) \cup (L \cap N)$. This concludes the part of the proof that $L \cap (M \cup N) \subseteq (L \cap M) \cup (L \cap N)$.

Now, if $x \in (L \cap M) \cup (L \cap N)$, then $x \in (L \cap M)$ or $x \in (L \cap N)$ from the definition of "$\cup$". In each of these cases $x \in L$; in the first case, $x \in M$ (by the definition of "$\cap$"), and in the second case, $x \in N$ (by the definition of "$\cap$"). Therefore, by definition of "$\cup$", $x \in (M \cup N)$. Hence, $x \in L \cap (M \cup N)$, if $x \in (L \cap M) \cup (L \cap N)$.

15. If S, T, L, M are sets such that $S \subseteq L$ and $T \subseteq M$, prove that

$$(S \cup T) \subseteq (L \cup M) \quad \text{and} \quad (S \cap T) \subseteq (L \cap M).$$

16. Prove that if L, M are sets

(a) $L = (L \square M) \cup (L \cap M)$.

(b) $L = L \cap (L \cup M)$.

(c) $(L \cap M)' = L' \cup M'$ } DeMorgan's Laws.

(d) $(L \cup M)' = L' \cap M'$ }

(e) $(L \square M)' = L' \cup M$.

(f) $L \cap M = (L' \cup M')'$.

(g) $(L \square M) \cup (M \square L) = (L \cup M) \square (L \cap M)$.

17. If A, B are sets such that $A \cap B = A$, what relation between A, B can be deduced? Prove your answer correct. Compare this with Example 1-9 and draw an analogous conclusion.

18. Let W and Z represent sets.

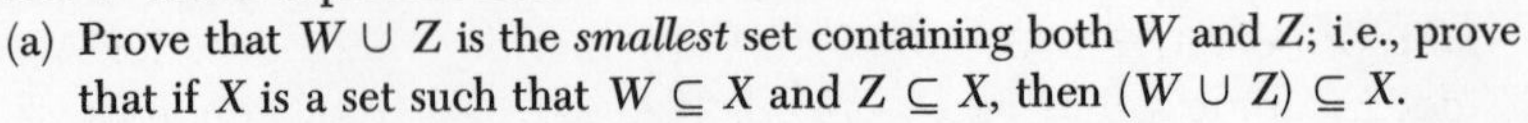

(a) Prove that $W \cup Z$ is the *smallest* set containing both W and Z; i.e., prove that if X is a set such that $W \subseteq X$ and $Z \subseteq X$, then $(W \cup Z) \subseteq X$.

(b) Prove that $W \cap Z$ is the *largest* set contained in both W and Z; i.e., prove that if X is a set such that $X \subseteq W$ and $X \subseteq Z$, then $X \subseteq (W \cap Z)$.

19. If A is a subset of the universal set U, prove the following.

(a) $A \cap A' = \varnothing$.
(b) $A \cup A' = U$.
(c) $(A')' = A$.
(d) $U' = \varnothing$.
(e) $\varnothing' = U$.

20. Prove that if $X \subseteq Y$, then $Y' \subseteq X'$.

1.3 Geometric Representation of Sets

A very convenient device for picturing sets geometrically is illustrated by the figures below. In a plane we represent a universal set U by the interior of some quadrilateral (or other closed figures for that matter). Then, the subsets of U are represented by closed figures interior to U as in Fig. 1-1. Letting the representative figures overlap, we may represent both the union and the intersection of sets by shading appropriate areas. In Fig. 1-1, $S \cap T$ is represented by the shaded area and the shaded area of Fig. 1-2 represents $S \cup T$.

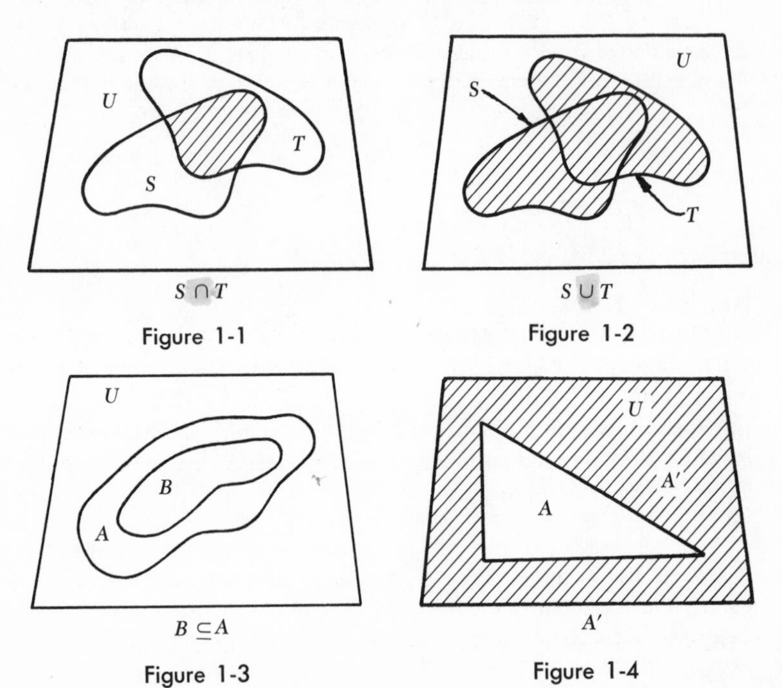

$S \cap T$

Figure 1-1

$S \cup T$

Figure 1-2

$B \subseteq A$

Figure 1-3

A'

Figure 1-4

We may represent the relation $B \subseteq A$ as in Fig. 1-3 simply by taking the representative figure for B entirely interior to the figure for A. Consider Example 1-9 of Sec. 1-2 with the aid of this representation. Other representations are suggested in Figs. 1-5, 1-6, and 1-7.

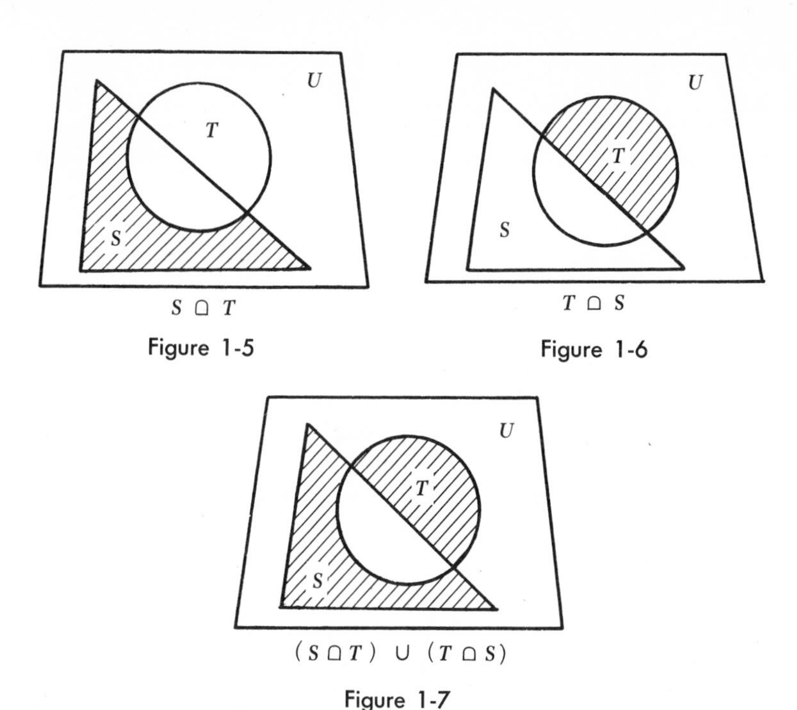

$S \square T$

Figure 1-5

$T \square S$

Figure 1-6

$(S \square T) \cup (T \square S)$

Figure 1-7

Example 1-11. We may illustrate Exercise 17 by an appropriate representation. See Fig. 1-3 where $A \cap B = B$.

Example 1-12. To illustrate the validity of Exercise 16(c), we construct separate figures for $(L \cap M)'$ and $L' \cup M'$. In the figures of the left-hand column of Fig. 1-8, we build up $(L \cap M)'$ by stages; in the right-hand column we do a similar thing for $L' \cup M'$. In the two separate columns the final stage is the same shaded area. This then suggests the validity of the statement $(L \cap M)' = L' \cup M'$.

Exercises

21. Illustrate the validity of Exercise 16(a), (b), (d) with appropriate geometric figures.

$(L \cap M)' = L' \cup M'$

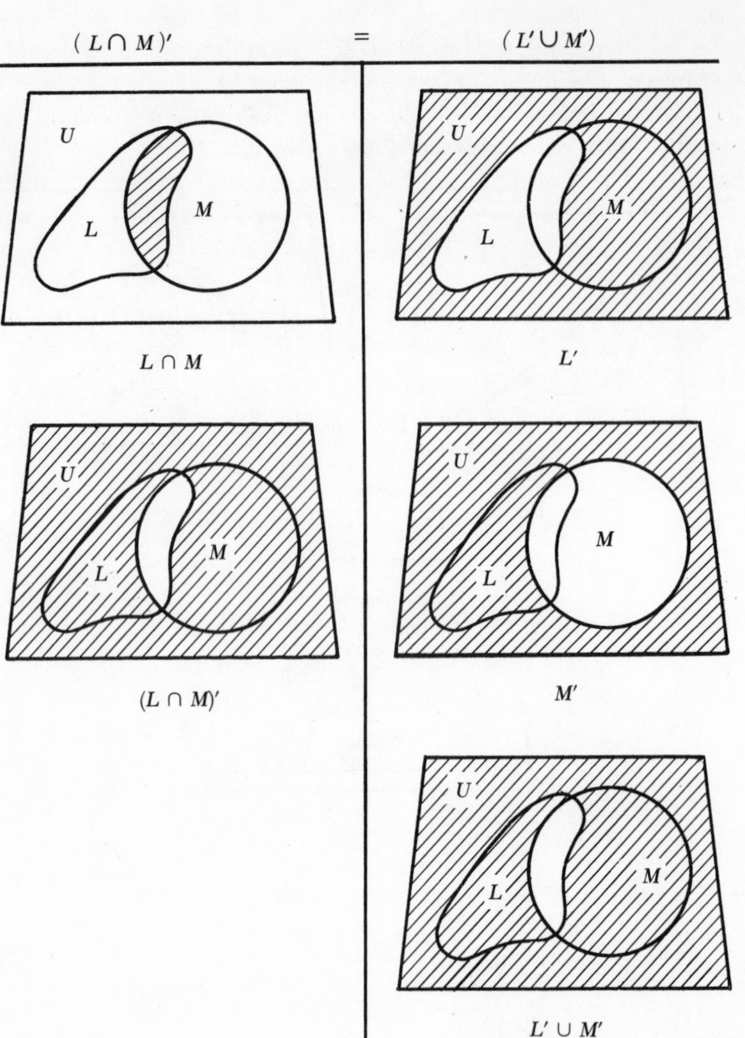

Figure 1-8

22. Illustrate the validity of Exercise 14(a) and (b), using suitable figures. Here three closed figures will be needed—one for each of the three sets L, M, N.

23. Illustrate the validity of Exercise 15.

1.4 Relations and Functions

In the previous section, the operations union, intersections, and difference of two sets were introduced. We now introduce another method of describing a set in terms of two given ones. In order to define this new concept, the notion of *ordered pair* must be considered.

An ordered pair is first of all a set; however, it is a set with an added property. By our definition of equality for sets, $\{a, b\} = \{b, a\}$. The idea behind the concept of ordered pair is simply that of imposing an order on the set $\{a, b\}$. Consequently, we denote by (a, b), the ordered pair having a as *first element* and b as *second element.* Now we *no longer have the equality* $(a, b) = (b, a)$ *as a general law.* Rather, we have the following rule governing equality of ordered pairs:

$$(a, b) = (c, d) \text{ if and only if } a = c \text{ and } b = d.^*$$

DEFINITION. If X, Y are sets, the *Cartesian product* of X, Y is

$$\{(a, b) \mid a \in X, b \in Y\}.$$

The Cartesian product is commonly denoted by $X \times Y$; i.e.,

$$X \times Y = \{(a, b) \mid a \in X, b \in Y\}.$$

Example 1-13. If $X = \{4, 3, 8\}$, $Y = \{a, 1\}$, then

$$\begin{aligned}
X \times Y &= \{(4, a), (4, 1), (3, a), (3, 1), (8, a), (8, 1)\} \\
Y \times X &= \{(a, 4), (1, 4), (a, 3), (1, 3), (a, 8), (1, 8)\} \\
X \times X &= \{(4, 4), (4, 3), (4, 8), (3, 4), (3, 3), (3, 8), (8, 4), (8, 3), (8, 8)\} \\
Y \times Y &= \{(a, a), (a, 1), (1, a), (1, 1)\}.
\end{aligned}$$

A useful geometric interpretation of $X \times Y$ may be obtained by representing the members of X and Y on intersecting lines (see Fig. 1-9), say, L_1 and L_2 respectively. Then through each point of L_1 which represents an element of X we take a line parallel to L_2; and through each point of L_2 representing a member of Y we draw a line parallel to L_1. The intersections of these various lines represent the members of $X \times Y$ as indicated in Fig. 1-9.

DEFINITION. If X, Y are sets, a subset G of $X \times Y$ is called a *relation.* The *domain* of G is the set

$$\mathfrak{D}(G) = \{x \mid (x, y) \in G, \text{ for some } y \in Y\}$$

and the *range* of G is the set

$$\mathfrak{R}(G) = \{z \mid (t, z) \in G, \text{ for some } t \in X\}.$$

---

* The notion of ordered pair, as we have introduced it, obviously lacks precision. This can be easily remedied by *defining* (a, b) to be the set $\{\{a, b\}, \{b\}\}$. It is then an easy matter to prove the above law of equality. The reader may find the proof of this fact a somewhat interesting exercise.

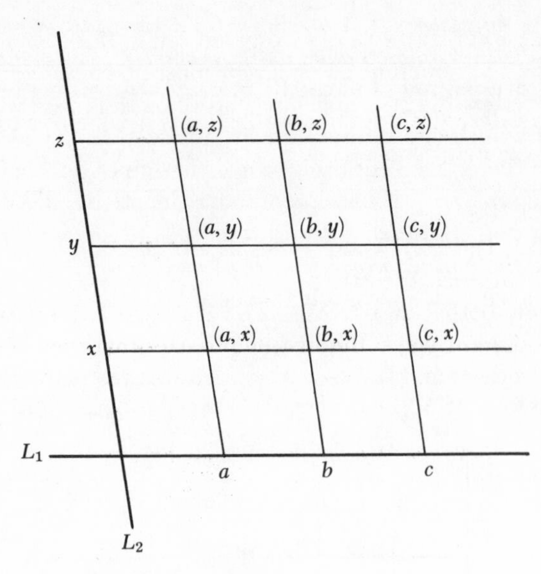

Figure 1-9

It is a rather simple matter to convince oneself that this definition of relation corresponds to our common use of the word. For example, if $X = \{1, 2, 3\}$, then

$$X \times X = \{(1, 1), (1, 2), (1, 3), (2, 1), (2, 2), (2, 3), (3, 1), (3, 2), (3, 3)\}.$$

Consider now the property "is the same as." This property we ordinarily consider a relation. We may define a set using this property:

$$\{(x, y) \mid x \in X, y \in X, x \text{ is the same as } y\}.$$

This is the set $\{(1, 1), (2, 2), (3, 3)\}$, a subset of $X \times X$, and therefore a relation by our definition. The domain as well as the range of this relation is X.

Again, consider the property "is less than." With $X = \{1, 2, 3\}$ as before, define $L = \{(x, y) \mid x \in X, y \in X, x \text{ is less than } y\}$. Then L is the subset $\{(1, 2), (1, 3), (2, 3)\}$ of $X \times X$. One should not conclude from these examples that all relations are as familiar as these; the set $\{(1, 1), (2, 1), (2, 2), (3, 3)\}$ is a relation by our definition, but does not appear to be as familiar as the two examples we have just seen.

One of our major concerns here will be the study of certain kinds of relations which we call *functions*.

DEFINITION. Let G be a relation having the property that if $(a, b) \in G$, and $(a, c) \in G$, then $b = c$. Then G is called a *function*.

This definition states that *a relation is a function provided it contains no two distinct ordered pairs with the same first element.* Thinking of a relation as a pairing of elements in its domain with elements in its range, we can describe a function as a relation which pairs with each element in its domain *one and only one* element in its range.

Example 1-14. The relation $F = \{(1, 1), (2, 2), (3, 3)\}$ is a function, while $G = \{(1, 1), (1, 2)\}$ is not. The second relation is not a function by our definition since 1 is paired with two (not just one) elements in its range—namely both 1 and 2. We illustrate these two relations in Fig. 1-10 in two different ways: the first emphasizes that they are subsets of a Cartesian product, and the second emphasizes the pairing.

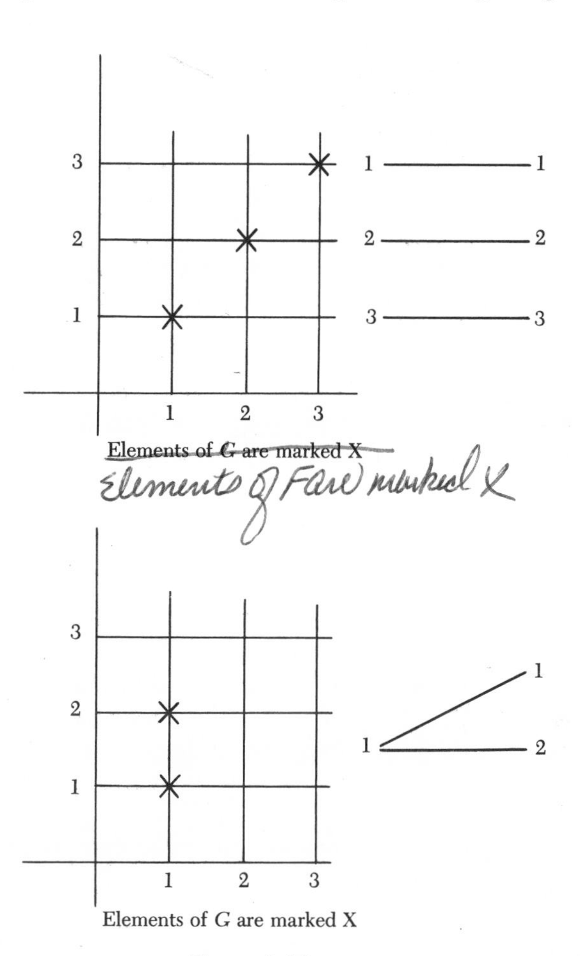

Figure 1-10

Example 1-15. Let $X = \{a, b, c, d\}$ and $Y = \{7, 4, 9\}$. Then each of the following relations is a function with domain X.

$$F = \{(a, 7), (b, 4), (c, 9), (d, 9)\}.$$
$$G = \{(a, 7), (b, 7), (c, 7), (d, 7)\}.$$
$$H = \{(a, 9), (b, 7), (c, 9), (d, 4)\}.$$

The relation $J = \{(a, 9), (b, 9), (a, 7), (c, 4), (d, 4)\}$ is not a function since $(a, 9) \in J$ and $(a, 7) \in J$ but $9 \neq 7$. We illustrate F, G, H, and J in Fig. 1-11 in two ways.

Note the fact that J is not a function is reflected on the grid-type "picture" (Fig. 1-11) in that the line through a parallel to L_2 has two $\times$-marks, and that in the other picture of J, two lines go *from a*. This will clearly always be the case for such representations when the relation represented is not a function.

If F is a function and the pair $(x, y) \in F$, it is customary to write $y = F(x)$. In other words, $F(x)$ is used to denote the second member of the ordered pair whose first member is x. $F(x)$ is said to be a *functional value* of F or the *value* of F at x. In Example 1-15 we have

$$7 = F(a),\ 4 = F(b),\ 9 = F(c) \text{ and } 9 = F(d).$$
$$7 = G(a),\ 7 = G(b),\ 7 = G(c) \text{ and } 7 = G(d).$$
$$9 = H(a),\ 7 = H(b),\ 9 = H(c) \text{ and } 4 = H(d).$$

Note that this notation is inappropriate for J since we would have $9 = J(a)$ and also $7 = J(a)$.

Suppose that X, Y are sets and that the relation R is a subset of $X \times Y$. Then we may associate with R a relation—called the *inverse* of R and denoted by R^{-1}—which is a subset of $Y \times X$. R^{-1} is defined to be the set

$$\{(w, z) \mid (z, w) \in R\}.$$

In other words, $(w, z) \in R^{-1}$ if and only if $(z, w) \in R$.

From Example 1-15 again, we have

$$F^{-1} = \{(7, a), (4, b), (9, c), (9, d)\}.$$
$$G^{-1} = \{(7, a), (7, b), (7, c), (7, d)\}.$$
$$H^{-1} = \{(9, a), (7, b), (9, c), (4, d)\}.$$

From the definition of function, we see that F^{-1} is not a function unless $c = d$; G^{-1} is not a function unless $a = b = c = d$; H^{-1} is not a function unless $a = c$.

In case R is a function, we may use the notation described above and write

$$(w, z) \in R^{-1} \text{ if and only if } w = R(z).$$

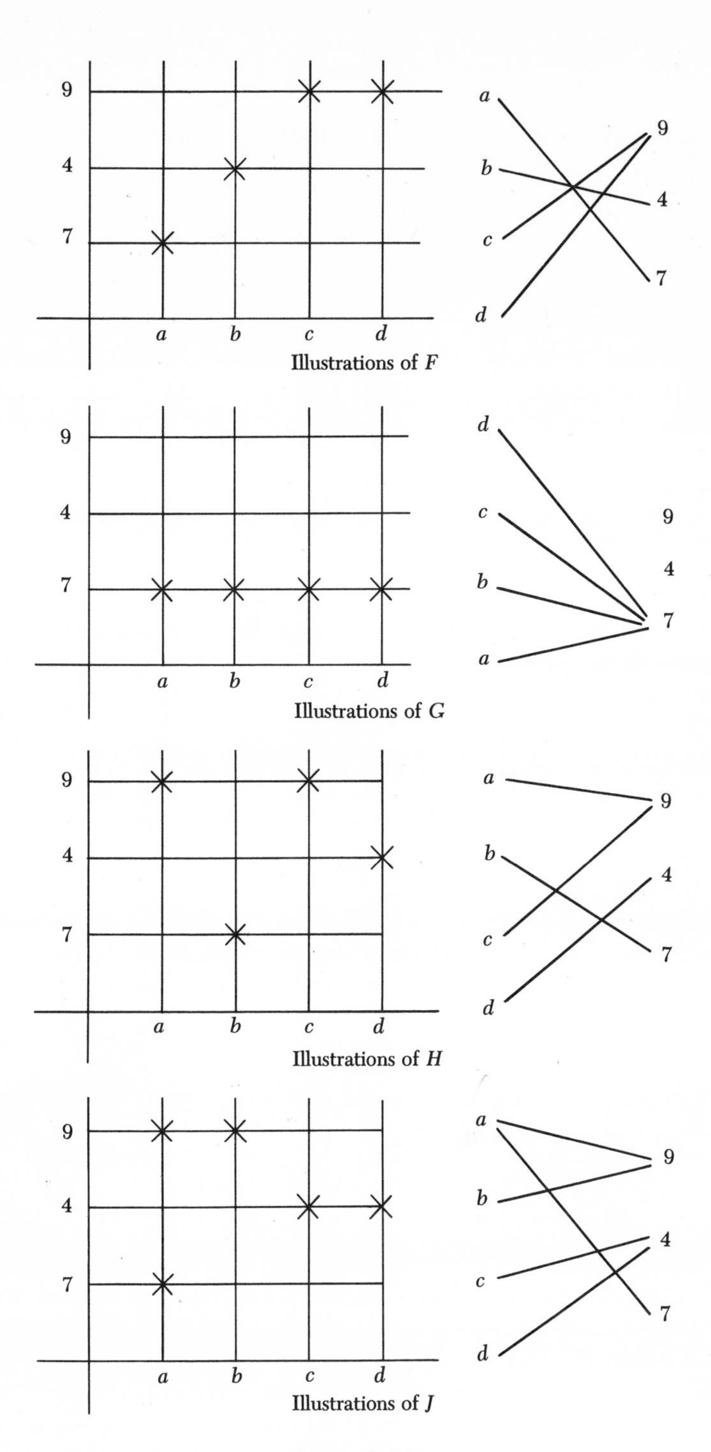

9
4
7
a
b
c
d
Illustrations of F
Illustrations of G
Illustrations of H
Illustrations of J

Figure 1-11

Also if R and R^{-1} are both functions,

$$z = R^{-1}(w) \text{ if and only if } w = R(z).$$

If R is a function with domain X and range Y, let us consider the question of whether R^{-1} is a function. According to the definition, R^{-1} is a function if and only if the following is true:

$$(w, z_1) \in R^{-1} \text{ and } (w, z_2) \in R^{-1} \text{ implies } z_1 = z_2.$$

Using the definition of R^{-1} we may state this condition as:

$$(1) \qquad (z_1, w) \in R \text{ and } (z_2, w) \in R \text{ implies } z_1 = z_2.$$

DEFINITION. A function R is a *one-one* function if and only if it has the property expressed in (1).

In terms of pairing we may state the condition that a function R be *one-one* as follows: *A function R is one-one if and only if each element in the range of R is paired with only one element in the domain of R.*

Returning to the question of whether R^{-1} is a function, it is evident that R^{-1} is a function if and only if R is a *one-one* function.

Most of the functions with which we will be concerned have domains and ranges which are sets of numbers. For this reason, the further study of functions will be postponed until numbers have been studied in the following chapter.

Exercises

24. List the members of each of the following sets:
(a) $\{1, 2\} \times \{2\}$. (b) $\{0, 5\} \times \{8, 5\}$.

25. Determine the domain and range of each of the following relations:
(a) $\{(3, 2), (2, 2)\}$.
(b) $\{(1, 2), (1, 5), (1, 7), (3, 5), (2, 2), (2, 7)\}$.
(c) $\{(2, 4), (2, 3), (7, 1), (5, 4)\}$.

26. Represent each of the relations in Exercise 25 geometrically in two ways.

27. Determine which of the following sets are functions; which are one-one functions; calculate the inverse of each.
(a) $\{(3, 2), (2, 2)\}$.
(b) $\{(3, 2), (2, 2), (3, 7), (4, 5)\}$.
(c) $\{(1, 2), (2, 5), (3, 7)\}$.
(d) $\{(2, 2), (3, 5), (4, 7)\}$.
(e) $\{(3, 7), (2, 5)\}$.

28. Represent geometrically each of the relations in Exercise 27 in two ways.

* 1.5 More About Relations and Their Graphs

In Sec. 1.4 we discussed a grid-type pictorial representation of relations. This is such a useful device for studying relations that it seems appropriate to pursue this topic further. The relations considered here will have both range and domain which are subsets of the same set, say X. That is, we consider sets of ordered pairs which are subsets of some $X \times Y$ where $X = Y$. If $R \subseteq (X \times X)$, we shall say that R is a relation *on* X.

The set of points that have $\times$-marks in the pictorial representation of a relation will be referred to as its *graph.*

DEFINITION. Let R be a relation on a set X.

(a) R is *reflexive* on X if and only if $(x, x) \in R$ for all $x \in X$;
(b) R is *symmetric* on X if and only if $(x, y) \in R$ implies $(y, x) \in R$ for all $x, y \in X$;
(c) R is *transitive* on X if and only if $(x, y) \in R$ and $(y, z) \in R$ implies $(x, z) \in R$ for all $x, y, z \in X$;
(d) R is an *equivalence relation* on X if and only if R is reflexive, symmetric, and transitive on X.

Example 1-16. The set $R = \{(1, 1), (2, 2), (2, 3), (3, 3), (3, 1)\}$ is a relation on the set $\{1, 2, 3\}$. R is reflexive since $(1, 1) \in R$, $(2, 2) \in R$ and $(3, 3) \in R$. R is not symmetric since $(2, 3) \in R$ but $(3, 2) \notin R$. R is not transitive since $(2, 3) \in R$, $(3, 1) \in R$ but $(2, 1) \notin R$. R is not an equivalence relation.

Example 1-17. $R = \{(1, 1), (2, 2), (3, 3)\}$ is an equivalence relation on $\{1, 2, 3\}$ as can easily be seen from the definition. The reflexive and symmetric properties are easily seen to hold, and there is nothing to check for the transitive property. What is the common name for this relation?

Example 1-18. $R = \{(1, 2), (2, 1), (1, 1)\}$ is not reflexive on $\{1, 2\}$ since $(2, 2) \notin R$. R is symmetric and transitive. Is R an equivalence relation?

Example 1-19. $R = \{(1, 2), (2, 3), (1, 3)\}$ is not reflexive on $\{1, 2, 3\}$ nor is it symmetric. R is, however, transitive on $\{1, 2, 3\}$.

Notice that by the definition of transitive relation, if we wish to determine whether R is transitive on a set X, we need consider only pairs $(a, b) \in R$ and $(b, c) \in R$. Then R is transitive on X if and only if for each such pair of pairs $(a, c) \in R$. *Obviously this is the case if either* $a = b$ *or* $b = c$. This observation will shorten the work in checking some relations for transitivity since we may ignore both the following situations:

$$(a, a) \in R, (a, b) \in R,$$

and

$$(a, b) \in R, (b, b) \in R.$$

Returning now to graphs of relations, we may ask how the reflexive, symmetric, and transitive properties are reflected in graphs. If R is a relation on the set $X = \{x_1, x_2, x_3, \ldots\}$, we will "picture" R on a frame such as that in Fig. 1-12. (Notice that the angle at A is a right angle, and that points $q \in X$ on AC are the same distance apart as on AD.) The line AB of Fig. 1-12 is called the *diagonal.* The reflexive property is

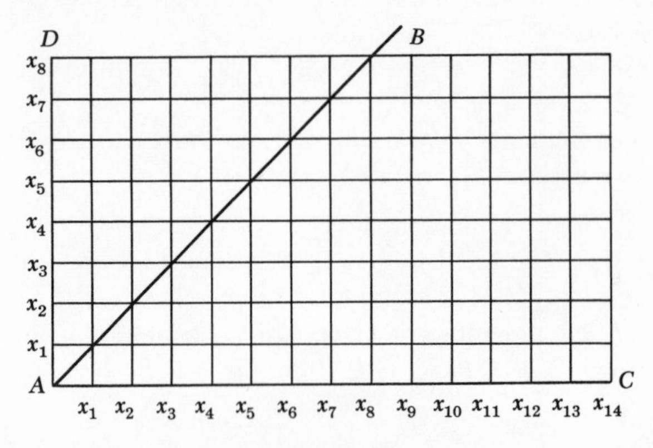

Figure 1-12

easily interpreted on this frame: *A relation R is reflexive on X if and only if each point of the diagonal which is also a point of the grid has an* $\times$*-mark.* For example, Fig. 1-13(a) is the graph of a non-reflexive relation; Fig. 1-13(b) shows a reflexive relation.

Suppose that a relation R is symmetric and that $(a, b) \in R$. Then by definition of "symmetric," we know that $(b, a) \in R$. Now, assuming that $a \neq b$, compare the relative positions for the points on the grid corresponding to the pairs (a, b) and (b, a). In Fig. 1-14, these pairs have been plotted. Observe that in Fig. 1-14 if a line is drawn through the point representing (a, b) perpendicular to the line AB, this line passes

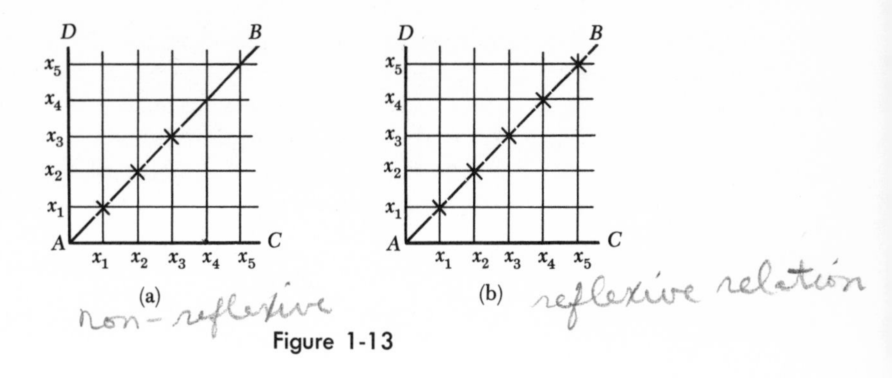

Figure 1-13

through the point representing (b, a). *The points representing* (a, b) *and* (b, a) *are said to be symmetric with respect to the line AB.*

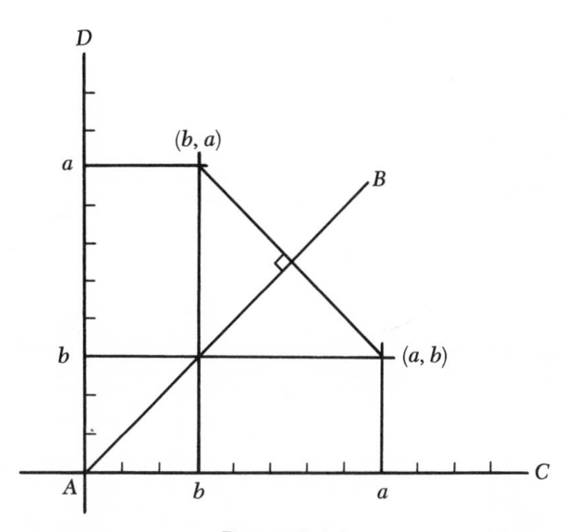

Figure 1-14

On graphs of this type, then, we may interpret a symmetric relation: *A relation R is symmetric on X if and only if its graph is symmetric with respect to the diagonal.*

In Fig. 1-15, we have the graph of a symmetric relation (a) and a non-symmetric relation (b). In Fig. 1-15(b), the point representing (x_3, x_5) is circled—indicating that (x_3, x_5) is *not* an element of the relation which has been graphed. This fact prevents the relation from being symmetric since the graph indicated that (x_5, x_3) *is* a member of the relation.

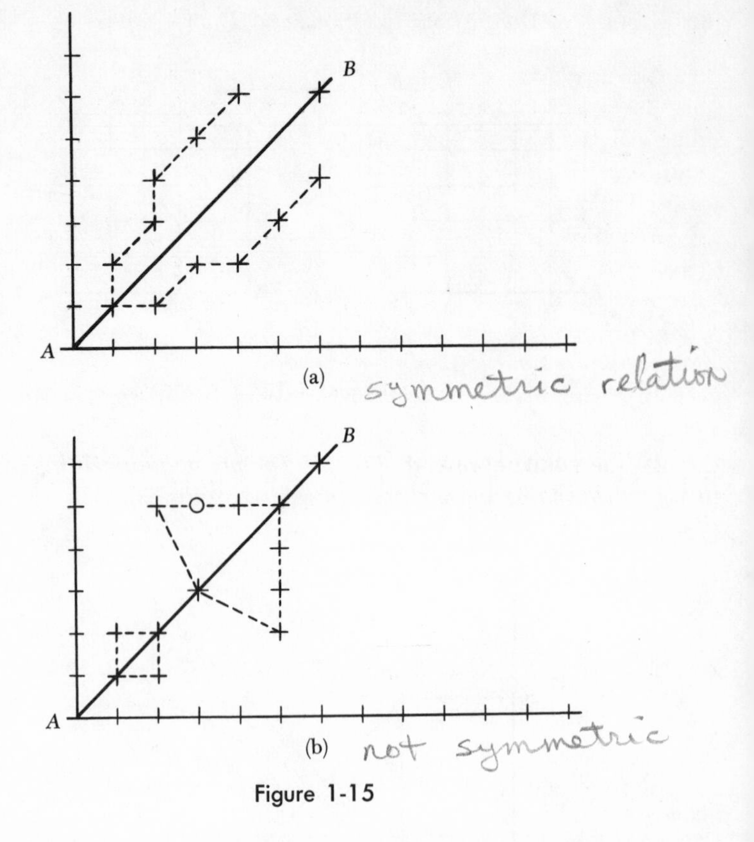

Figure 1-15

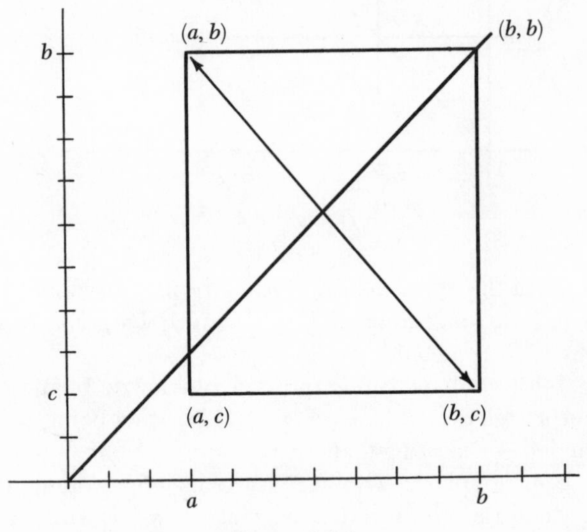

Figure 1-16

Consider two pairs (a, b) and (b, c) of a relation R (assuming that R has such pairs). Let us call the points corresponding to these pairs diagonal points of the relation. In Fig. 1-16 below, we have plotted (a, b) and (b, c). It should be clear from this figure why the word "diagonal" is used here.

According to the definition of transitive relation R: if $(a, b) \in R$ and $(b, c) \in R$, then $(a, c) \in R$. We may interpret graphically the transitive property of a relation R as follows: *If the graph of R contains two diagonal points, corresponding to (a, b) and (b, c), then the graph contains the point corresponding to (a, c).*

In Fig. 1-17, we have the graph of a transitive relation (a) and a non-transitive relation (b).

If R is a relation, let us consider the problem of obtaining the graph of R^{-1} from that of R. Recall that by the definition of R^{-1}, $(a, b) \in R^{-1}$

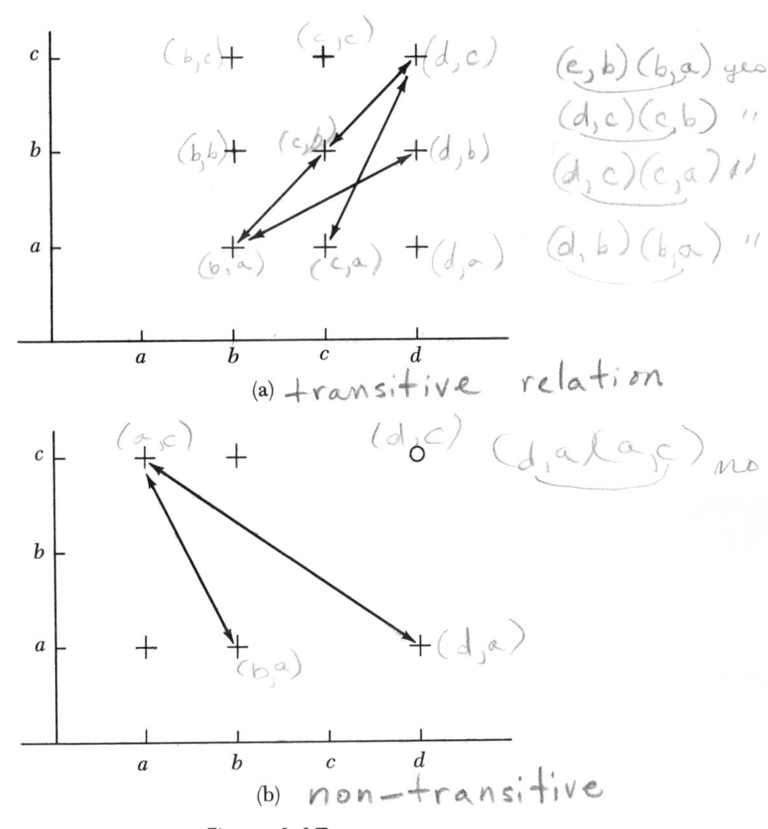

Figure 1-17

if and only if $(b, a) \in R$. Since we have already seen that the points corresponding to (a, b) and (b, a) are symmetric with respect to the diagonal, the graph of R^{-1} may be constructed as follows: *For each point P of the graph of R, plot the point Q which is symmetric to P with respect to the diagonal.*

In Fig. 1-18, we have plotted (a) the graph of a relation R, and (b) the graph of R^{-1}.

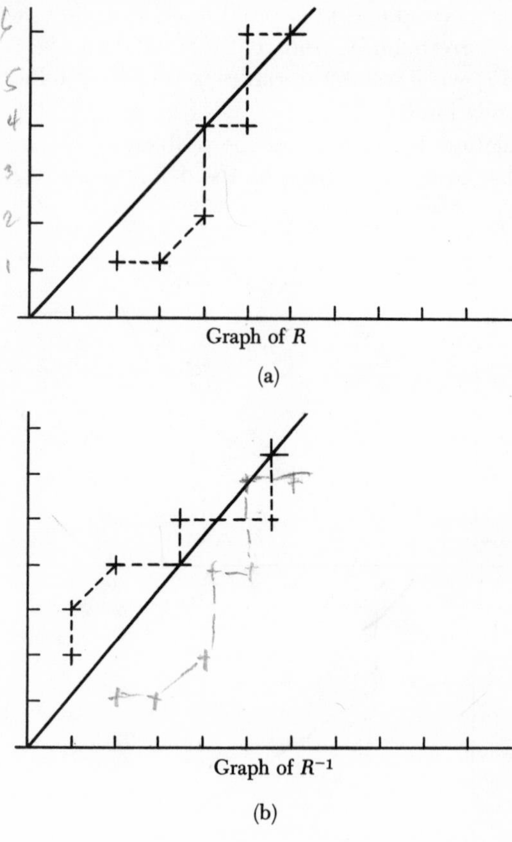

Graph of R

(a)

Graph of R^{-1}

(b)

Figure 1-18

*Exercises

29. Let $X = \{a, b, c, d\}$. Determine for each of the following whether the relation is reflexive, symmetric, or transitive.

(a) $\{(a, b), (a, a), (a, d)\}$.
(b) $\{(a, a), (b, b), (c, c), (b, a)\}$.

(c) $\{(a, a), (b, b), (c, c), (d, d)\}$.
(d) $\{(a, b), (b, c), (a, c)\}$.
(e) $\{(a, a), (b, b), (c, c), (d, d), (a, b), (b, a)\}$
(f) $X \times X$.

30. Calculate the inverse of each relation in Exercise 29 and answer the questions of Exercise 29 for the resulting relations.

31. Graph each of the relations in Exercise 29 and 30.

32. Listed below in Fig. 1-19 are the graphs of some relations on the set $\{0, 1, 2, 3, 4\}$. Check each graph for symmetry with respect to the diagonal, reflexiveness, and transitivity.

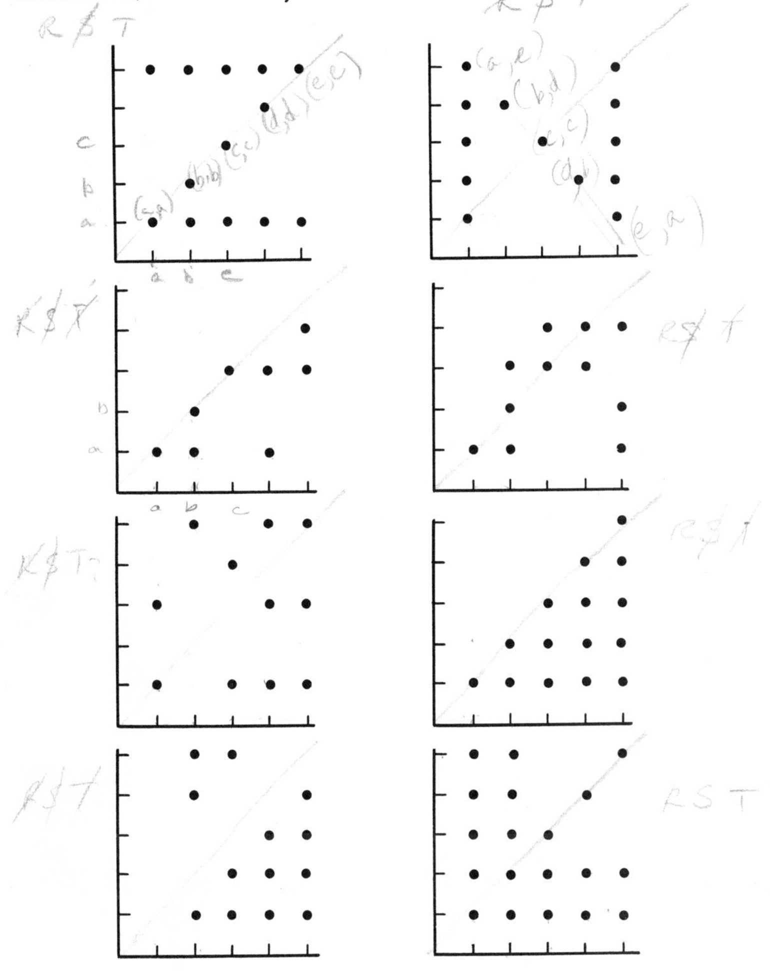

Figure 1-19

33. From the graphs of the relations given in Exercise 32, determine the graphs of the inverse relations. For each of these relations so determined, answer the questions of whether they are reflexive, symmetric, or transitive.

34. For each relation of Exercises 29, 30, 32, 33, determine which are functions, and which are one-one functions.

2

The Real Numbers

We assume on the part of the reader a certain familiarity with real numbers. From previous mathematical experience, he will possess many "facts" about these numbers. What he may lack, however, is an understanding of the foundations of these facts. No exhaustive development of the real number system will be attempted here. Rather, we will take *real number* to mean anything which satisfies the *field axioms, order axiom* and *completeness axiom* given below. Some of the axioms (or postulates) will be familiar to the student as "facts" about real numbers. But for us, these axioms are simply assumed. From these assumptions it is then possible to prove everything else that is true about the real numbers—we indicate how this is done in some theorems below. By proceeding in this manner, we hope to impart understanding, as well as information, about the real numbers.

2.1 Field Axioms

Many of the properties with which the reader is familiar will be found below in the list of axioms for what is called a *field.* The set of real numbers is an example of this concept of field and for that reason we may study the reals by making a study of these axioms.

Axiom 1. *Closure Axiom.* The sum, $a + b$, and the product, ab, of any real numbers a and b is a unique real number.

Axiom 2. *Commutative Axiom.* For any two real numbers a and b,

$$a + b = b + a, \qquad \text{and} \qquad ab = ba.$$

Axiom 3. *Associative Axiom.* If a, b, c, are real numbers, then

$$a + (b + c) = (a + b) + c, \qquad \text{and} \qquad a(bc) = (ab)c.$$

Axiom 4. *Distributive Axiom.* If a, b, c, are real numbers, then

$$a(b + c) = ab + ac.$$

Axiom 5. *Identity Element Axiom.*

(a) There is a number, called *zero,* and denoted by 0, with the property that $a + 0 = a$ for each real number a.

(b) There is a number, different from 0, called *one,* and denoted by 1, with the property that $a(1) = a$ for each real number a.

Axiom 6. *Inverse Element Axiom.*

(a) For each real number a there is a real number, called the *additive inverse* of a, and denoted by $-a$, with the property that $a + (-a) = 0$.

(b) For each non-zero real number a there is a real number, called the *multiplicative inverse* of a, and denoted by a^{-1}, with the property that $a(a^{-1}) = 1$.

Before illustrating some elementary deductions from the axioms, a word about the meaning of equality, as we shall use it, is in order. When we assert that "$a = b$," we mean that "a" and "b" are names for the same number. From this definition of equality, we can quickly deduce the following familiar rules:

1. $a = a$, for all real numbers a.
2. $a = b$ implies $b = a$ for all real numbers a, b.
3. $a = b$ and $b = c$ imply $a = c$ for all real numbers a, b, c.

These rules are sometimes referred to as the *reflexive, symmetric* and *transitive* properties, respectively, for equality. Observe that the transitive property is simply a concise statement of the rule: "Things equal to the same thing are equal to each other." In the proofs which follow, certain steps will be justified because of our definition of equality. When this is the case, we will indicate this with the abbreviation "MOE" (meaning of equality).

Theorem 1. If x is a real number, then (a) $0 + x = x$ and (b) $(-x) + x = 0$.

Proof:

Statement	*Reason*
(a) 1. $0 + x = x + 0$	Axiom 2
2. $x + 0 = x$	Axiom 5(a)
3. $0 + x = x$	1, 2, and MOE
(b) 1. $(-x) + x = x + (-x)$	Axiom 2
2. $x + (-x) = 0$	Axiom 6(a)
3. $(-x) + x = 0$	1, 2, and MOE

Theorem 2. If x is a real number, then (a) $1 \cdot (x) = x$ and (b) if $x \neq 0$, $(x^{-1}) \cdot x = 1$.

Proof: Left as an exercise.

Theorem 3. If a and x are real numbers, then $(-a) + (a + x) = x$.

Proof:

Statement	*Reason*
1. $(-a) + (a + x) = ((-a) + a) + x$	Axiom 3
2. $((-a) + a) + x = 0 + x$	Theorem 1, MOE
3. $0 + x = x$	Theorem 1
4. $(-a) + (a + x) = x$	1, 2, 3, and MOE

Theorem 4. If a, b, and c are real numbers and $a + b = a + c$, then $b = c$.

Proof:

Statement	*Reason*
1. $a + b = a + c$	Given
2. $(-a) + (a + b) = (-a) + (a + c)$	MOE, Axiom 6
3. $(-a) + (a + b) = b$ and $(-a) + (a + c) = c$	Theorem 3
4. $b = c$	MOE

Theorem 5. If a, b, and c are real numbers such that $a \neq 0$ and $ab = ac$, then $b = c$.

Proof: Left as an exercise. p 32, #2

Theorem 6. If a is a real number, then $a0 = 0$.

Proof:

Statement	*Reason*
1. $0 + 0 = 0$	Axiom 5(a)
2. $a0 = a(0 + 0)$	1, MOE
3. $a(0 + 0) = a0 + a0$	Axiom 4
4. $a0 = a0 + a0$	2, 3, MOE
5. $a0 + 0 = a0$	Axiom 5(a)
6. $a0 + 0 = a0 + a0$	4, 5, MOE
7. $0 = a0$	Theorem 4

In proving further properties, it is helpful to know that for any given real number which is different from zero there is just one multiplicative inverse.

Theorem 7. The multiplicative inverse of each non-zero real number is unique.

Proof: Axiom 6(b) states that each real number a has at least one multiplicative inverse, but does not exclude the possibility that a might have more than one inverse. Let us suppose, then, that both the numbers h and k are multiplicative inverses of a; i.e., $ah = 1$ and also $ak = 1$. Then $ah = ak$, and since we are assuming that $a \neq 0$, it follows by Theorem 5 that $h = k$.

Theorem 8. The additive inverse of a real number is unique.

Proof: Left as an exercise.

We now prove a theorem which justifies a "rule" which is sometimes stated as "minus times plus is minus." It really says that the product of the additive inverse of a and the number b is equal to the additive inverse of the product of a and b.

Theorem 9. If a and b are real numbers, then $(-a)(b) = -(ab)$.

Proof: We will show that when $(-a)(b)$ is added to (ab), the result is zero. This means that $(-a)(b)$ is the additive inverse of (ab) and, since the additive inverse of (ab), namely $-(ab)$, is unique (Theorem 8), we conclude that $(-a)(b) = -(ab)$.

Statement	*Reason*
1. $(ab) + (-a)(b) = (ba) + (b)(-a)$	Commutative axiom
2. $(ba) + (b)(-a) = b(a + (-a))$	Distributive axiom
3. $b(a + (-a)) = b(0) = 0$	Axiom 6(a) MOE, and Theorem 6

We conclude that, therefore, since $(ab) + (-a)(b) = 0$, $(-a)(b)$ is the additive inverse of (ab), thus $(-a)(b) = -(ab)$.

Theorem 10. $(-a)(-b) = (ab)$

Proof: (Supply reasons for each step.)

$$
\begin{aligned}
&1.\ (-a)(-b) = (-a)(-b) + 0 = (-a)(-b) + [-(ab) + (ab)] \\
&2.\ \qquad = (-a)(-b) + [(-a)(b) + (ab)] \\
&3.\ \qquad = [(-a)(-b) + (-a)(b)] + (ab) \\
&4.\ \qquad = (-a)(-b + b) + (ab) \\
&5.\ \qquad = (-a)(0) + (ab) = 0 + (ab) \\
&6.\ (-a)(-b) = (ab)
\end{aligned}
$$

Another very useful property of the real numbers, or of any set satisfying Axioms 1–6, is the following:

Theorem 11. If $ab = 0$, then either $a = 0$ or $b = 0$.

Proof: Suppose that $a \neq 0$. In this case we know that a^{-1} exists and we have:

Statement	*Supply reasons*:
1. $ab = 0$	
2. $a^{-1}(ab) = a^{-1}(0)$	
3. $(a^{-1}a)b = 0$	
4. $b = 0$	

Let us consider now the kinds of numbers which Axioms 1–6 have placed at our disposal. Axiom 5(b) gives us the number 1 and hence, by Axiom 1 all the following:

$$1, 1 + 1, 1 + 1 + 1, 1 + 1 + 1 + 1, \ldots$$

These we call the *positive integers*, and write

$$1, 2, 3, 4, \ldots$$

i.e., 4 *means* $1 + 1 + 1 + 1$, for example. Next, Axiom 6(a) states that each of these positive integers has an additive inverse:

$$-1, -2, -3, -4, \ldots$$

These are called the *negative integers*. The positive integers, and the negative integers, together with zero (Axiom 5(a)) are referred to as the *integers*.

Axiom 6(b) guarantees that each non-zero integer n has a multiplicative inverse, n^{-1}. Using Axiom 1, then, we have all the numbers of the form $m \cdot n^{-1}$ where m, n are integers and $n \neq 0$. Each of these real numbers we call a *rational* number and denote by "m/n". So far we have:

Non-negative Integers: $0, 1, 2, 3, 4, \ldots$
Negative Integers: $-1, -2, -3, -4, \ldots$
Rational numbers: all numbers m/n, where m, n are integers and $n \neq 0$.

Without additional axioms, we do not know that numbers other than those listed above exist. We cannot say, for instance, that there is a number x such that $x^3 = 10$. In Sec. 2.3, an axiom will be introduced which will guarantee the existence of such numbers.

Exercises

1. Prove that if a, b, c, d are real numbers,
   (a) $(a + b) + c = (c + b) + a$.
   (b) $ac + ad + bc + bd = (a + b) \cdot (c + d)$.

2. Prove Theorems 2, 5 and 8.

3. Use the axioms (and MOE) to justify the steps in finding a solution for the equation $5(x + 2) = 37$.

4. Prove that if x is a real number and $x^2 + x - 6 = 0$, then $x = 2$ or $x = -3$. [*Hint:* factor and use Theorem 11].

5. For real numbers a, b we define $a - b$ to be the number $a + (-b)$. Use this definition and the axioms (and/or theorems) to prove the following:
   (a) $a(b - c) = ab - ac$.
   (b) $-(a - b) = b - a$.
   (c) If $a - b = a - c$, then $b = c$.
   (d) $(a + b)(a - b) = a^2 - b^2$.
   (e) $(a - b) \cdot (a^2 + ab + b^2) = a^3 - b^3$.

6. Prove the following properties of rational numbers:
   (a) $-(m/n) = (-m)/n = m/(-n)$, where m, n are integers and $n \neq 0$.
   (b) $(m/n) + (a/b) = (mb + na)/(nb)$, for $n \neq 0$, $b \neq 0$.
   (c) $(m/n) - (a/b) = (mb - na)/(nb)$, for $n \neq 0$, $b \neq 0$.
   (d) $m/1 = m$; $m/m = 1$, $m \neq 0$.
   (e) $(m/n) \cdot (a/b) = (ma)/(nb)$, for $n \neq 0$, $b \neq 0$.
   (f) $(ma)/(na) = m/n$, for $n \neq 0$, $a \neq 0$.
   (g) $(m/n) \cdot (n/m) = 1$, for $n \neq 0$, $m \neq 0$.

7. Prove that the sum and product of two rational numbers is a rational number.

2.2 The Order Axiom

If we now add to the field axioms another one called the *order axiom* we obtain what is usually referred to as an *ordered field.*

Axiom 7. *The Order Axiom.* There is a non-empty subset of real numbers called the *positive numbers* and denoted by P with the following properties:
   (a) If $a \in P$ and $b \in P$, then $(a + b) \in P$ and $(ab) \in P$.
   (b) If a is a real number, then one and only one of the following is true:

$$a \in P, \qquad \text{or} \qquad -a \in P, \qquad \text{or} \qquad a = 0.$$

We emphasize here that no information is available concerning *positive* numbers except that which is contained in the above axiom.

Statement (a) of the axiom may be expressed by saying: *The sum and product of positive numbers is positive.*

Statement (b) may be rendered: *If a number is not zero, then either it is positive or its additive inverse is positive—but not both.*

Axiom 7 enables us to define precisely what we mean when we say that one real number is less than another. This has the effect of "arranging" the reals in a fixed order; hence, the name for the axiom.

DEFINITION. The real number a is *less than* the real number b, denoted by $a < b$, if and only if $(b - a) \in P$.

A consequence of this definition is that for any two real numbers a and b, exactly one of the statements

$$a < b; \qquad b < a; \qquad a = b$$

is true. To see this, consider the number $a - b$. By Axiom 7 one, and only one, of the following is true:

$$(a - b) \in P; \qquad -(a - b) \in P; \qquad a - b = 0.$$

These statements lead immediately to the result by definition of "$<$."

If we observe that for any real number x

$$0 < x \qquad \text{if and only if} \qquad x \in P,$$

we see that if $x \neq 0$, $0 < x$ or $x < 0$. We may apply this when $x = 1$ since by Axiom 5(b), $1 \neq 0$. We then have that $1 < 0$ or $0 < 1$. If $1 < 0$, it follows that $-1 \in P$ by definition, and hence that $(-1)(-1) \in P$ by Axiom 7. But by Theorem 10, $(-1)(-1) = 1$ and we have $1 \in P$ *and* $-1 \in P$ in contradiction to Axiom 7. Therefore, we conclude that $0 < 1$. This proves the following theorem.

THEOREM 12. $0 < 1$.

Questions such as "For what numbers x is the number $2x - 7$ negative?" arise in the study of calculus. Expressions of the type "$2x - 7 < 0$" are called inequalities, and they can be "solved" by using those properties of real numbers already established, together with three special properties of the "less than" relation. Stated informally, the three properties are: (1) Any real number may be added to both sides of an equality which is a true statement and the resulting inequality is a true statement. (2) If both sides of an inequality which is a true statement are multiplied by the same *positive* number, the resulting inequality is a true statement. (3) If both sides of an inequality which is a true statement are multiplied by the same negative number and the "sense" or "direction" of the inequality is reversed, then the resulting inequality is a true statement. We now state these formally as theorems, giving proofs for two of them.

Theorem 13. If $a < b$, then $a + c < b + c$.

Proof: (The commutative and associative axioms are used freely here without mention.) If $a < b$ then $b - a \in P$, by the definition of "less than," and, since $c - c = 0$, we have

$$b - a = b + {}^-a + c + {}^-c = b + c + {}^-a + {}^-c = (b + c) - (a + c) \in P.$$

Again, by the definition of "less than," we see that this last statement means that $a + c < b + c$.

Theorem 14. If $a < b$ and $0 < c$, then $ac < bc$.

Proof: Since $a < b$ and $0 < c$ we know from the definition of "less than" that $b - a \in P$ and $c \in P$. Then by the order axiom $(b - a)c \in P$, that is, $bc - ac \in P$ and thus $ac < bc$.

Theorem 15. If $a < b$ and $c < 0$, then $bc < ac$.

Proof: Left as an exercise.

Some examples illustrating the use of these ideas follow after a few words about notation.

The expression "$a > b$" is read "a is greater than b" and it means that b is less than a; i.e., $a > b$ if and only if $b < a$. The expression "$a \leq b$" is read "a is less than or equal to b" and is an abbreviated way of writing "$a < b$ or $a = b$." All the results established for "$<$" hold for "$\leq$" and can be easily proved by considering separately the cases where equality holds.

Example 2-1. Find all real numbers x for which $2x - 7 < 0$.

Solution. If x is a real number such that $2x - 7 < 0$, by Theorem 12 we have $(2x - 7) + 7 < 0 + 7$ or $2x < 7$. From this, by Theorem 13, since $0 < \frac{1}{2}$ (Why?), $\frac{1}{2} \cdot (2x) < \frac{1}{2} \cdot 7$ or $x < \frac{7}{2}$. This shows that *if there are any numbers* x *such that* $2x - 7 < 0$, *then* $x < \frac{7}{2}$. On the other hand, if $x < \frac{7}{2}$, $2x < 7$ (Why?) and $2x - 7 < 0$ (Why?). And this shows that *every* number x which is less than $\frac{7}{2}$ works; i.e., the *solution set* for this problem is $\{x \mid x < \frac{7}{2}\}$.

Notice in this example that there are two important parts: First, we assumed that there was a number x such that $2x - 7 < 0$, and from this we deduced that $x < 7/2$. Then we reversed the steps to show that if $x < 7/2$, then $2x - 7 < 0$. This shows, of course, that

$$\{x \mid 2x - 7 < 0\} = \{x \mid x < 7/2\}.$$

Both of these steps are important, and should be observed in solving any inequalities of this type. In the following examples, we do not supply all these details, but the reader is urged to supply them for himself.

Example 2-2. Find the solution set of the inequality $5x + 7 < 8x - 3$.

Solution. If x is a real number such that $5x + 7 < 8x - 3$, then

$$\begin{aligned} &5x - 8x < -3 - 7 \\ &-3x < -10 \\ &(-1/3)(-3x) > -1/3(-10) \qquad \text{Theorem 15} \\ &x > 10/3. \end{aligned}$$

Since these steps are reversible, we conclude that the solution set for the inequality $5x + 7 < 8x - 3$ is the set $\{x \mid x > 10/3\}$.

Example 2-3. Solve the inequality $(3x - 5)/x < 2$; i.e., find the solution set.

Solution. Note first of all that

$$\{x \mid (3x - 5)/x < 2\}$$
$$= \{x \mid (3x - 5)/x < 2 \text{ and } x > 0\} \cup \{x \mid (3x - 5)/x < 2 \text{ and } x < 0\}.$$

Considering first

$$\{x \mid (3x - 5)/x < 2 \text{ and } x > 0\}$$

we have that if

$$x > 0$$

and

$$(3x - 5)/x < 2$$

then,

$$3x - 5 < 2x$$

and

$$x < 5.$$

Hence,

$$\{x \mid (3x - 5)/x < 2 \text{ and } x > 0\} = \{x \mid x < 5\} \cap \{x \mid x > 0\}.$$

Next, we consider $\{x \mid (3x - 5)/x < 2 \text{ and } x < 0\}$. If $x < 0$ and $(3x - 5)/x < 2$, then

$$3x - 5 > 2x,$$

and

$$x > 5.$$

But there are no numbers x such that $x < 0$ and $x > 5$. (Why?) Hence,

$$\{x \mid (3x - 5)/x < 2 \text{ and } x < 0\} = \varnothing.$$

Thus, we have

$$\begin{aligned}\{x \mid (3x - 5)/x < 2\} &= \{x \mid (3x - 5)/x < 2 \text{ and } x > 0\} \\ &= \{x \mid x < 5\} \cap \{x \mid x > 0\} \\ &= \{x \mid 0 < x \text{ and } x < 5\}.\end{aligned}$$

In other words, the set of all numbers x such that $(3x - 5)/x < 2$ is the set of positive numbers less than 5.

DEFINITION. The *absolute value* of the real number a, denoted $|a|$, is defined as follows:

(1) $|a| = a$ if $a \geq 0$.
(2) $|a| = -a$ if $a < 0$.

Some examples will help illustrate the meaning and use of this definition.

Example 2-4. Since $\frac{1}{2} > 0$, $|\frac{1}{2}| = \frac{1}{2}$.

Example 2-5. $|-3| = -(-3)$ since $-3 < 0$. Hence $|-3| = 3$.

Example 2-6. For what numbers x is it true that $|x| = 3$?

Solution. The definition gives rise to two cases. If $x \geq 0$, then $|x| = x$, and the equation $|x| = 3$ becomes $x = 3$. If $x < 0$, then $|x| = -x$, hence $|x| = 3$ becomes $-x = 3$ or $x = -3$. We also see by the definition that $|\pm 3| = 3$ and we obtain $\{x \mid |x| = 3\} = \{3, -3\}$.

THEOREM 16. If a is a real number, then $|a| \geq 0$.

Proof: By Axiom 7, $a \geq 0$ or $a < 0$. If $a \geq 0$, $|a| = a$ by definition. Thus, $|a| \geq 0$. If $a < 0$, then by definition $|a| = -a$. But in this case $-a > 0$. Hence in either case $|a| \geq 0$.

THEOREM 17. Let a, x be real numbers such that $a > 0$. Then

$$|x| < a \quad \text{if and only if} \quad -a < x < a.$$

Proof: (Here, the notation $-a < x < a$ means that $-a < x$ *and* $x < a$.)
First, we prove that if $|x| < a$, then $-a < x < a$.

Case 1. If $x \geq 0$, then $|x| = x$ by definition. So if $|x| < a$, $x < a$.

Hence, $0 \leq x < a$. But since $a > 0$, $-a < 0$ giving

$$-a < x < a.$$

Case 2. If $x < 0$, $|x| = -x$ by definition. So if $|x| < a$, $-x < a$, or, by Theorem 15, $-a < x$. Since $x < 0$ and $0 < a$, $x < a$ so that

$$-a < x < a.$$

Now we prove that if $-a < x < a$, then $|x| < a$.

Case 1. If $x \geq 0$, then $|x| = x$ by definition. So if $-a < x < a$, then $x = |x| < a$.

Case 2. If $x < 0$, then $|x| = -x$ by definition. So if $-a < x$, then $-x < a$ by Theorem 15, or, $-x = |x| < a$.

In both cases we have that if $-a < x < a$, then $|x| < a$.

Example 2-7. For which real numbers x is it true that $|2x + 3| < 4$?

Solution. We use Theorem 17 with $2x + 3$ playing the role of x. According to the theorem there is a number x such that $|2x + 3| < 4$ if and only if $-4 < 2x + 3 < 4$; i.e., if and only if $-7 < 2x < 1$ or $-7/2 < x < 1/2$.

Example 2-8. Find all real numbers x for which $|x - 3| \geq 7$.

Solution. If we first observe that $|x - 3| \geq 7$ is true for all numbers x *except* those for which $|x - 3| < 7$, we may again use Theorem 17. Now $|x - 3| < 7$ is true if and only if $-7 < x - 3 < 7$, and thus, if and only if $-4 < x < 10$. The solution to the original inequality is, then, all those numbers x except those satisfying $-4 < x < 10$. The solution thus has to be those numbers x such that $x \leq -4$ or $x \geq 10$.

Additional discussion of this concept will be found in Chapter 3 where an interesting geometrical interpretation is given.

Exercises

8. Find all real numbers x for which:
   (a) $3x + 4 < 17$.
   (b) $x + 8 < 3x - 19$.
   (c) $3(x - 4) \geq 13 - 8x$.
   (d) $(x + 5)/x < 3$.
   (e) $(3x - 5)/2 \leq x^{-1}$.
   (f) $|x + 2| < 8$.
   (g) $|3x - 5| \leq 7/2$.
   (h) $|x - 4| \geq 3$.

9. Prove that if $a < b$ and $c < 0$, then $ac > bc$.

10. Prove that if $a < b$ and $b < c$, then $a < c$.

11. Show that if $x < 0$ and $5 < y$, then $x < y$.

12. We have seen on page 35 that for a non-zero number x, $0 < x$ or $x < 0$. In case $0 < x$, $x \in P$ or x is positive. We define x to be *negative* in case $x < 0$. Prove the following:

(a) The product of a negative number and a positive number is a negative number.

(b) The product of two negative numbers is a positive number. (Compare (a) to Theorem 9 and (b) to Theorem 10 and discuss how they are related to each other.)

(c) If ab is positive, then a, b are both positive or a, b are both negative.

(d) If ab is negative, then a is positive and b is negative or a is negative and b is positive.

(e) The sum of two negative numbers is negative.

(f) The number $-x$ is negative only if x is positive.

(g) The number x is negative only if $-x$ is positive.

13. Prove that if $a > 0$, then $a^{-1} > 0$ and if $a < 0$, then $a^{-1} < 0$.

14. (a) Prove that if $0 \leq a < b$, then $a^2 < b^2$.

(b) Prove that if $b < a \leq 0$, then $a^2 < b^2$.

(c) Show by an example that the following is not true:

$$\text{If } a < b, \text{ then } a^2 < b^2.$$

15. Show that for a real number x

(a) $-|x| \leq x \leq |x|$.

(b) $|x|^2 = x^2$.

16. If a is a real number, show that

$$\sqrt{a^2} = |a|.$$

[*Hint:* If $x \geq 0$ is a real number, $\sqrt{x}$ *means* that *non-negative* real number whose square is x.]

17. Prove each of the following:

(a) If $x \neq 0$, then $x^2 > 0$.

(b) There is no number x such that $x^2 + 1 = 0$.

(c) If $x \leq y$, then $-y \leq -x$.

(d) If $0 < x < y$, then $0 < y^{-1} < x^{-1}$.

(e) If $x < y$ and $w < z$, then $x + w < y + z$.

(f) If $x < y$, then $x < (1/2)(x + y) < y$.
(g) If $x < y < z$, then $x < (1/3)(x + y + z) < z$.
(h) Prove that $(1/2)(x + y + |x - y|)$ is the larger number of x, y.

18. Solve the following equations:
(a) $|x| = 0$.
(b) $|2x| = 4$.
(c) $|x - 1| = 0$.
(d) $|7x + 2| = 5$.
(e) $|y - 2| = -3$.
(f) $|x + 1| = |1 - x|$.
(g) $|2x| = |(1/2)x + 2|$.
(h) $|x - y| = 0$.

19. Obtain the solution set for each of the following:
(a) $|x - 1| \leq |x - 2|$.
(b) $|7x + 2| < |5 - x|$.
(c) $|4 - x|^{-1} < 1$.
(d) $7 < |x + 1|$.

*2.3 The Completeness Axiom

We come now to our last axiom. This axiom in a sense "completes" the system of real numbers. We say "completes" because it is this axiom which allows us to show that we have all the numbers which we desire. For example, without the completeness axiom we could not show that there is a real number x such that $x^2 = 2$; i.e., we would not know that $\sqrt{2}$ exists. We must go beyond the collection of rational numbers to obtain such a number as the following shows.

Theorem 18. There is no rational number x such that $x^2 = 2$.

Proof: Suppose that there is a rational number m/n such that $(m/n)^2 = 2$, where m, n are integers and $n \neq 0$. We may assume that m, n have no common factor [see Exercise 6(f)]. Then if $(m/n)^2 = 2$, $m^2 = 2n^2$ and m^2 is even. If m is an odd integer, there is an integer k such that $m = 2k + 1$ (by definition of odd integer). Thus $m^2 = 2(2k^2 + 2k) + 1$ which shows that m^2 is odd contrary to the above result that it is even. Therefore, m cannot be odd and must be even. Hence, there is an integer k such that $m = 2k$. Then $m^2 = 4k^2$, and substituting in the above equation $m^2 = 2n^2$ gives $4k^2 = 2n^2$ or $2k^2 = n^2$. This last equation shows that n^2 is even and, as before, n is even. Since we have already shown that m is even, the two integers, m, n have a common factor of 2 contrary to the fact m/n is in "reduced form." From this contradiction we conclude that there is no rational number m/n such that $(m/n)^2 = 2$.

We need a few preliminary ideas before stating the Completeness Axiom.

DEFINITION. If S is a non-empty set of real numbers, then a real number x is an *upper bound* of S if and only if

$$s \leq x \qquad \text{for all} \qquad s \in S.$$

Some sets have upper bounds and some do not, as the following examples show.

Example 2-8. The set of real numbers has no upper bound since if x is any real number, then $x < x + 1$.

Example 2-9. The set $\{\frac{1}{2}, -8, 2, \frac{7}{8}, \sqrt{2}\}$ has the numbers 2, 3, $11\frac{1}{2}$, 100, 4086 as some of its upper bounds. Of course, these are not all the upper bounds of this set, since *any* number larger than the given upper bounds is also an upper bound.

Example 2-10. Let $S = \{t \mid t \text{ is a real number and } t^3 < 10\}$. The number 1 is not an upper bound for S since $1 < 2$ and $2 \in S (2^3 < 10)$. However, we claim that 4 is an upper bound for S. Suppose that $t \geq 4$. Then $t^3 \geq 64 > 10$ so that $t^3 > 10$. Hence $t \notin S$. Therefore, if $t \in S$, $t < 4$.

DEFINITION. Let S be a non-empty set of real numbers and let t be an upper bound of S such that if u is any upper bound of S, then

$$t \leq u.$$

Then t is called the *least upper bound* of S.

We may describe a least upper bound of a set (if it has one) as the *smallest* of all its upper bounds.

Example 2-11. Of all the upper bounds for the set $\{\frac{1}{2}, -8, 2, \frac{7}{8}, \sqrt{2}\}$ we see that 2 is the smallest. Hence, 2 is the least upper bound of this set.

Example 2-12. Let $S = \{x \mid x < 1\}$. Then 1 is clearly an upper bound for S. Also, 1 is the smallest of all the upper bounds for S, for we can show that no number smaller than 1 can be an upper bound for S. To do this, suppose that t is a number such that $t < 1$. Then $t < (\frac{1}{2})(t + 1) < 1$. [See Exercise 17(f)]. Therefore $(\frac{1}{2})(t + 1)$ is an element of S which is larger than t so that t cannot be an upper bound for S.

Observe that the least upper bound of the set $\{\frac{1}{2}, -8, 2, \frac{7}{8}, \sqrt{2}\}$ is a member of the set, while the least upper bound of $\{x|x < 1\}$ is not a member since $1 \notin \{x|x < 1\}$.

Suppose that u is the least upper bound of some set S. Then, in particular, u is an upper bound for S; i.e., $x \leq u$ for all $x \in$ S. Also, if d is *any* positive number, there is an element $y \in$ S such that $u - d < y$. This is true because if there is no such $y \in$ S, then $x \leq u - d$ for *all* $x \in$ S and this would imply that $u - d$ is an upper bound for S. But since d is positive, $u - d < u$, and u was supposed to be the *least* upper bound for S. Therefore, if u is the least upper bound of S, we may say the following:

(a) $x \leq u$ for all $x \in$ S.

(b) There is an element $y \in$ S for each positive number d such that

$$u - d < y.$$

The reader may be familiar with the fact that not every set of real numbers contains a least or smallest element. For example, the set $D = \{t|0 < t < 10\}$ contains no smallest element. Suppose to the contrary that $d \in D$ and $d \leq t$ for *all* $t \in D$. Then since $d \in D$, $0 < d < 10$. But $0 < (½)d < d$ or $0 < (½)d < 10$, which shows that $(½)d \in D$ and is smaller than the element which was supposed to be smallest. Thus, the set D contains no smallest element.

The content of our final axiom is that certain kinds of sets of real numbers *always* have least members. We start with a set of real numbers S $\neq \varnothing$ which has upper bounds. Then we consider the set $\triangle$ of *all* upper bounds of S. The completeness axiom asserts that $\triangle$ contains a smallest or least member.

Axiom 8. *Completeness Axiom* (or Least Upper Bound Axiom). Let S be a set of real numbers such that S $\neq \varnothing$ and S has upper bounds. Then S has a least upper bound.

If a non-empty set S of real numbers has upper bounds, then we say that S is *bounded above.* Using this terminology, Axiom 8 may be expressed as follows: *Every non-empty set of real numbers which is bounded above has a least upper bound.*

The use of this axiom will now be illustrated in proving some results.

Theorem 19. The set Z of positive integers is not bounded above.

Proof: Suppose to the contrary that there is a real number y such that $n \leq y$ for all $n \in$ Z. Then, by Axiom 8, Z has a least upper bound, say x. Since $x - 1 < x$, there is an integer $m \in$ Z such that

$x - 1 < m$ and $x < m + 1$. But $m + 1 \in Z$. Hence x is *not* an upper bound for Z. This contradiction thus proves the theorem.

Theorem 20. If d is any positive real number, then there is an integer n such that $(1/n) < d$.

Proof: By Theorem 19 the set of positive integers is not bounded above. Hence there is an integer n such that $n > 1/d$. Then $1/n < d$.

Theorem 21. Let x, y be real numbers such that $y > 0$. Then there is a positive integer m such that $x < my$.

Proof: If x is negative or zero, then, since $y > 0$, $x < 1 \cdot y$ and we may take $m = 1$. If x is positive, then y/x is positive and by Theorem 20 there is an integer $m > 0$ such that $(1/m) < y/x$. Hence $x < my$.

It was pointed out earlier that without the completeness property of the real numbers, we do not know that there is a number x such that $x^2 = 2$. With the completeness axiom we may prove that there is such a number x. First, we define

$$S = \{y \mid y \text{ is a positive rational number and } y^2 < 2\}.$$

Then $1 \in S$ so that $S \neq \varnothing$. Also, 3 is an upper bound for S (for if $y \geq 3$, then $y^2 \geq 9$ so that $y \notin S$). Therefore, by Axiom 8, S has a least upper bound, say x. It is now possible to show that $x^2 = 2$. ($\sqrt{2}$ is by definition this number x.) We shall not give the proof here; the reader may find this carried further in *Introduction to Analysis*, Vol. I, by N. B. Haaser, J. P. LaSalle, J. A. Sullivan, Ginn & Co., 1959, or in *The Number System* by B. K. Youse, Dickenson Publishing Co., 1965.

*Exercises

20. Formulate definitions for the following terms: *lower bound, greatest lower bound, largest element.*

21. For each of the following sets, find some lower bounds and upper bounds when these exist.
    (a) $\{1/10, -\sqrt{2}, 1/2, 0.78\}$.
    (b) $\{n^2 \mid n \text{ is an integer}\}$.
    (c) $\{m^2 \mid m \text{ is an integer and } m < 101\}$.
    (d) $\{(1/2)n \mid n \text{ is an integer and } n \geq 0\}$.

(e) $\{1/m \mid m \text{ is an integer and } m > 0\}$.
(f) $\{1 - 1/n \mid n \text{ is a positive integer}\}$.

22. For each of the sets in 21,
(a) find the least upper bound if it exists;
(b) find the greatest lower bound when it exists.

23. Use Axiom 8 to prove that a non-empty set S of real numbers which has lower bounds has a greatest lower bound. [*Hint:* consider the set $N = \{-x \mid x \in S\}$.]

24. Show that the set $\{1 - 1/n \mid n \text{ is a positive integer}\}$ has no largest element.

25. (a) Show that if a set $S \neq \varnothing$ of real numbers has a largest member q, then q is the least upper bound of S.
(b) Show that if a set $S \neq \varnothing$ has a smallest member p, then p is the greatest lower bound of S.

26. Prove that every real number x is between two integers; i.e., prove that there are integers n, m such that $n < x < m$.

27. As indicated above, $\sqrt{2}$ is defined to be the least upper bound of the set

$$\{y \mid y \text{ is a positive rational number and } y^2 < 2\}.$$

In a similar fashion formulate definitions for each of the following:

(a) $\sqrt[3]{2}$. (b) $\sqrt[3]{7}$. (c) $3^{3/5}$.

Be sure in each case to show that the set which you use in your definition is not empty and that it has an upper bound.

2.4 The Natural Numbers and Mathematical Induction

The reader will recall that the set N of natural numbers or positive integers consists of the numbers $1, 1 + 1, 1 + 1 + 1, 1 + 1 + 1 + 1$, etc., and that these are denoted by

$$1, 2, 3, 4, \ldots.$$

A basic characteristic of the set N of natural numbers is the so-called well ordering property which we assume to be true. (This may be proved from the axioms above.)

Well-Ordering Property of the Natural Numbers: Let S be a subset of the natural numbers such that $S \neq \varnothing$. Then there is a natural number $t \in S$ such that $t \leq x$ for all $x \in S$.

The number t of this statement is called the *least* member of S. In this language we may say that *every non-void set of natural numbers contains a least element.*

Example 2-13. The least natural number in the set N of all natural numbers is 1; 2 is the least element of the set of even natural numbers.

Example 2-14. Show that there are no natural numbers x such that $0 < x < 1$.

Solution. Suppose there is at least one natural number x such that $0 < x < 1$. Then if

$$S = \{x \mid x \text{ is a natural number and } 0 < x < 1\},$$

$S \neq \varnothing$. By the well-ordering property there is a least member, say t, of S. Hence, $0 < t < 1$. If we multiply by t, we have

$$0 < t^2 < t < 1.$$

But since the product of natural numbers is a natural number, $t^2 \in S$ with $t^2 < t$. This is a contradiction and, therefore, proves the statement.

Example 2-15. Prove that if m is any natural number, then $m < 2^m$.

Solution. Suppose that there is some natural number n such that $n \geq 2^n$. Then the set

$$S = \{k \mid k \text{ is a natural number and } k \geq 2^k\}$$

is not empty. So S has a least member, say t. Thus t is the smallest natural number such that

$$t \geq 2^t.$$

We note that $t > 1$ since $1 < 2$. Therefore, $t - 1 \geq 1$ and is a natural number smaller than t. Since t is the smallest natural number such that $t \geq 2^t$, we conclude that $t - 1 < 2^{t-1}$. Then, by adding 1, we have $t < 2^{t-1} + 1$. But since $1 < 2^{t-1}$,

$$2^{t-1} + 1 < 2^{t-1} + 2^{t-1} = 2 \cdot 2^{t-1} = 2^t.$$

Hence $t < 2^t$, contrary to the fact that t was assumed to be the smallest natural number such that $t \geq 2^t$. We conclude that our original supposition that there was at least one natural number n such that $n \geq 2^n$ is incorrect, and that $m < 2^m$ for all natural numbers m.

In Example 2-15 we have the statement

$$m < 2^m.$$

In fact, we have many statements here—one for each natural number m—and we wish to prove that they are all true. It quite often happens that we have a function P which associates with each natural number n a statement $P(n)$ and we wish to show that the set

$$\{P(n) \mid n \text{ is a natural number}\}$$

contains only true statements. In the example above the statement $P(n)$ for each natural number n was

$$n < 2^n,$$

and we were able to prove that these are all true by using the well-ordering property of the natural numbers. Another method of doing this, which is based on the well-ordering property, is called mathematical induction.

Principle of Mathematical Induction. Let P be a function which associates with each natural number n a statement $P(n)$ and suppose that the following are true:

(a) $P(1)$ is true.

(b) if, for any natural number k, $P(k)$ is true, then $P(k + 1)$ is true.

Then $P(n)$ is true for all natural numbers n.

Proof: Suppose that there is at least one natural number s such that $P(s)$ is not true. Then the set

$$S = \{s \mid s \text{ is a natural number and } P(s) \text{ is false}\}$$

is not empty. Let t be the least element of S. Then $1 \notin S$ since by (a) $P(1)$ is true. Thus $t > 1$ and $t - 1$ is a natural number not in S (the smallest element of S is t and $t - 1 < t$). Hence, $P(t - 1)$ is true. By (b), then, $P(t - 1 + 1)$ is true; i.e., $P(t)$ is true. But $t \in S$ so that $P(t)$ is false—a contradiction. This implies that our supposition that there was at least one natural number s such that $P(s)$ is false is incorrect. Therefore $P(n)$ is true for all natural numbers n.

Let us apply the principle of mathematical induction to the statement

$$n < 2^n.$$

The principle states that we can conclude that this statement is true for all natural numbers if we can show that it has properties (a) and (b).

It has property (a) since $P(1)$ is the statement

$$1 < 2,$$

and this is true. If we know that $P(k)$ is a true statement for a natural number k; i.e., that

$$k < 2^k,$$

then,

$$k + 1 < 2^k + 1 < 2^k + 2^k = 2^{k+1}$$

or $P(k + 1)$ is true. This shows that (b) also is satisfied by P. Hence, we conclude that $P(n)$ is true for all natural numbers.

The procedure we have just used in applying the principle of mathematical induction must be observed generally; i.e., to prove that a statement is true for all natural numbers by mathematical induction we must:

(a) Show that the statement is true for 1.

(b) Show that if the statement is true for a natural number k, then it is true for $k + 1$.

Example 2-16. Let $P(n)$ be the statement

$$n = n + 1.$$

Show that P has property (b) but does not have property (a).

Solution. $P(1)$ is the statement

$$1 = 1 + 1$$

which is not true, so that P does not have property (a). To show that P has property (b) we must show that *if* $P(k)$ is true, then $P(k + 1)$ is true. If $P(k)$ is true, then

$$k = k + 1,$$

and adding 1 gives

$$k + 1 = (k + 1) + 1.$$

Hence, if $k = k + 1$, then $(k + 1) = (k + 1) + 1$. Thus (b) is satisfied. (The reader has no doubt decided that $n = n + 1$ is false for every natural number n.)

Example 2-17. Show that the statement

$$I(n)\colon n \neq n + 1$$

satisfies both conditions (a) and (b) of the principle of mathematical induction.

Solution. The statement $I(1)$ is

$$1 \neq 1 + 1$$

and this is true, so (a) is satisfied. Now suppose that $k \neq k + 1$. We need to demonstrate that this assumption implies that $k + 1 \neq (k + 1) + 1$. But if we did not have $k + 1 \neq (k + 1) + 1$, we would have $k + 1 = (k + 1) + 1$, and subtracting 1 would give $k = k + 1$. Hence, (b) is satisfied and we may conclude that $n \neq n + 1$ for all natural numbers n.

Example 2-18. Prove that $[n(n + 1)(n + 2)]/3$ is a natural number for all natural numbers n.

Solution. We apply the principle of mathematical induction to the statement $P(n)$: $[n(n + 1)(n + 2)]/3$ is a natural number. For $n = 1$ the statement $P(n)$ is

$$[1(1 + 1)(1 + 2)]/3 \text{ is a natural number;}$$

i.e., "2 is a natural number," and this is true, so $P(n)$ satisfies condition (a) of the induction principle. To show that condition (b) is also satisfied, suppose that $P(k)$ is true:

$$[k(k + 1)(k + 2)]/3 \text{ is a natural number.}$$

We wish to show that $P(k + 1)$ is true if $P(k)$ is true. The statement $P(k + 1)$ is

$$[(k + 1)(k + 2)(k + 3)]/3 \text{ is a natural number.}$$

Using the distributive and commutative axioms we may write

$$(k + 1)(k + 2)(k + 3) = k(k + 1)(k + 2) + 3(k + 1)(k + 2)$$

and therefore,

$$[(k + 1)(k + 2)(k + 3)]/3 = [k(k + 1)(k + 2)]/3 + [(k + 1)(k + 2)].$$

Since $(k + 1)(k + 2)$ is a natural number, the sum on the right above is a natural number if $[k(k + 1)(k + 2)]/3$ is a natural number. In other words, $[(k + 1)(k + 2)(k + 3)]/3$ is a natural number if $[k(k + 1)(k + 2)]/3$ is a natural number. This shows that $P(n)$ satisfies condition (b) and concludes the proof that $[n(n + 1)(n + 2)]/3$ is a natural number for all natural numbers n.

Example 2-19. Prove that for all natural numbers n

$$2 + 4 + 6 + \cdots + 2n = n(n + 1).$$

Solution. We are to prove that the sum of the first n even natural numbers is $n(n + 1)$. The induction principle may be applied to the statement

$$P(n)\colon 2 + 4 + 6 + \cdots + 2n = n(n + 1).$$

$P(1)$ is the statement: "$2 \cdot 1 = 1(1 + 1)$". Thus, $P(1)$ is true. The statements $P(k)$ and $P(k + 1)$ are

$$P(k)\colon 2 + 4 + 6 + \cdots + 2k = k(k + 1),$$

and

$$P(k + 1)\colon 2 + 4 + 6 + \cdots + 2k + 2(k + 1) = (k + 1)(k + 2).$$

Now suppose that $P(k)$ is true. Then,

$$\begin{aligned} 2 + 4 + 6 + \cdots + 2k + 2(k + 1) \\ &= (2 + 4 + 6 + \cdots + 2k) + 2(k + 1) \\ &= k(k + 1) + 2(k + 1) \\ &= (k + 1)(k + 2). \end{aligned}$$

This shows that if $P(k)$ is true, then so is $P(k + 1)$.

Exercises

28. Prove that for all natural numbers n each of the following is a natural number.
(a) $[n(n + 1)]/2$.
(b) $[n(n + 1)(n + 2)]/6$.
(c) $[n(n + 1)(n + 2)(n + 3)]/24$.

29. Prove the following generalization of the induction principle: Let $P(n)$ be a statement that is associated with every natural number n such that $n \geq a$ where a is a natural number. Suppose the following is true:
(a) $P(a)$ is true.
(b) If $P(k)$ is true for any natural number $k \geq a$, $P(k + 1)$ is true.
Then $P(n)$ is true for all natural numbers $n \geq a$.

30. Prove each of the following is true for all natural numbers n:
(a) $1 + 2 + 3 + \cdots + n = [n(n + 1)]/2$.
(b) $1 + 3 + 5 + \cdots + (2n - 1) = n^2$.
(c) $1 + 5 + 9 + \cdots + (4n - 3) = n(2n - 1)$.
(d) $1 + 4 + 9 + \cdots + n^2 = [n(n + 1)(2n + 1)]/6$.
(e) $1 + 8 + 27 + \cdots + n^3 = [n^2(n + 1)^2]/4$.
(f) $1/(1 \cdot 2) + 1/(2 \cdot 3) + 1/(3 \cdot 4) + \cdots + 1/[n(n + 1)] = n/(n + 1)$.
(g) $2 + 2(2^2) + 3(2^3) + \cdots + n(2^n) = 2 + (n - 1)2^{n+1}$.
(h) $a + ar + ar^2 + \cdots + ar^{n-1} = (ar^n - a)/(r - 1)$, where a, r are real numbers and $r \neq 1$.

(i) $2 \cdot 3 + 2 \cdot 3 + 2 \cdot 3^2 + \cdots + 2 \cdot 3^{n-1} = 3^n - 1.$

(j) $1 + \frac{1}{\sqrt{2}} + \frac{1}{\sqrt{3}} + \cdots + \frac{1}{\sqrt{n}} \geq \sqrt{n}.$

31. Prove each of the following:

(a) If n is a positive integer and if x is a number such that $0 < x < 1$, then $0 < x^n < 1$.

(b) If n is a natural number such that $n \geq 4$, then $2^n < n!$ ($n!$ means $1 \cdot 2 \cdot 3 \ldots n$). [*Hint:* use the induction principle of Exercise 29.]

(c) If a line segment of unit length is given, then a line segment of length $\sqrt{n}$ can be constructed with ruler and compass for any natural number n.

(d) If x, y are real numbers and n is a natural number, then $x^n - y^n = (x - y)(x^{n-1} + x^{n-2}y + x^{n-3}y^2 + \cdots + xy^{n-2} + y^{n-1})$.

(e) The sum of the interior angles of a convex polygon of n sides is $180° \cdot (n - 2)$, where $n \geq 3$.

(f) Let $a, b, x_1, x_2, x_3, \ldots, x_n$ be real numbers and n a natural number. If $a < x_1 < b, a < x_2 < b, a < x_3 < b, \ldots, a < x_n < b$, then,

$$a < (x_1 + x_2 + x_3 + \cdots x_n)/n < b.$$

(g) If x is a real number such that $x \geq -1$ and n is a natural number, then

$$(1 + x)^n \geq 1 + nx.$$

32. Use the well-ordering property of the natural numbers to prove the following.

Let Z be a subset of the natural numbers N which satisfies the following two conditions:

(a) $1 \in Z$.

(b) If $k \in Z$, then $(k + 1) \in Z$.

Then $Z = N$.

3

Real Relations, Functions and Their Graphs

3.1 Real Coordinate Systems

It will be recalled that a grid type representation for a relation on a set X requires that points of a line be chosen to represent the elements of the set X. Since we are now concerned with *real* relations, we wish to represent the set of all real numbers as points on a line. There are many ways of doing this; we describe below a way which is the one most in use.

On any line L choose two district points, say A and B, with B to the right of A. Let 0 be represented by A and let 1 be represented by the point B, called the *unit point*. (See Fig. 3-1.) Now to the right and left

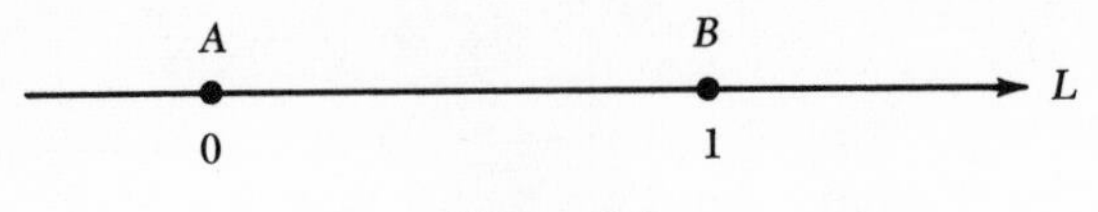

Figure 3-1

of A mark off segments equal in length to segment AB. Let the resulting points represent the positive and negative integers as indicated in Fig. 3-2. It is evident in Fig. 3-2 that if n is any integer the point on L which

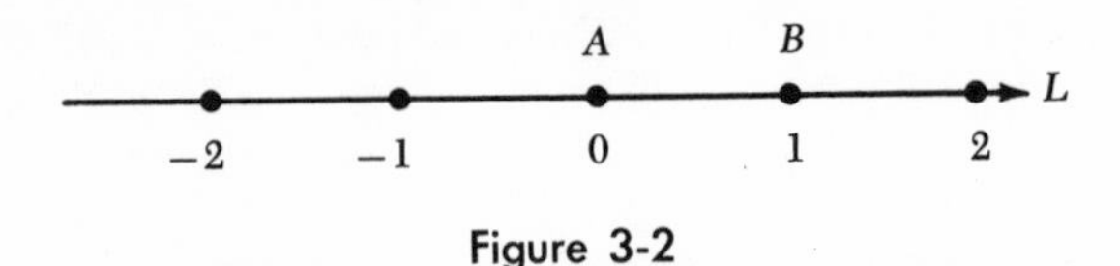

Figure 3-2

represents n is a distance $|n|$ from the point A. If a is any real number, we mark two points on line L, one to the right of A and one to the left of A. Both of these points will be taken at a distance $|a|$ from the point A. (See Fig. 3-3.) Then if $a > 0$, the point to the right of A

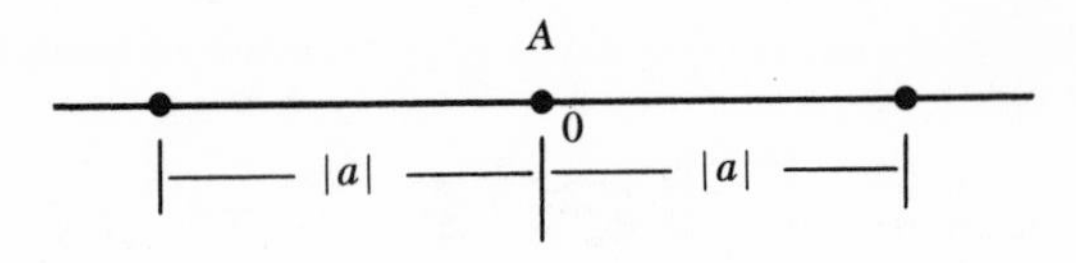

Figure 3-3

is taken to represent a; if $a < 0$, the point to the left of A is taken to represent a. (See Fig. 3-4.)

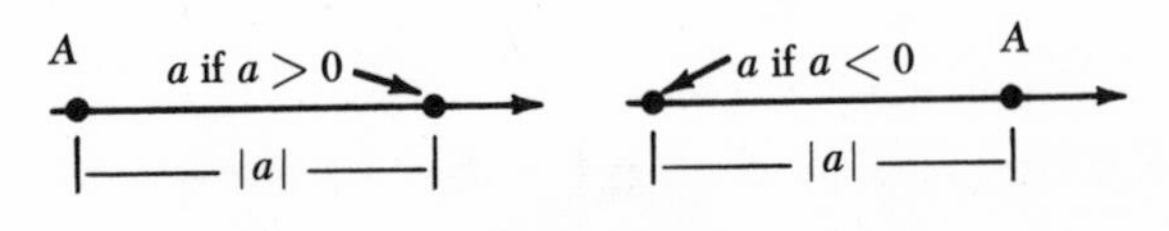

Figure 3-4

This discussion indicates how each real number is represented by a point on the line L. Conversely, we could reverse this process and indicate how each point of line L represents some number. That this process can be carried out is guaranteed by the completeness property of the real numbers—stated in Chapter 2. Such a representation of the real numbers is called a *one-dimensional coordinate system.* Let it be stressed that *if P is a point of the line and the number a is represented by P, then the distance between A and P is* $|a|$.

This particular way of representing real numbers on a line has the following convenient connection with "less than": $a < b$ *if and only if the point P representing a is to the left of the point M representing b.* Hence, $\{x|x > a\}$ is represented on the line L as the set of all points to the right of the point representing a. (See Fig. 3-5.) The relative

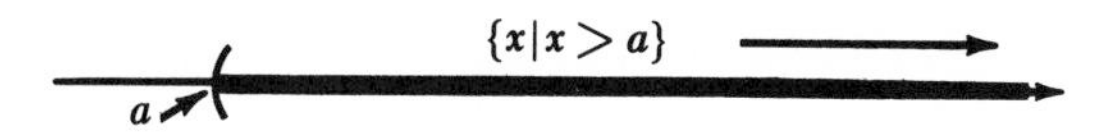

Figure 3-5

position of the sets $\{x|x < a\}$, $\{x|a < x < b\}$, $\{x|x > b\}$ on line L is indicated in Fig. 3-6.

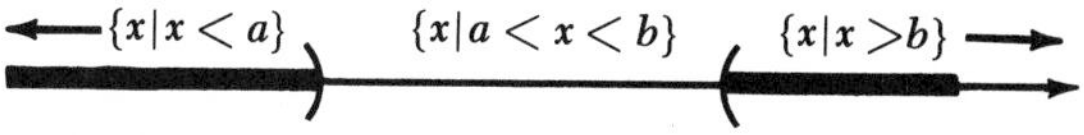

$\{x|x < a\}$ $\{x|a < x < b\}$ $\{x|x > b\}$

Figure 3-6

Now that we have described a method of associating a number with each point of a line, we may discuss *rectangular coordinate systems.* A rectangular two-dimensional coordinate system is established by taking two lines perpendicular to each other and, on each of these lines, a one-

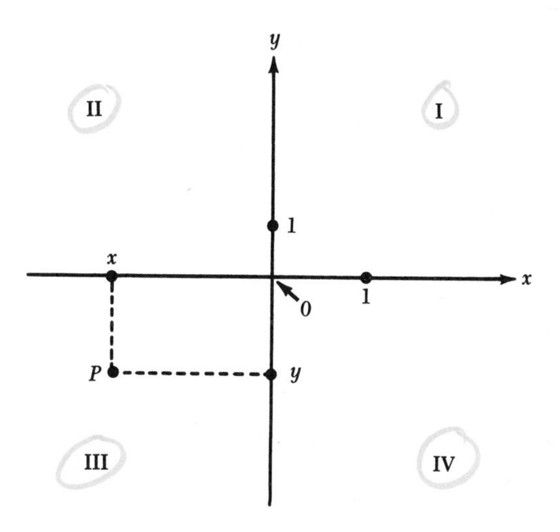

Figure 3-7

dimensional coordinate system is constructed as described above. We take one of the lines horizontal and the other vertical, and choose their point of intersection to correspond to 0, while the unit points are taken as indicated in Fig. 3-7.

The plane is now divided into four parts called *quadrants* as indicated in Fig. 3-7. Notice that the unit point on the vertical line is above the point corresponding to zero, and on the horizontal line it is to the right; also the unit lengths are not the same in the figure. In most of the work in this chapter the unit lengths chosen will be the same, although this is by no means necessary. It is now possible to associate with each point P of the plane an ordered pair (x, y) of real numbers. The method for doing this was described in Chapter 1 but for emphasis the procedure which establishes this association will now be reviewed.

First of all, if the point P in the plane is given, how is the ordered pair (x, y) which goes with P found? As usual, two lines are drawn through P: one line parallel to the horizontal line and the other one parallel to the vertical line. (See Fig. 3-7.) The two numbers obtained in this way, as indicated in Fig. 3-7, determine the ordered pair (x, y) that is associated with P. It should be stressed that the number x of the horizontal line is the first member of the ordered pair (x, y), and that the number y of the vertical line is the second member of the ordered pair.

It has become standard practice to use the letter x to name numbers corresponding to points of the horizontal line and to use the letter y to name numbers corresponding to points of the vertical line. Hence, these lines are referred to as the "x-axis" and the "y-axis" respectively. (A more appropriate name for them would be "axis of first coordinates" and "axis of second coordinates".) Of course other names would do just as well, but the x, y-terminology is well established. If the ordered pair (a, b) corresponds to the point Q, we say that a is the *first* or *x-coordinate* of Q and that b is the *second* or *y-coordinate* of Q.

Now, suppose that the ordered pair (x, y) is given and we wish to determine the point P associated with (x, y). Choose the point on the x-axis which corresponds to the number x and construct a line on this point parallel to the y-axis; on the y-axis construct a line parallel to the x-axis which passes through the point corresponding to the number y. These two lines intersect (Why?) and their intersection point is the point P which we seek.

Several consequences of this particular method for establishing a coordinate system are immediate. For example, *if a point Q is on the x-axis and (a, b) corresponds to Q, then $b = 0$.* Remember that b is obtained from the y-axis as the intersection of the y-axis and a line on Q drawn parallel to the x-axis. But since Q is on the x-axis, the line on Q parallel to the x-axis is the x-axis itself, and this line meets the y-axis at 0. Hence, $b = 0$. We may therefore conclude that *every point of the x-axis corresponds to an ordered pair of the form* $(x, 0)$; i.e., the second coordinate of every such point is 0.

By a similar argument we obtain: *if* (a, b) *corresponds to a point of the y-axis,* $a = 0$; *every point of the y-axis corresponds to an ordered pair of the form* $(0, b)$.

We might refer to our two-dimensional coordinate system as being "distance oriented" for the following reason: *If the point Q corresponds to the ordered pair* (a, b), *then the distance between Q and the y-axis is* $|a|$ *and the distance between Q and the x-axis is* $|b|$. This can be seen very easily by recalling the method for establishing the coordinates on the x- and y-axis. For example, let Q be a point in the second quadrant. Then our result is illustrated by Fig. 3-8.

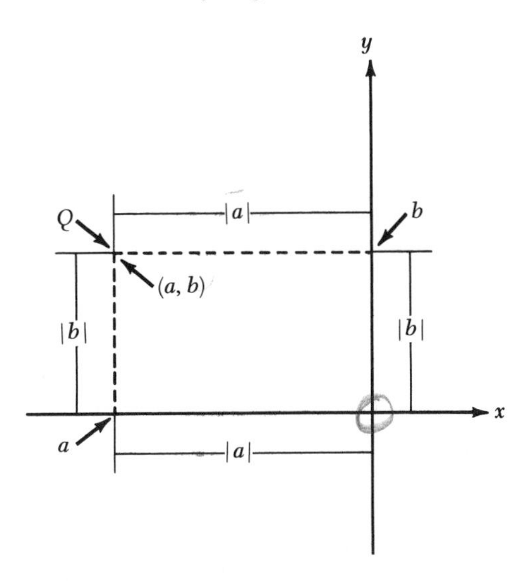

Figure 3-8

Example 3-1. Because of the way our coordinate system was constructed, we may easily verify the following:

(i) If F is a point in the first quadrant with coordinates (a, b), then $a \geq 0$ and $b \geq 0$.

(ii) If S is a point in the second quadrant with coordinates (a, b), then $a \leq 0$ and $b \geq 0$.

(iii) If T is a point in the third quadrant with coordinates (a, b), then $a \leq 0$ and $b \leq 0$.

(iv) If F is a point in the fourth quadrant with coordinates (a, b), then $a \geq 0$ and $b \leq 0$.

Example 3-2. Let k be a line which is 3.5 units below the x-axis and parallel to the x-axis. Show that if a point Q of k has coordinates (a, b) then $b = -3.5$.

Solution. By the above result, the point Q is a distance $|b|$ from the x-axis. But Q is on k, which is 3.5 units below the x-axis. Hence, $|b| = 3.5$ and $b = 3.5$ or $b = -3.5$. Since Q is *below* the x-axis, it is in either quadrant III or IV; from Example 3-1 (iii) and (iv), $b < 0$ so $b = -3.5$.

Example 3-3. Let m be the line which passes through the point with coordinates $(0, 0)$ (this point is called the *origin*) and bisects the second and fourth quadrants as indicated in Fig. 3-9. We mean by this that every point P of m is either in quadrant II or IV and P is the same distance from the x-axis as from the y-axis. Let us prove that if a point P of m has coordinates (a, b), then $b = -a$.

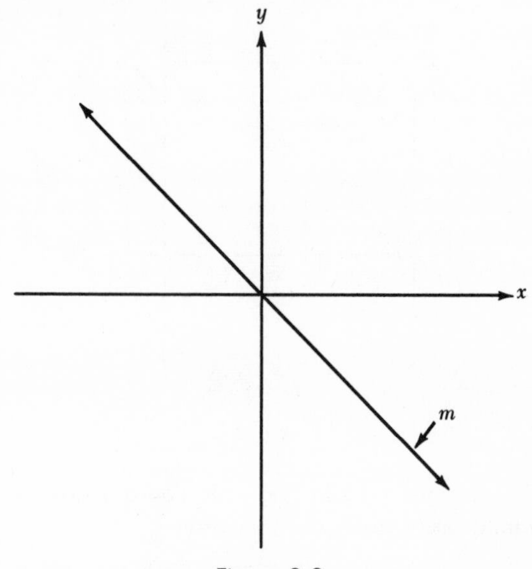

Figure 3-9

Solution. We are given that P is the same distance from the x-axis as from the y-axis; hence, $|a| = |b|$. If P is in quadrant II, $a \leq 0$ and $b \geq 0$ by Example 3-1 (ii). Then $|a| = -a$ and $|b| = b$, giving $b = -a$. If P is in quadrant IV, $a \geq 0$, $b \leq 0$ by Example 3-1 (iv). In this case, $|a| = a$, $|b| = -b$, and again $b = -a$. We may state this result by saying that *the second coordinate of every point on this line is the additive inverse of the first coordinate.*

Exercises

1. Construct a rectangular coordinate system with equal unit lengths on the two axes and plot the points having the following coordinates:
   (a) $(0, 0)$. (b) $(0, 1)$. (c) $(0, -1)$. (d) $(-1, 0)$.
   (e) $(\frac{1}{2}, -4)$. (f) $(-3, 3)$. (g) $(2.75, -8)$. (h) $(0, \frac{5}{8})$.

2. Construct a rectangular coordinate system with different unit lengths on the axes and plot the points having the coordinates of Exercise 1 above. In the rest of these problems take equal unit lengths.

3. Prove each of the following statements:
   (a) If n is a line 2 units to the right and parallel to the y-axis and (a, b) are coordinates of a point on n, then $a = 2$.
   (b) If m is a line d units to the left and parallel to the y-axis and (a, b) are coordinates of a point on m, then $a = -d$.
   (c) If k is a line t units above and parallel to the x-axis and (a, b) are coordinates of a point on k, then $b = t$.

4. Let W, Z be two points on the x-axis with a corresponding to W and b corresponding to Z. Show that the distance between W and Z is $|a - b|$.

5. If P is a point with coordinates (a, b), we say that the point with coordinates $(a, 0)$ is the *projection of P on the x-axis* and that the point having coordinates $(0, b)$ is the *projection of P on the y-axis.* Prove the following:
   (a) If A and B are points of a line parallel to the x-axis whose projections on the x-axis are $(a, 0)$ and $(b, 0)$ respectively, then the distance between A and B is $|a - b|$.
   (b) If C and D are points of a line parallel to the y-axis whose projections on the y-axis are $(0, c)$ and $(0, d)$ respectively, then the distance between C and D is $|c - d|$.

6. Let m be the line which passes through the origin and bisects the first and third quadrants. Show that if a point P of m has coordinates (a, b), then $b = a$. (See Example 3-3.)

7. Let t be the line on the two points with coordinates $(0, 1)$ and $(1, 0)$ respectively. Show that if Q is a point of t having coordinates (c, d), then $c + d = 1$.

8. Prove the statement on page 53 that says: On a one-dimensional coordinate system, if the number a corresponds to point P and the number b corresponds to the point M, then $a < b$ if and only if P is to the left of M.

3.2 The Distance Formula and Circles

We wish now to consider the following problem. Suppose that K and L are points of the plane having coordinates (a, b) and (c, d), respectively; can we express the distance between K and L in terms of the coordinates of the given points, i.e., in terms of the numbers a, b, c, d? We refer to Fig. 3-10 in the following consideration, but direct the reader's attention

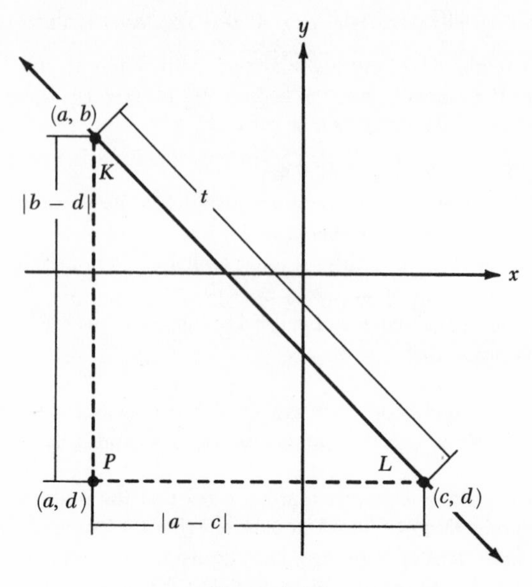

Figure 3-10

to the fact that only one of several possibilities for the location of the two points K and L with respect to the quadrants is pictured here. If a line on K is drawn parallel to the y-axis and a line on L is drawn parallel to the x-axis, these lines intersect at right angles in a point P having coordinates (a, d) as shown. Now, by Exercise 5, the lengths of the short sides of the right triangle formed are $|b - d|$ and $|a - c|$. Since the object here is to determine the distance t between K and L or the length of the line segment KL, we may use the pythagorean theorem (which says the sum of the squares of the lengths of the short sides of a right triangle is the square of the length of the long side) to obtain

$$|a - c|^2 + |b - d|^2 = t^2.$$

By a previous result $|a - c|^2 = (a - c)^2$ and $|b - d|^2 = (b - d)^2$ so that we may express the above equation as

$$t^2 = (a - c)^2 + (b - d)^2.$$

Since t is a length and must therefore be non-negative

$$t = \sqrt{(a - c)^2 + (b - d)^2}.$$

Thus, the question we started with has been answered: *If K and L are points having coordinates* (a, b) *and* (c, d) *respectively, then the distance between K and L is the number*

$$\sqrt{(a - c)^2 + (b - d)^2}.$$

This expression for the distance between points is known as the *distance formula.*

Example 3-4. If two points have coordinates $(-1, \sqrt{2})$ and $(\frac{1}{2}, 1)$, the distance between them is given by the distance formula as

$$\begin{aligned}\sqrt{(-1 - \tfrac{1}{2})^2 + (\sqrt{2} - 1)^2} &= \sqrt{\tfrac{9}{4} + (3 - 2\sqrt{2})} \\ &= \sqrt{\tfrac{21}{4} - 2\sqrt{2}} \\ &= \sqrt{(\tfrac{1}{4})(21 - 8\sqrt{2})} = \tfrac{1}{2}\sqrt{21 - 8\sqrt{2}}.\end{aligned}$$

Example 3-5. Show that a point having coordinates (a, b) is at a distance

$\sqrt{a^2 + b^2}$ from the origin.

Solution. The origin has coordinates $(0, 0)$ so that the distance between the point having coordinates (a, b) and the origin is given by the distance formula as

$$\sqrt{(a - 0)^2 + (b - 0)^2} = \sqrt{a^2 + b^2}.$$

Example 3-6. Let S be the set of coordinates (x, y) of points which are equidistant from the points having coordinates $(1, 1)$ and $(-1, -1)$, respectively. Now let

$$W = \{(x, y) \mid y = -x\}.$$

We will show that $W = S$. (See Fig. 3-11 and compare this with Example 3-3.)

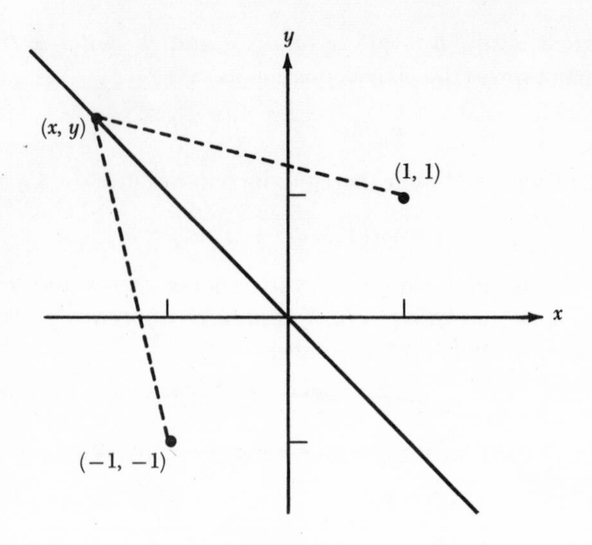

Figure 3-11

Solution. Let $(x, y) \in W$. Then $y = -x$ and the distance formula gives

$$\sqrt{(x-1)^2+(y-1)^2} = \sqrt{(x-1)^2+(-x-1)^2} = \sqrt{(x-1)^2+(x+1)^2}$$

and

$$\sqrt{(x+1)^2+(y+1)^2} = \sqrt{(x+1)^2+(-x+1)^2} = \sqrt{(x+1)^2+(x-1)^2}$$

as the distance between (x, y) and $(1, 1)$ and (x, y) and $(-1, -1)$ respectively. This shows that the distance between (x, y) and $(1, 1)$ is the same as the distance between (x, y) and $(-1, -1)$. Therefore, by definition of S, $(x, y) \in S$, which shows that every member of W is a member of S or $W \subseteq S$. Now, if (x, y) is a member of S we must have

$$\sqrt{(x-1)^2+(y-1)^2} = \sqrt{(x+1)^2+(y+1)^2}$$

by definition of S and the distance formula. This equation reduces to

$$\begin{aligned}(x-1)^2+(y-1)^2 &= (x+1)^2+(y+1)^2\\ x^2-2x+1+y^2-2y+1 &= x^2+2x+1+y^2+2y+1\\ -2x-2y &= 2x+2y\\ -4y &= 4x\\ y &= -x.\end{aligned}$$

But this shows that $(x, y) \in W$ and that $S \subseteq W$. It then follows that $S = W$.

The distance formula is extremely useful in analyzing circles in terms of coordinates of points. The reader will recall that a circle is a set of points in a plane having a center D and radius r, and that each of the points is a distance $r > 0$ from the point D. In other words, *a point P is on the circle of radius r and center D if and only if the distance between P and D is r.* If P has coordinates (x, y) and D has coordinates (a, b), then the distance between P and D is, according to the distance formula,

$$\sqrt{(x - a)^2 + (y - b)^2}.$$

Therefore, P is a point of the circle if and only if

$$\sqrt{(x - a)^2 + (y - b)^2} = r$$

or if and only if

$$(x - a)^2 + (y - b)^2 = r^2.$$

The circle of radius r and center D (a, b) may then be described as the set*

$$\{(x, y) \mid (x - a)^2 + (y - b)^2 = r^2\}.$$

Example 3-7. The circle with center at the origin and radius 2 is

$$\{(x, y) \mid (x - 0)^2 + (y - 0)^2 = 2^2\}, \qquad \text{or} \qquad \{(x, y) \mid x^2 + y^2 = 4\}.$$

Example 3-8. The set $\{(x, y) \mid x^2 + y^2 + 2x + 4y = 0\}$ describes the circle with center at $(-1, -2)$ and radius $\sqrt{5}$ since

$$x^2 + y^2 + 2x + 4y = 0$$

is equivalent to

$$(x - (-1))^2 + (y - (-2))^2 = (\sqrt{5})^2.$$

This is obtained by completing the squares in the equation above as follows:

$$\begin{aligned} x^2 + y^2 + 2x + 4y &= x^2 + 2x + y^2 + 4y \\ &= (x^2 + 2x + 1) + (y^2 + 4y + 4) - 5 \\ &= (x + 1)^2 + (y + 2)^2 - 5 \\ &= (x - (-1))^2 + (y - (-2))^2 - (\sqrt{5})^2. \end{aligned}$$

* This is a common notation that means D is a point whose coordinates are (a, b).

Hence,

$$\{(x, y) \mid x^2 + y^2 + 2x + 4y = 0\}$$
$$= \{(x, y) \mid (x - (-1))^2 + (y - (-2))^2 = (\sqrt{5})^2\}.$$

(See Fig. 3-12.)

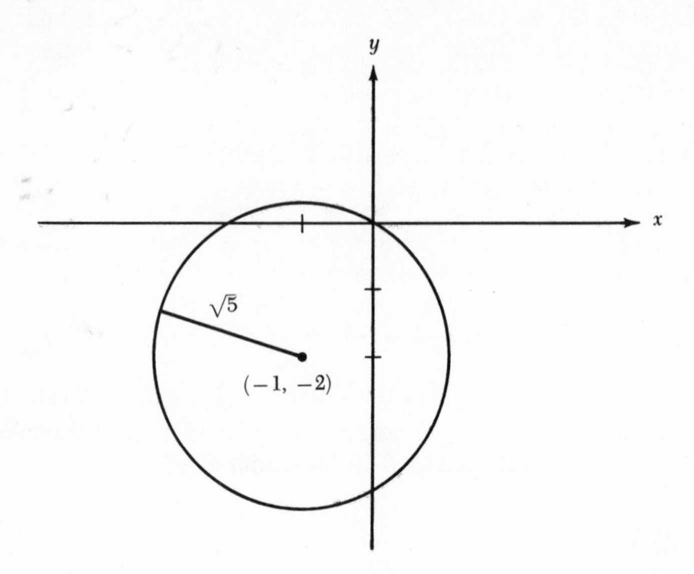

Figure 3-12

Exercises

9. Calculate the distance between the following pairs of points.

(a) $(1, 1)$; $(1, 2)$.
(b) $(0, 0)$; $(7, 9)$.
(c) $(\frac{1}{4}, -5)$; $(-1, 0)$.
(d) $(-\sqrt{2}, 1)$; $(1, -\frac{1}{8})$.

10. (a) In the proof of the distance formula, only the case in which one point is in quadrant II and the other is in quadrant IV was considered. List all the other possibilities and draw an appropriate figure for each.

(b) The results of Exercise 5 give the distance between points which lie on lines parallel to one of the axes. Show that the distance formula gives the same result.

11. Plot the following points and determine the area of the triangle obtained:

$$(-2, 0), (0, 2), (5, 0).$$

12. Determine whether the following sets are circles; if they are, give the center and radius.

(a) $\{(x, y) \mid x^2 + y^2 = 1\}$.

(b) $\{(x, y) \mid x^2 + y^2 = 0\}$.
(c) $\{(x, y) \mid (x - 1)^2 + y^2 = -1\}$.
(d) $\{(s, t) \mid (s - 1)^2 + (t - 1)^2 = 4\}$.
(e) $\{(a, b) \mid a^2 - 4 = b^2\}$.
(f) $\{(p, m) \mid (p + 8)^2 + (m + 5)^2 = \sqrt{2}\}$.
(g) $\{(p, m) \mid 4(p^2 + p) + 4(m^2 - 2m) = -1\}$.

13. Describe each of the following circles in set terminology.
(a) The circle of radius 1, center at $(0, 1)$.
(b) The circle of radius $\frac{1}{2}$, center at $(\sqrt{2}, -4)$.
(c) The circle of radius $\frac{3}{8}$, center at $(-1, -2)$.
(d) The circle of radius $\sqrt{6}$, center at $(-\frac{8}{9}, 0.6)$.

14. Show that the triangle with vertices $(-3, -1)$, $(2, 5)$ and $(4, \frac{10}{3})$ is a right triangle. [*Hint:* Use the converse of the pythagorean theorem.]

3.3 Graphs of Real Relations

By a *graph* of a relation we mean a set of points, and only those points, in the plane corresponding to the ordered pairs of the relation. For example, the circle of Fig. 3-13 is a graph of

$$\{(x, y) \mid x^2 + (y - 1)^2 = 4\}.$$

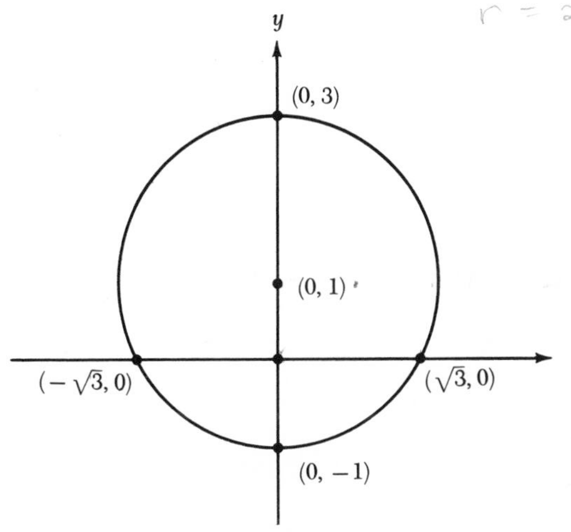

Figure 3-13

It will be recalled from Section 3-1 that on a one-dimensional coordinate system a set of the form $\{x \mid a \leq x \leq b\}$ is represented by a line segment as in Fig. 3-14. This set is called a *closed interval* and is denoted

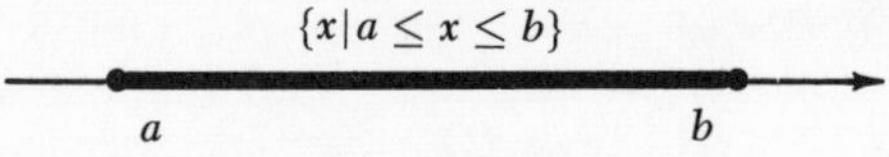

$\{x \mid a \leq x \leq b\}$

a b

Figure 3-14

by $[a, b]$; i.e., by definition

$$[a, b] = \{x \mid a \leq x \leq b\}.$$

Variations are:

$$(a, b) = \{x \mid a < x < b\},$$

called an *open interval;*

$$[a, b) = \{x \mid a \leq x < b\},$$

called a *right half-open interval;*

$$(a, b] = \{x \mid a < x \leq b\},$$

called a *left half-open interval.*

Example 3-9. Construct the graph of the relation $\{(x, y) \mid x \in [-1, 1]\}$.

Solution. We claim that the shaded area of Fig. 3-15 is the graph of this relation, since any (x, y) of this relation must have $x \in [-1, 1]$ or

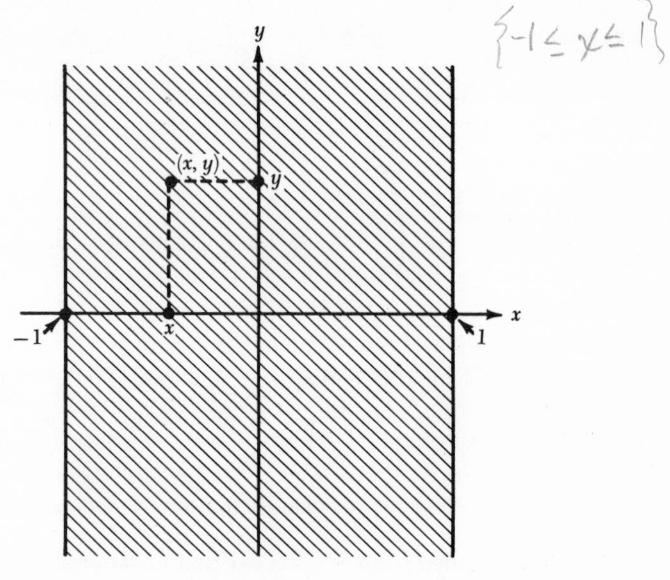

Figure 3-15

$-1 \leq x \leq 1$. On the other hand, if (x, y) is a point of the shaded area, then $-1 \leq x \leq 1$ and (x, y) is a member of the relation. Observe that this relation is the Cartesian product $[-1, 1] \times R$, where R is the set of reals.

Example 3-10. Construct the graph of the relation $\{(x, y) \mid |x| \leq 1\}$.

Solution. It is clear that $\{(x, y) \mid |x| \leq 1\} = \{(x, y) \mid -1 \leq x \leq 1\}$ since $|x| \leq 1$ if and only if $-1 \leq x \leq 1$. Hence, the graph of $\{(x, y) \mid |x| \leq 1\}$ is given by Fig. 3-15.

Example 3-11. Construct the graph of the relation $\{(x, y) \mid y = -x\}$.

Solution. In example 3-3, it is shown that if a point (a, b) is on the line which bisects the quadrants II and IV, then $b = -a$; i.e., every point on this line represents an element of the relation $\{(x, y) \mid y = -x\}$. Conversely, suppose the ordered pair $(a, b) \in \{(x, y) \mid y = -x\}$. Then $b = -a$ and $|b| = |-a| = |a|$. But $|a|$ is the distance that (a, b) is from the y-axis and $|b|$ is the distance that (a, b) is from the x-axis. Therefore, the point (a, b) is the same distance from the x-axis as from the y-axis. We cannot conclude at this point that (a, b) is a point of the line which bisects quadrants II and IV because points of the line bisecting quadrants I and III are also the same distance from one axis as from the other. But in this case the condition that $b = -a$ requires a and b to have *different signs* unless $a = b = 0$; and this is *not* true for the points of the line bisecting quadrants I and III. Hence, we conclude that if $b = -a$, (a, b) represents a point of the line bisecting quadrants II and IV. (See Fig. 3-11.)

Example 3-12. Construct the graph of the relation $\{(x, y) \mid x < y\}$.

Solution. If x is negative and $y \geq 0$, the condition $x < y$ is obviously met, and thus it is easy to see that every point to the left of the y-axis in quadrant II represents an element (x, y) of our relation. [See Fig. 3-16 (a).] If both x and y are positive, then $x = |x|$ and $y = |y|$ [the distance (x, y) is from the y-axis and x-axis, respectively] and the condition that $x < y$ requires that the point (x, y) be closer to the y-axis than to the x-axis. [See Fig. 3-16 (a).] We conclude from this that every point in quadrant I between the y-axis and the line bisecting quadrant I represents an element (x, y) of $\{(x, y) \mid x < y\}$. Next, if x and y are both negative $|x| = -x$ and $|y| = -y$ and since $x < y$, $-y < -x$ or the distance the point (x, y) is from the x-axis is less than the distance it is from the y-axis. [See Fig. 3-16 (b).] This tells us that every point of quadrant

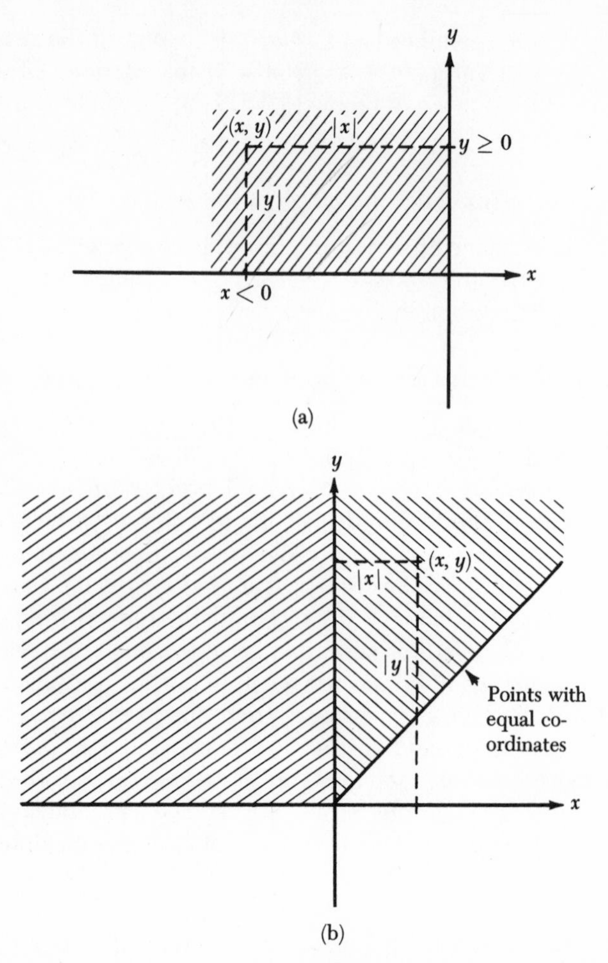

Figure 3-16

III between the x-axis and the line of Fig. 3-16 (c) (where $x = y$) represents a point of the given relation. (Obviously we cannot have $x < y$ if x is positive and y is negative, so all possible cases have been considered.) Conversely, it is evident that every point of the shaded region (not including the line L) of Fig. 3-16 (d) represents an ordered pair (x, y) such that $x < y$. Thus, the graph of the relation $\{(x, y) | x < y\}$ is the shaded region of Fig. 3-16 (d).

Of particular importance is the so-called *linear* relation

$$\{(x, y) | Ax + By = C\},$$

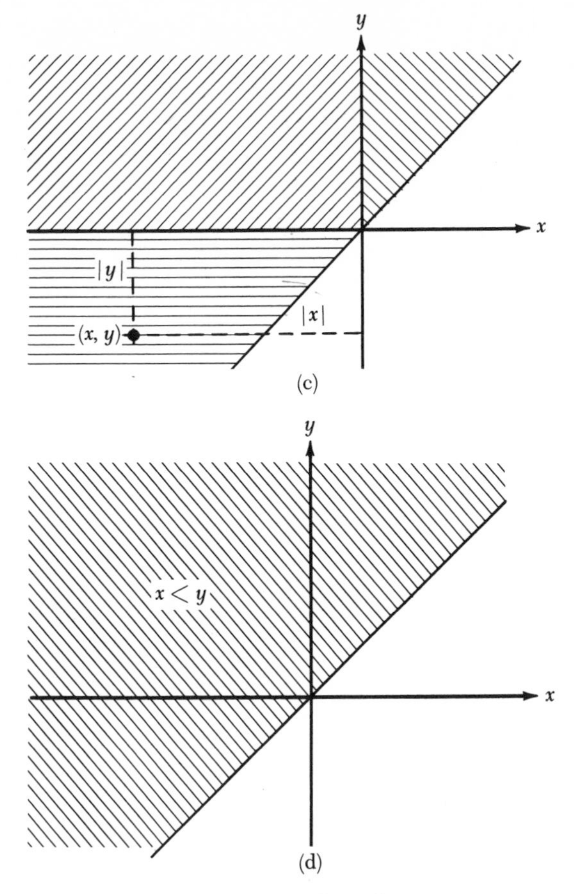

Figure 3-16 (cont.)

where A, B, C are real numbers and not both of A and B are zero. We now investigate the graphs of linear relations. If $B = 0$, then (since not both of A and B are zero) $A \neq 0$ and

$$\{(x, y) \mid Ax + By = C\} = \{(x, y) \mid Ax = C\}$$
$$= \{(x, y) \mid x = C/A\}.$$

If $C/A > 0$, every (x, y) of the linear relation is $|x| = |C/A| = C/A$ units from the y-axis and to the right of the y-axis. Thus, every (x, y) lies on the line parallel to, and C/A units to the right of, the y-axis. Conversely, every point of this line is C/A units from the y-axis and to the right, and hence represents a pair (x, y) where $x = C/A$. This line is the graph of the linear relation in this case. We have a similar situation if $C/A < 0$, except that the line is to the left of the y-axis. (See Fig. 3-17.)

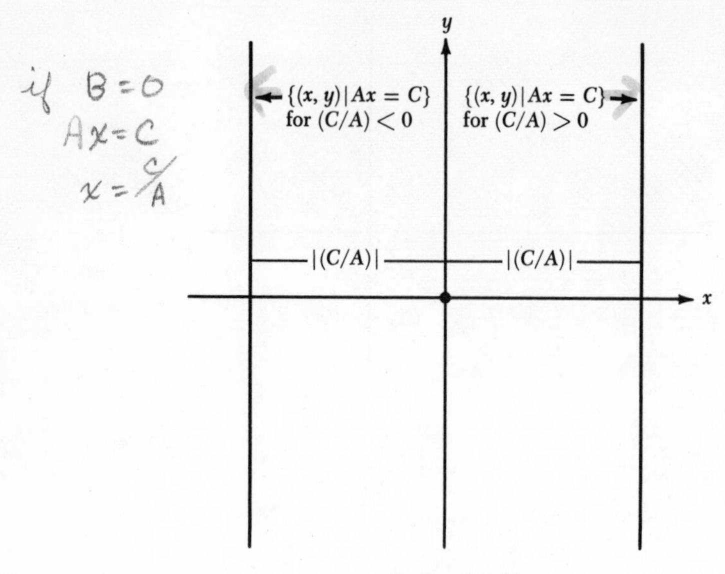

Figure 3-17

In case $B \neq 0$ and $A = 0$, $\{(x, y) \mid Ax + By = C\} = \{(x, y) \mid y = C/B\}$, and this case is similar to that above except that the line is parallel to the x-axis instead of to the y-axis. (See Fig. 3-18.)

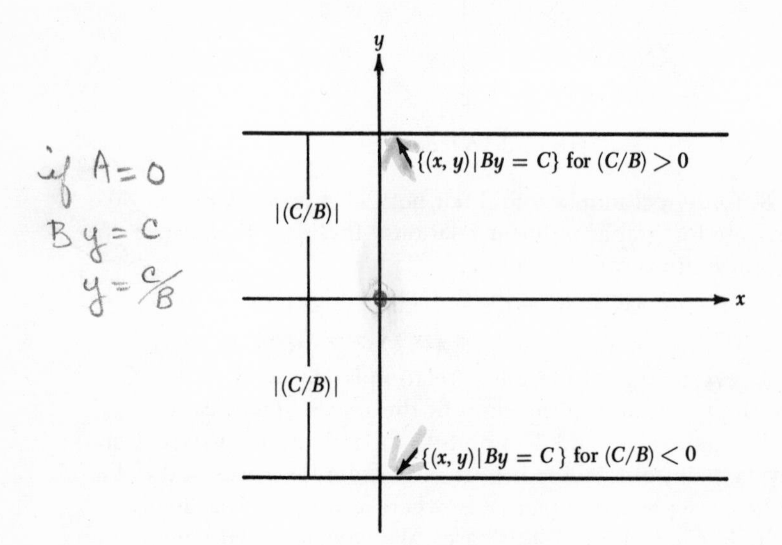

Figure 3-18

For $A \neq 0$ and $B \neq 0$ we may observe that

$$(0, C/B) \in \{(x, y) \mid Ax + By = C\}$$

and

$$(C/A, 0) \in \{(x, y) \mid Ax + By = C\}.$$

The point $(0, C/B)$ is called the ***y*-intercept** and the point $(C/A, 0)$ is called the ***x*-intercept** of the linear relation. We have indicated these points in Fig. 3-19 in the case $C/B > 0$ and $C/A < 0$. It turns out that if $C \neq 0$, the line on these two points is the graph of $\{(x, y) \mid Ax + By = C\}$. To demonstrate this fact let (x, y) be any point on this line different from

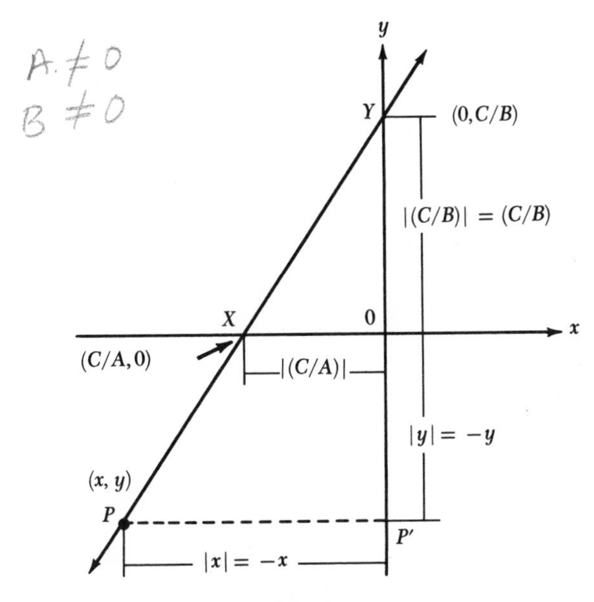

Figure 3-19

X, Y as in Fig. 3-19. From the figure we have two similar triangles: $\triangle YOX$ is similar to $\triangle YPP'$. Thus from geometry we have

$$(C/B)/(-C/A) = [C/B + (-y)]/(-x) \qquad \text{or} \qquad (A/B)x = (C/B) - y.$$

Now, multiplying by B gives

$$Ax = C - By \qquad \text{or} \qquad Ax + By = C.$$

Hence, if (x, y) is on the line connecting X and Y, then $Ax + By = C$ and so

$$(x, y) \in \{(x, y) \mid Ax + By = C\}.$$

If (p, q) is a point *not* on the line connecting X and Y, then we may show that $(p, q) \notin \{(x, y) \mid Ax + By = C\}$. For we may find a point of the line, say R, whose first coordinate is p. (See Fig. 3-20.) If t is the

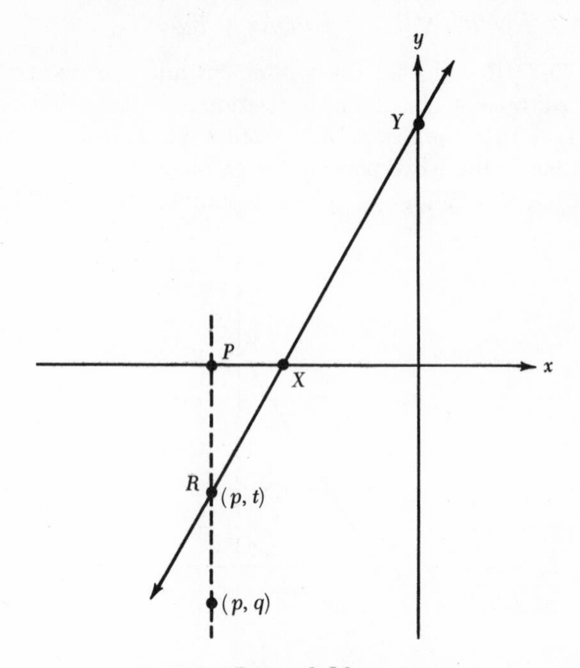

Figure 3-20

second coordinate of R, it has just been shown above that

$$Ap + Bt = C \qquad \text{or} \qquad t = C/B - (A/B)p.$$

Now since the point (p, t) is different from the point (p, q), $q \neq t$, and since $t = C/B - (A/B)p$, therefore we have

$$Ap + Bq \neq C,$$

which proves that $(p, q) \notin \{(x, y) \mid Ax + By = C\}$. *We may now conclude that a point* (a, b) *is on the line connecting* X, Y *if, and only if,* $(a, b) \in \{(x, y) \mid Ax + By = C\}$.

The above argument shows that in this particular case ($C/B > 0$ and $C/A < 0$) *the graph of the linear relation* $\{(x, y) \mid Ax + By = C\}$ *is a line.* The other cases arising when $C \neq 0$ present no new problems and may be handled just as has been done above. However, if $C = 0$, $C/B = 0$ and $C/A = 0$ (assuming $B \neq 0$ and $A \neq 0$) making the x- and y- intercepts the same point. Thus the above argument cannot be used. (See Exercise 18.)

Exercises

15. Construct the graph of each of the following relations.

(a) $\{(x, y) \mid y \leq |2.5|\}$.
(b) $\{(x, y) \mid x^2 + y^2 = 1\}$.
(c) $\{(x, y) \mid x^2 + y^2 < 1\}$.
(d) $\{(x, y) \mid x^2 + y^2 > 1\}$.
(e) $\{(x, y) \mid (x + 1)^2 + (y - 1)^2 = 1 \text{ and } |y| < 1\}$.
(f) $\{(x, y) \mid (x + 1)^2 + (y - 1)^2 < 1 \text{ and } |y| = 1\}$.
(g) $\{(x, y) \mid (x + 1)^2 + (y - 1)^2 > 1 \text{ and } |y| > 1\}$.

16. Construct graphs for the following:

(a) $\{(p, m) \mid p \geq m\}$.
(b) $\{(a, b) \mid a > b \text{ and } b \leq 0\}$.
(c) $\{(x, y) \mid |x + 1| \leq 3\}$.
(d) $\{(k, r) \mid k^2 + r^2 \leq 1 \text{ and } k \leq r\}$.

17. Graph the following:

(a) $\{(p, q) \mid p + q = 1\}$.
(b) $\{(m, n) \mid 2m - 5n = 2\}$.
(c) $\{(s, t) \mid 4s + t = 3\}$.
(d) $\{(s, t) \mid 4s + t < 3\}$.
(e) $\{(s, t) \mid 4s + t > 3\}$.

18. Show that the graph of the linear relation $\{(x, y) \mid Ax + By = 0\}$ is a line. [*Hint:* Consider the two points $(0, 0)$ and $(B, -A)$.]

19. What are the relations which have the graphs of Fig. 3-21?

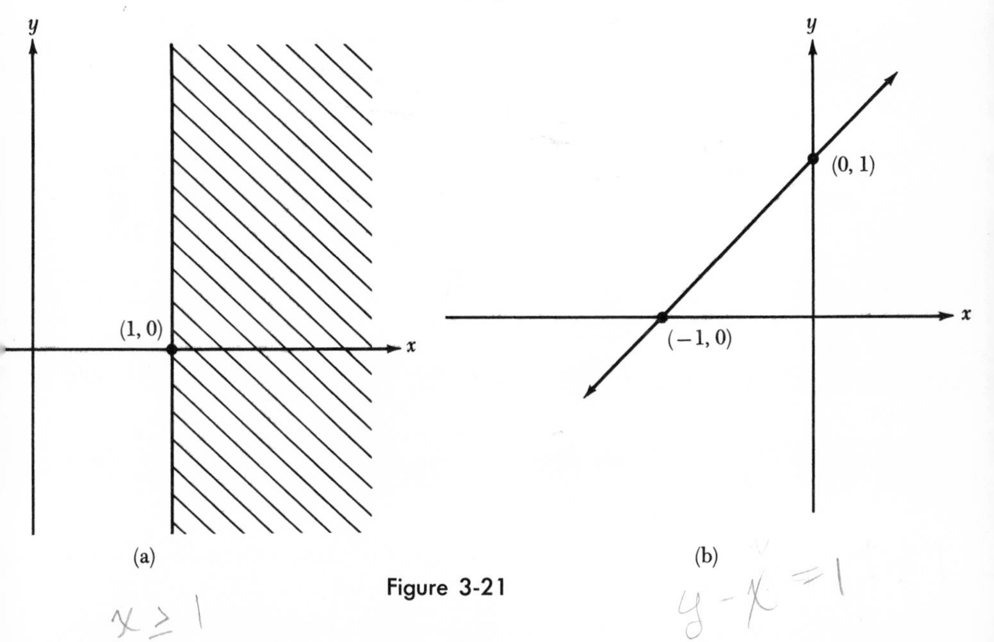

Figure 3-21

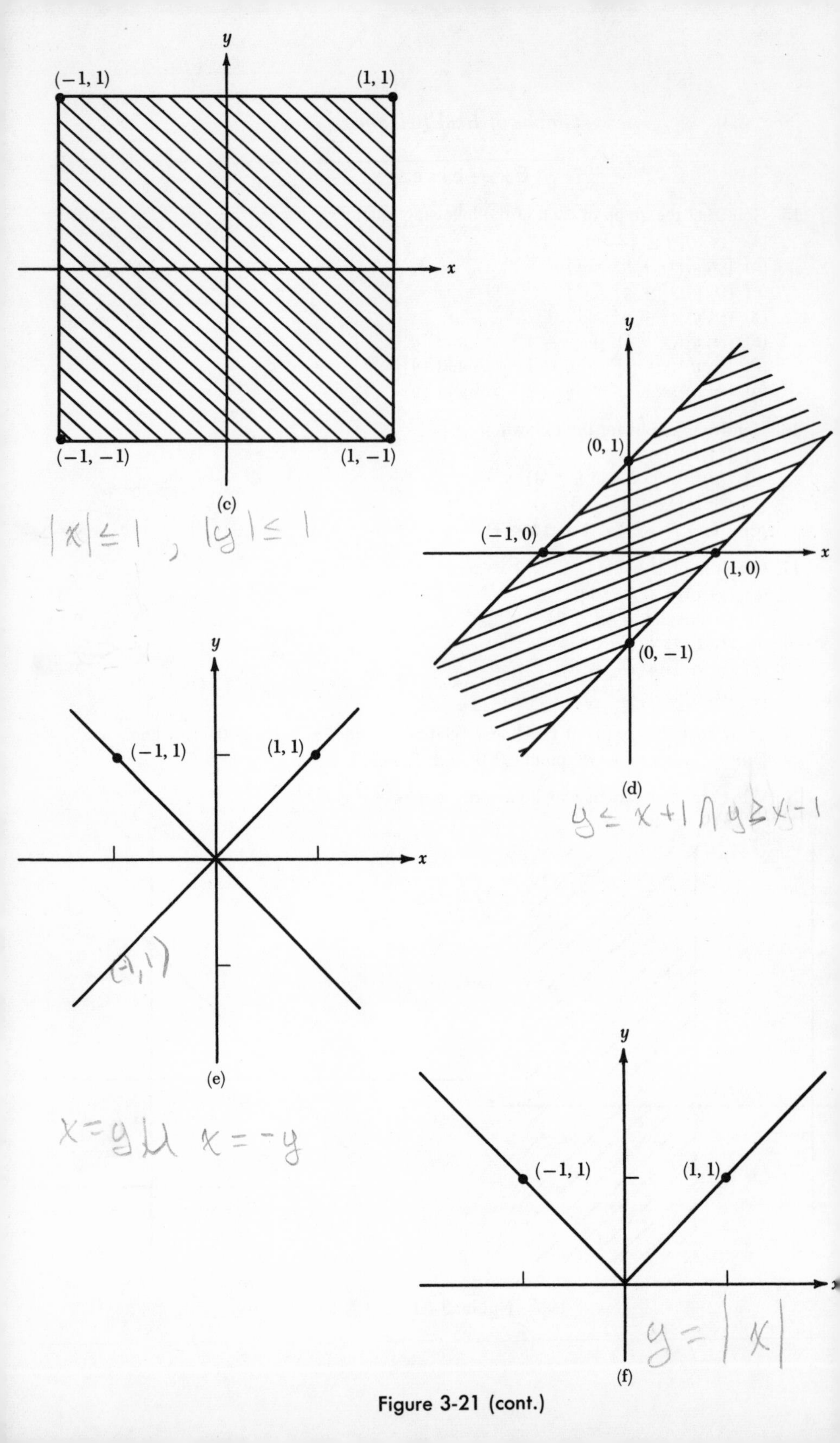

Figure 3-21 (cont.)

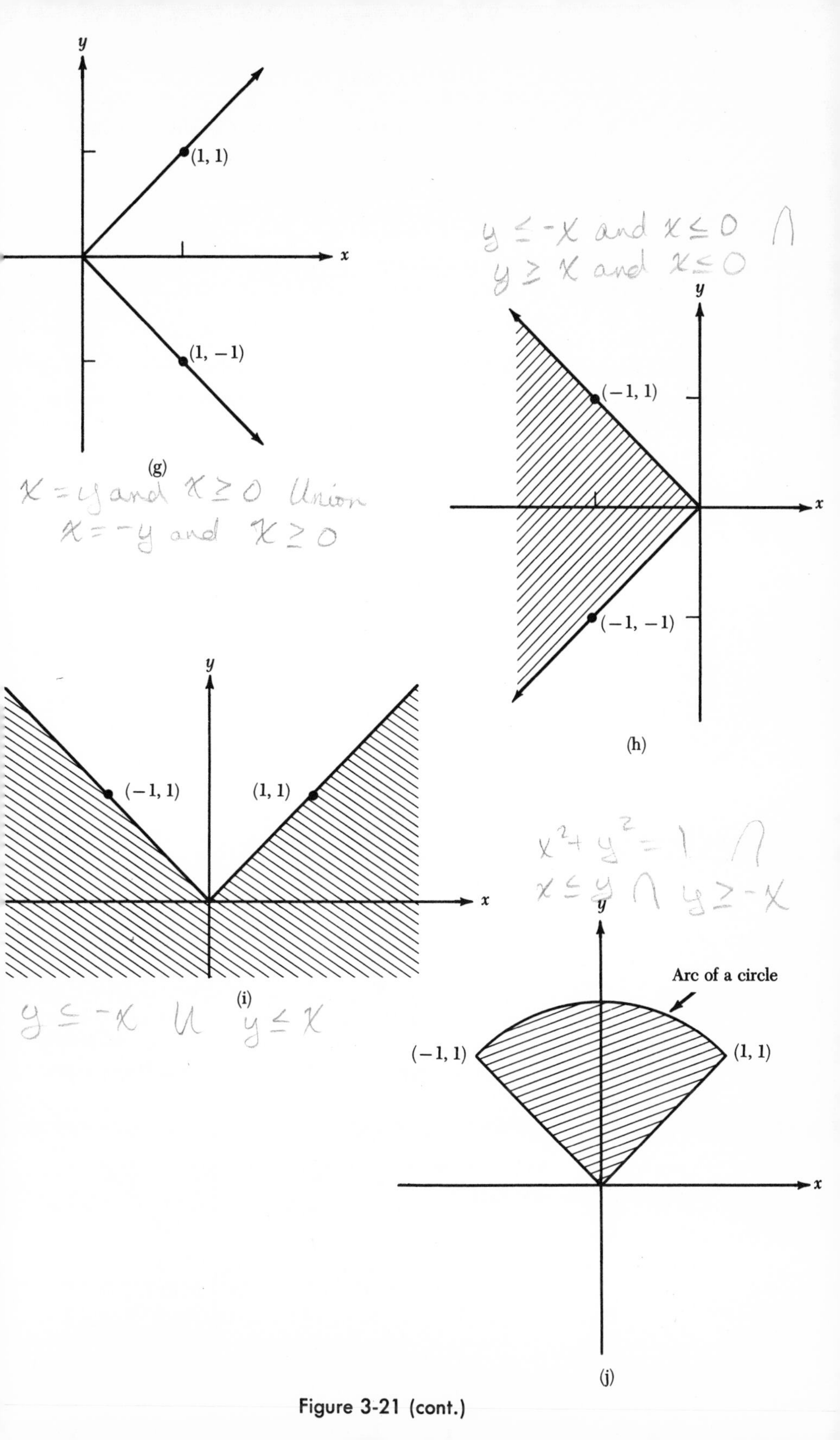

Figure 3-21 (cont.)

3.4 Real Functions

We now consider those real relations which are functions; i.e., those real relations R having the property:

$$(a, b) \in R \text{ and } (a, c) \in R \text{ imply } b = c.$$

As before, let us rephrase this definition: *R contains no two distinct ordered pairs with the same first element; R pairs no more than one element in the range of R with each element of the domain.*

In terms of the graph of R, if $(a, b) \in R$ and $(a, c) \in R$, we have a situation as indicated in Fig. 3-22 if $b \neq c$. The important aspect of

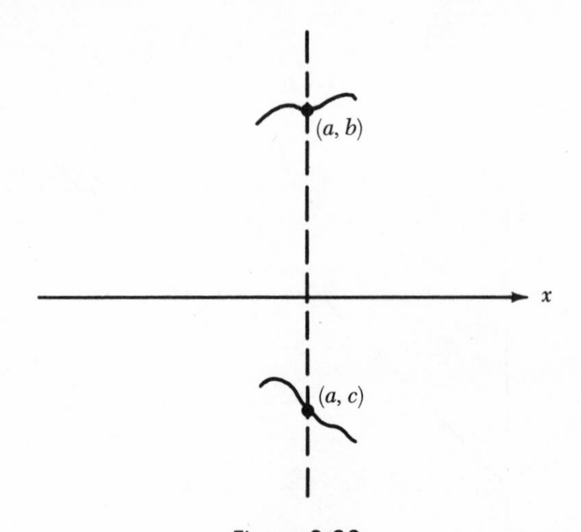

Figure 3-22

Fig. 3-22 is that if $b \neq c$, then $(a, b) \neq (a, c)$ and the two points (a, b), (a, c) are the same distance from the y-axis and hence on a line parallel to the y-axis. The conclusion to be drawn from this is that *the relation R is not a function if its graph is cut more than once by any line parallel to the y-axis.*

Example 3-13. All linear relations are functions except those having a graph parallel to the y-axis.

Example 3-14. A circle is not the graph of a function since an infinite number of lines parallel to the y-axis cut it in two points. [See Fig. 3-23 (a).] However, a circle is the union of two parts, each of which is

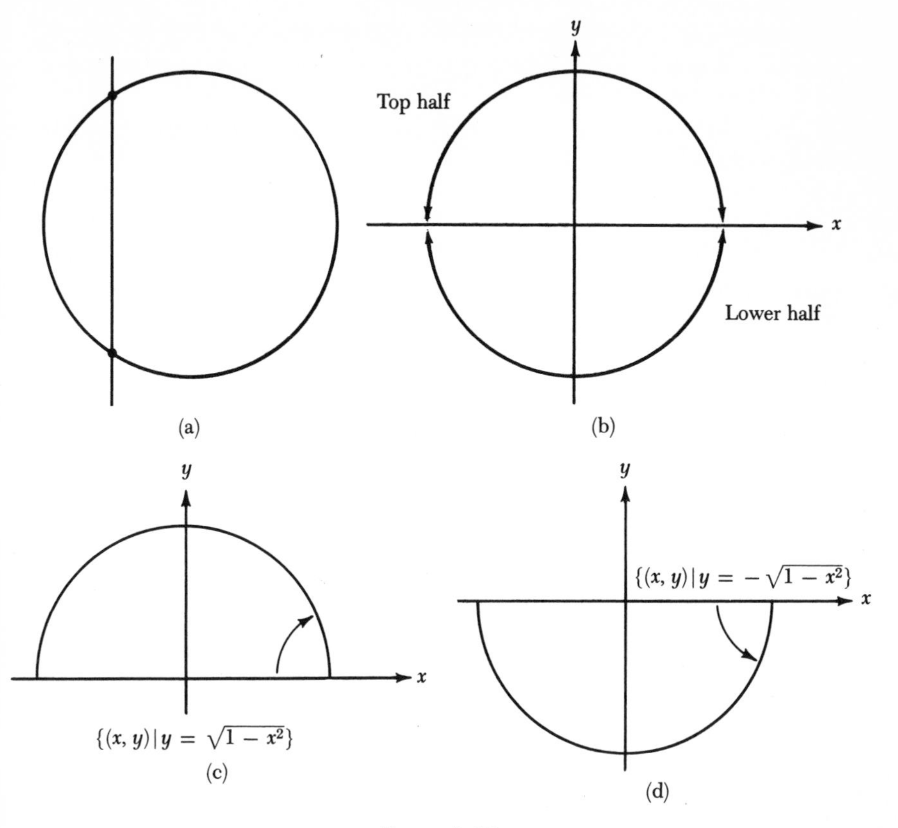

Figure 3-23

the graph of a function; for example,

$$\{(x, y) \mid x^2 + y^2 = 1\} = \{(x, y) \mid x^2 + y^2 = 1, y \geq 0\} \cup \{(x, y) \mid x^2 + y^2 = 1, y \leq 0\}.$$

The first member of the above union is the top half and the second member is the lower half of the circle as indicated in Fig. 3-23 (b). For a pair (x, y) of the top half we have $y \geq 0$ and $x^2 + y^2 = 1$ or $y^2 = 1 - x^2$. Hence, y is the non-negative number whose square is $1 - x^2$, i.e., $y = \sqrt{1 - x^2}$. If (x, y) is an ordered pair belonging to the lower half, $x^2 + y^2 = 1$ and $y \leq 0$ or $y^2 = 1 - x^2$. In this instance y is the non-positive number whose square is $1 - x^2$ or $y = -\sqrt{1 - x^2}$. We may then write

$$\{(x, y) \mid x^2 + y^2 = 1\} = \{(x, y) \mid y = \sqrt{1 - x^2}\} \cup \{(x, y) \mid y = -\sqrt{1 - x^2}\}.$$

[See Fig. 3-23 (c), (d).]

Example 3-15. The relation $F = \{(x, y) \mid y = x^2\}$ is a function since if $(a, b) \in F$ and $(a, c) \in F$, $b = a^2$ and $c = a^2$ so that $b = c$. The graph of F is indicated in Fig. 3-24.

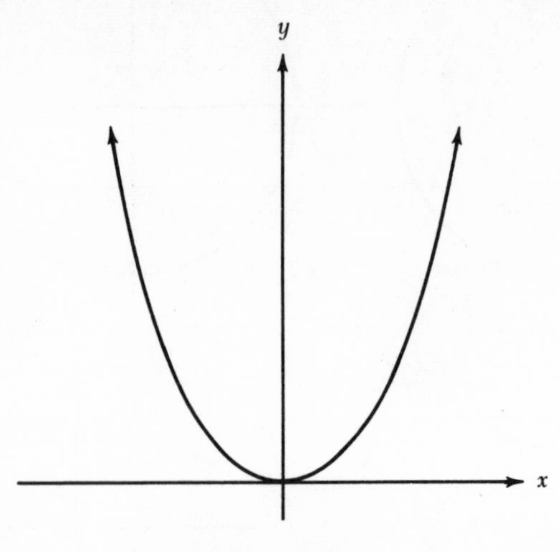

Figure 3-24

Example 3-16. The relation $G = \{(x, y) \mid x = y^2\}$ is not a function since $(1, 1) \in G$ and $(1, -1) \in G$. Observe that G is the inverse relation of the function in Example 3-15 above; i.e., $G = F^{-1}$. The graph of G is indicated in Fig. 3-25.

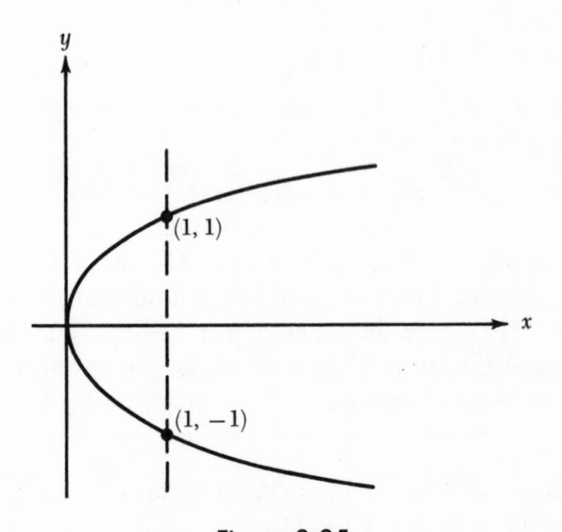

Figure 3-25

Example 3-17. The relation $A = \{(a, b) | b = |a|\}$ is a function whose graph is indicated in Fig. 3-26. The graph is easily constructed by using

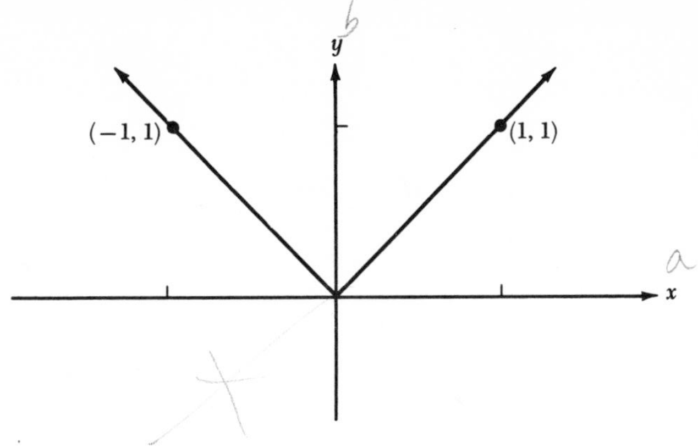

Figure 3-26

the definition of absolute value:

$$b = |a| = a \text{ if } a \geq 0$$

and

$$b = |a| = -a \text{ if } a < 0$$

so that

$$A = \{(a, b) | b = a \text{ and } a \geq 0\} \cup \{(a, b) | b = -a \text{ and } a < 0\}.$$

Hence, A is the union of two linear functions.

Example 3-18. Let $C = \{(w, z) | z = (-1)^w \cdot w \text{ and } w \text{ is an integer } \geq 0\}$. Since w is an integer, $(-1)^w = 1$ for even w and $(-1)^w = -1$ for odd w. Therefore,

$$C = \{(w, z) | z = w \text{ and } w \text{ is an even integer } \geq 0\} \cup \{(w, z) | z = -w \text{ and } w \text{ is an odd integer } \geq 0\}.$$

(See Fig. 3-27 for the graph of C.)

Example 3-19. Define $G = \{(a, b) | a \text{ is a real number, } a \geq 0, \text{ and } b \text{ is an integer such that } a - 1 < b \leq a\}$.

G is called the *greatest integer* function; this is a quite natural name for this function since it will be noted that b—in the definition of G—is the *largest integer* which is not greater than a. Some ordered pairs in G are $(1, 1)$, $(\frac{1}{2}, 0)$, $(\sqrt{2}, 1)$. Suppose that $(x, b) \in G$ and $x \in [0, 1)$, i.e., $0 \leq x < 1$. Then, evidently 0 is the largest integer which is not larger

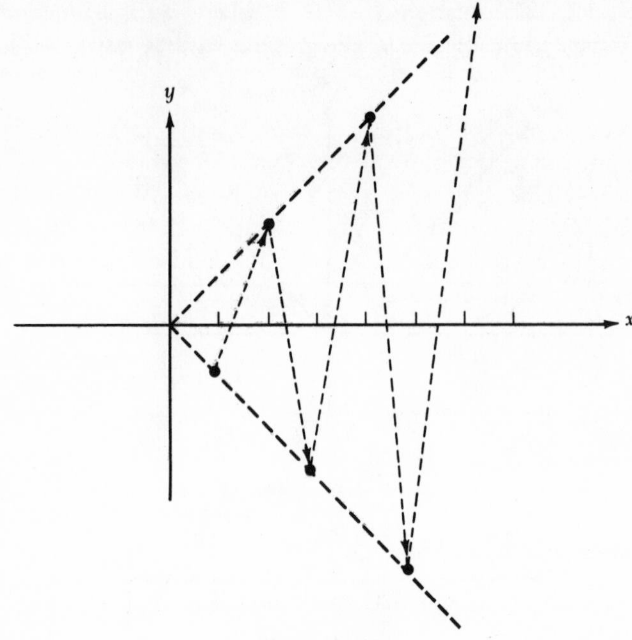

Figure 3-27

than x. Hence, $b = 0$. Similar reasoning shows that if $(x, b) \in G$ and $x \in [1, 2)$, $b = 1$; generally if $(x, b) \in G$ and $x \in [n, n + 1)$, where $n \geq 0$ and n is an integer, then $b = n$. It is thus clear that G can be expressed

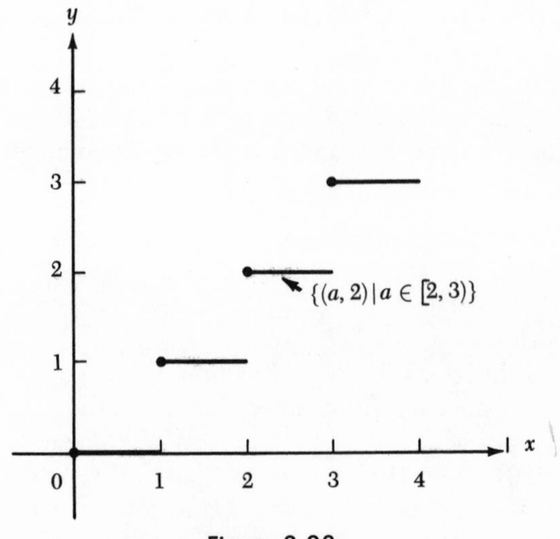

Figure 3-28

as follows:

$$G = \{(a, 0) \mid a \in [0, 1)\} \cup \{(a, 1) \mid a \in [1, 2)\} \cup \{(a, 2) \mid a \in [2, 3)\} \cup \ldots.$$

G is an example of a kind of function known as a *step function;* this term is clearly justified as the graph of G in Fig. 3-28 shows.

The domain and range of a function can be easily seen from the graph of the function. Remembering that the domain is the set of all first coordinates and the range is the set of all second coordinates, we may determine these as indicated in Fig. 3-29.

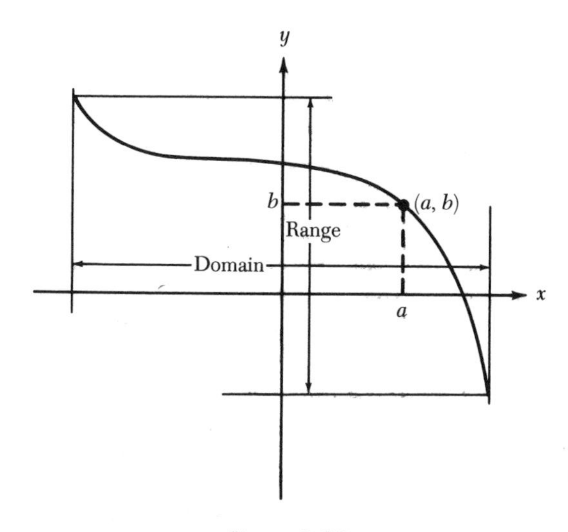

Figure 3-29

We wish to emphasize again other notations for functions; the most common ways of indicating that $(x, y) \in F$, where F is a function, are the following:

(1) $y = F(x)$.
(2) $F: x \rightarrow y$.

These are read respectively: "y is F of x" and "F maps x into y." Although notation (2) is in common use, we will use only the $F(x)$ notation here. The reader should always bear in mind that both (1) and (2) mean simply that $(x, y) \in F$.

Quite frequently, a function F will be defined in the $F(x)$ notation by giving $F(x)$ by some formula. For example, we may say: "Let F be defined by the formula: $F(x) = 1/x$." This is another way of expressing

$$F = \{(x, y) \mid y = 1/x \text{ and } x \neq 0\}.$$

Here no mention was made of the domain of F. We follow the convention *that when no domain is explicitly given, the domain of F is to be taken as the largest set of real numbers for which the defining formula has meaning.* Using this convention for the function F defined by

$$F(x) = 1/x,$$

we have

$$\mathfrak{D}(F) = \mathbf{R} \sqcap \{0\},$$

where $\mathbf{R}$ denotes the set of real numbers.

A very convenient use of the notation $y = F(x)$ is in the defining of new functions in terms of given ones; this is seen in the following definition.

DEFINITION. Let F and G be real functions. Then

(1) $F + G = \{(x, F(x) + G(x)) \mid x \in \mathfrak{D}(F) \cap \mathfrak{D}(G)\}$.
(2) $F - G = \{(x, F(x) - G(x)) \mid x \in \mathfrak{D}(F) \cap \mathfrak{D}(G)\}$.
(3) $F \cdot G = \{(x, F(x) \cdot G(x)) \mid x \in \mathfrak{D}(F) \cap \mathfrak{D}(G)\}$.
(4) $F/G = \{(x, F(x)/G(x)) \mid x \in \mathfrak{D}(F) \cap \mathfrak{D}(G) \text{ and } G(x) \neq 0\}$.

The relations defined above are known as the *sum, difference, product* and *quotient,* respectively, of F and G. Notice that the definition states that the second members of ordered pairs in these relations are obtained by adding, subtracting, multiplying or dividing *corresponding* second members of ordered pairs in F and G. The requirement that $x \in \mathfrak{D}(F) \cap \mathfrak{D}(G)$ is obviously a natural one since, for example, $F(x) + G(x)$ has no meaning if $x \notin \mathfrak{D}(F) \cap \mathfrak{D}(G)$.

Example 3-20. Let $F = \{(x, y) \mid y - x = 1\}$ and $G = \{(x, y) \mid y = 1\}$.
Both F and G are linear functions, and we have

$$y = F(x) = x + 1$$

and

$$y = G(x) = 1,$$

so that

$$\begin{aligned} F + G &= \{(x, F(x) + G(x)) \mid x \text{ is a real number}\}. \\ &= \{(x, x + 2) \mid x \text{ is a real number}\}. \\ &= \{(x, y) \mid y = x + 2,\ x \text{ is real}\}. \\ F - G &= \{(x, x) \mid x \text{ is a real number}\} = \{(x, y) \mid y = x,\ x \text{ is real}\}. \\ F \cdot G &= \{(x, x + 1) \mid x \text{ is real}\} = \{(x, y) \mid y = x + 1,\ x \text{ is real}\}. \\ F/G &= \{(x, x + 1) \mid x \text{ is real}\} = \{(x, y) \mid y = x + 1,\ x \text{ is real}\}. \end{aligned}$$

(See Fig. 3-30 for the graph of $F + G$.)

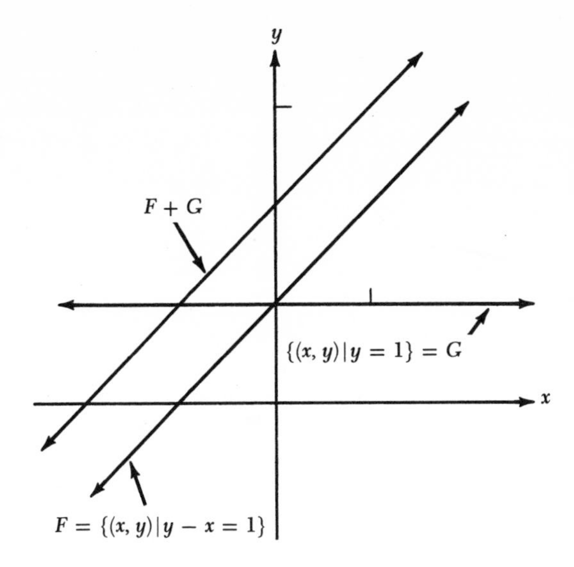

Figure 3-30

Example 3-21. If $\mathfrak{D}(F) \cap \mathfrak{D}(G) = \varnothing$, then

$$F + G = F - G = F \cdot G = F/G = \varnothing.$$

Example 3-22. Let $T = \{(a, b) \mid b = \sqrt{1 - a^2}\}$

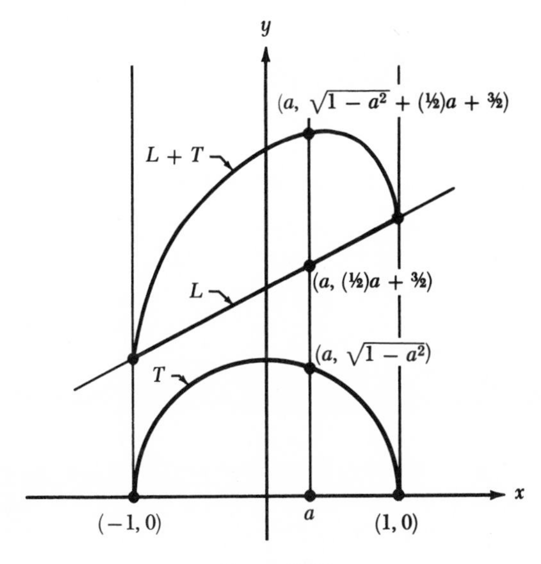

Figure 3-31

and

$$L = \{(a, b) \mid b = (1/2)a + 3/2,\ a \in [-1, 1]\}.$$

Then

$$T + L = \{(a, b) \mid b = \sqrt{1 - a^2} + (1/2)a + 3/2 \text{ and } a \in [-1, 1]\}.$$

(See Fig. 3-31.)

Example 3-23. In notation (1) for $F + G$, etc., we have

$$\begin{aligned} y &= (F + G)(x) \\ y &= (F - G)(x) \\ y &= (F \cdot G)(x) \\ y &= (F/G)(x). \end{aligned}$$

But since y is the second member of an ordered pair (x, y) in $F + G$, etc., the definition gives

$$\begin{aligned} y &= (F + G)(x) = F(x) + G(x) \\ y &= (F - G)(x) = F(x) - G(x) \\ y &= (F \cdot g)(x) = F(x) \cdot G(x) \\ y &= (F/G)(x) = F(x)/G(x),\ G(x) \neq 0. \end{aligned}$$

Example 3-24. In Example 3-22, the functions may be specified in notation (1) as follows:

$$\begin{aligned} b &= T(a) = \sqrt{1 - a^2} \\ b &= L(a) = (1/2)a + 3/2,\ a \in [-1, 1]. \end{aligned}$$

Then,

$$\begin{aligned} b = (T + L)(a) &= T(a) + L(a) \\ &= \sqrt{1 - a^2} + (1/2)a + 3/2 \\ b = (T - L)(a) &= T(a) - L(a) \\ &= \sqrt{1 - a^2} - [(1/2)a + 3/2] \\ b = (T \cdot L)(a) &= (T(a)) \cdot (L(a)) \\ &= (\sqrt{1 - a^2})[(1/2)a + 3/2] \\ b = (T/L)(a) &= T(a)/L(a) \\ &= \sqrt{1 - a^2}/[(1/2)a + 3/2]. \end{aligned}$$

It is no doubt evident to the reader that *if F and G are functions, then the relations $F + G$, $F - G$, $F \cdot G$, F/G are also functions.* To show that $F + G$ is a function, for example, suppose that

$$(a, b) \in (F + G) \text{ and } (a, c) \in (F + G).$$

This means that

$$b = (F + G)(a) = F(a) + G(a).$$

and

$$c = (F + G)(a) = F(a) + G(a).$$

Therefore,

$$b = c \text{ and } F + G \text{ is a function.}$$

DEFINITION. If H and W are functions such that $\mathcal{R}(W) \subseteq \mathcal{D}(H)$, then the *composite of H by W* is

$$\{(x, y) \mid y = H(W(x))\}.$$

The composite of H by W is denoted by "$H(W)$".

Example 3-25. If $H(x) = x^2$ and $W(x) = x + 2$ then

$$H(W(x)) = H(x + 2) = (x + 2)^2 = x^2 + 4x + 4$$

so that $H(W) = \{(x, y) \mid y = x^2 + 4x + 4\}$. (See Fig. 3-32.)

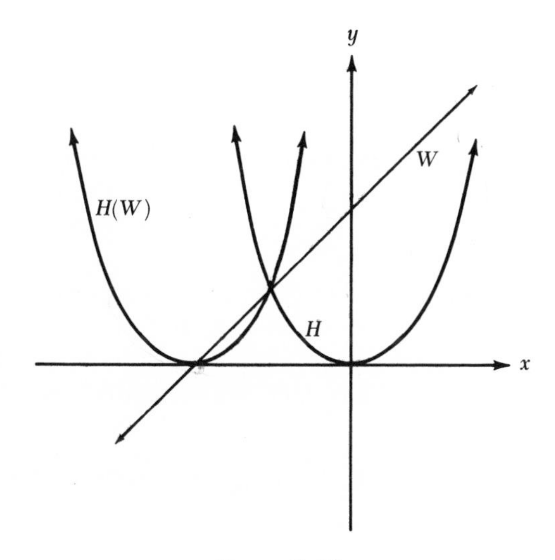

Figure 3-32

Example 3-26. If $H(x) = \sqrt{1 - x^2}$ and $W(x) = (½)x + 3/2$, $x \in [-1, 1]$, then $H(W)$ does not exist since $\mathcal{R}(W) \not\subseteq \mathcal{D}(H)$. To show that the range of W is not in the domain of H, we only have to note that

$$W(1) = ½ \cdot 1 + 3/2 = 2 \notin \mathcal{D}(H).$$

An interesting geometric interpretation of $H(W)$ is illustrated by Fig. 3-33; this figure, also, illustrates a technique which may be used to

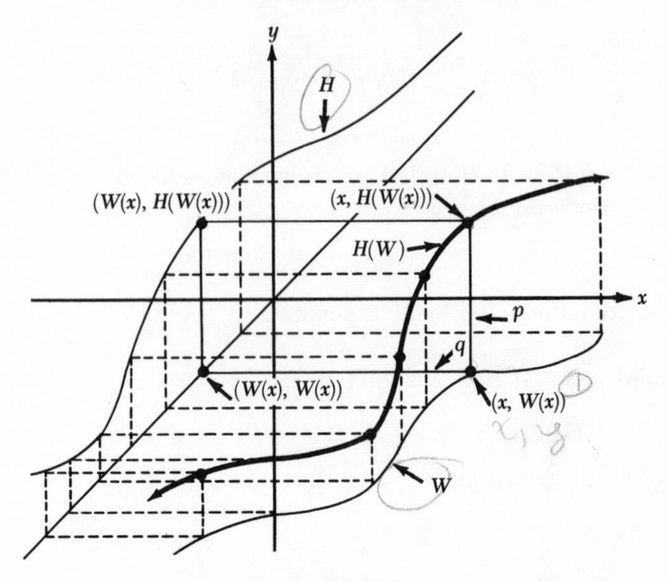

Figure 3-33

construct the graph of $H(W)$ from the graphs of H and W. If the graphs of H and W are given, we proceed to the graph of $H(W)$ as follows: choose the point on the graph of W which corresponds to $(x, W(x))$ and on this point construct the line q parallel to the x-axis and the line p parallel to the y-axis. The line q so constructed intersects the line bisecting quadrants I and III at a point having coordinates $(W(x), W(x))$. On the point $(W(x), W(x))$ we now construct the line parallel to the y-axis and this line cuts the graph of H in a point $(W(x), H(W(x)))$. Now on this point $(W(x), H(W(x)))$, take the line which is parallel to the x-axis and this will intersect the line p in a point having coordinates $(x, H(W(x)))$.

Example 3-27. If $H(x) = \sqrt{1 - x^2}$ and $W(x) = 1/x$ for $x > 1$, then $\mathcal{R}(W) \subseteq \mathcal{D}(H)$ since if $x > 1$,

$$0 < 1/x < 1.$$

Hence, $H(W)$ exists, and we have

$$\begin{aligned} H(W(x)) &= \sqrt{1 - [W(x)]^2} \\ &= \sqrt{1 - (1/x)^2} \\ &= \sqrt{(1/x^2)(x^2 - 1)} = (1/x)\sqrt{x^2 - 1}. \end{aligned}$$

The graph of H is given in Fig. 3-34 (a), and that of W in Fig. 3-34 (b). In Fig. 3-34 (c) the technique for graphing composites given in (b) above is used to obtain the graph of $H(W)$.

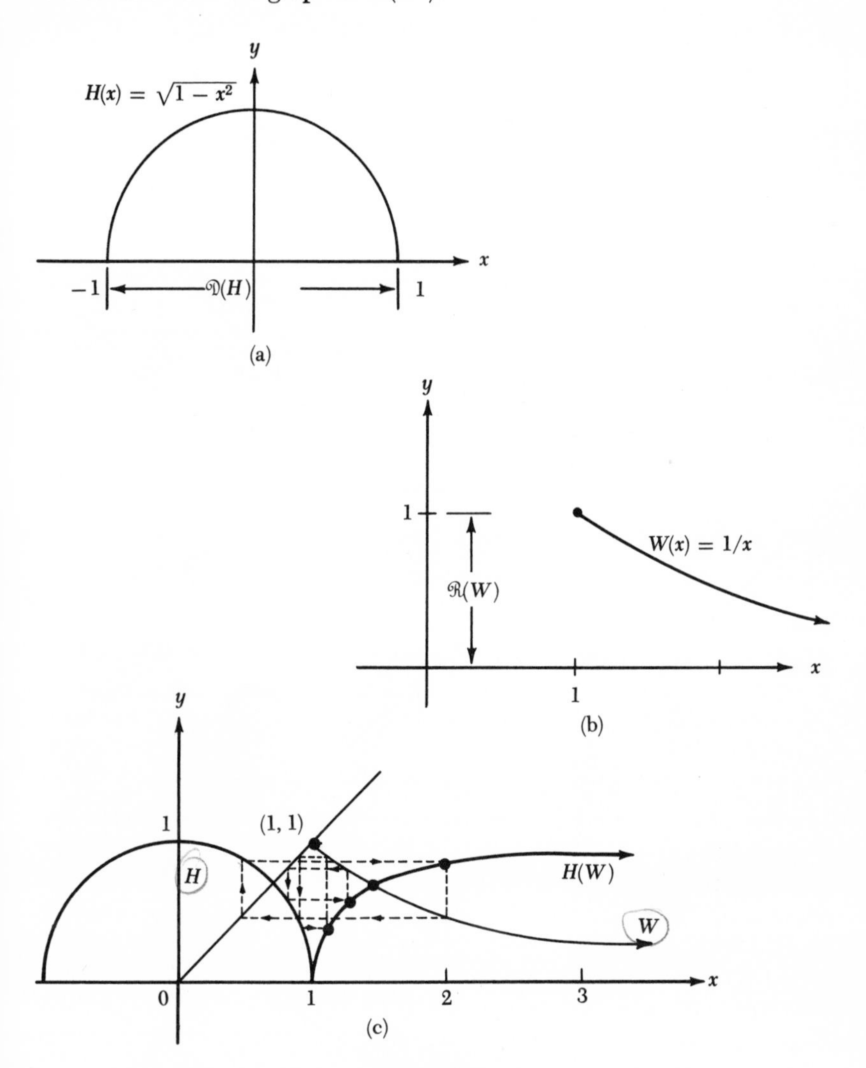

Figure 3-34

Exercises

20. The graphs given in Fig. 3-35 are graphs of real relations; which are graphs of functions?

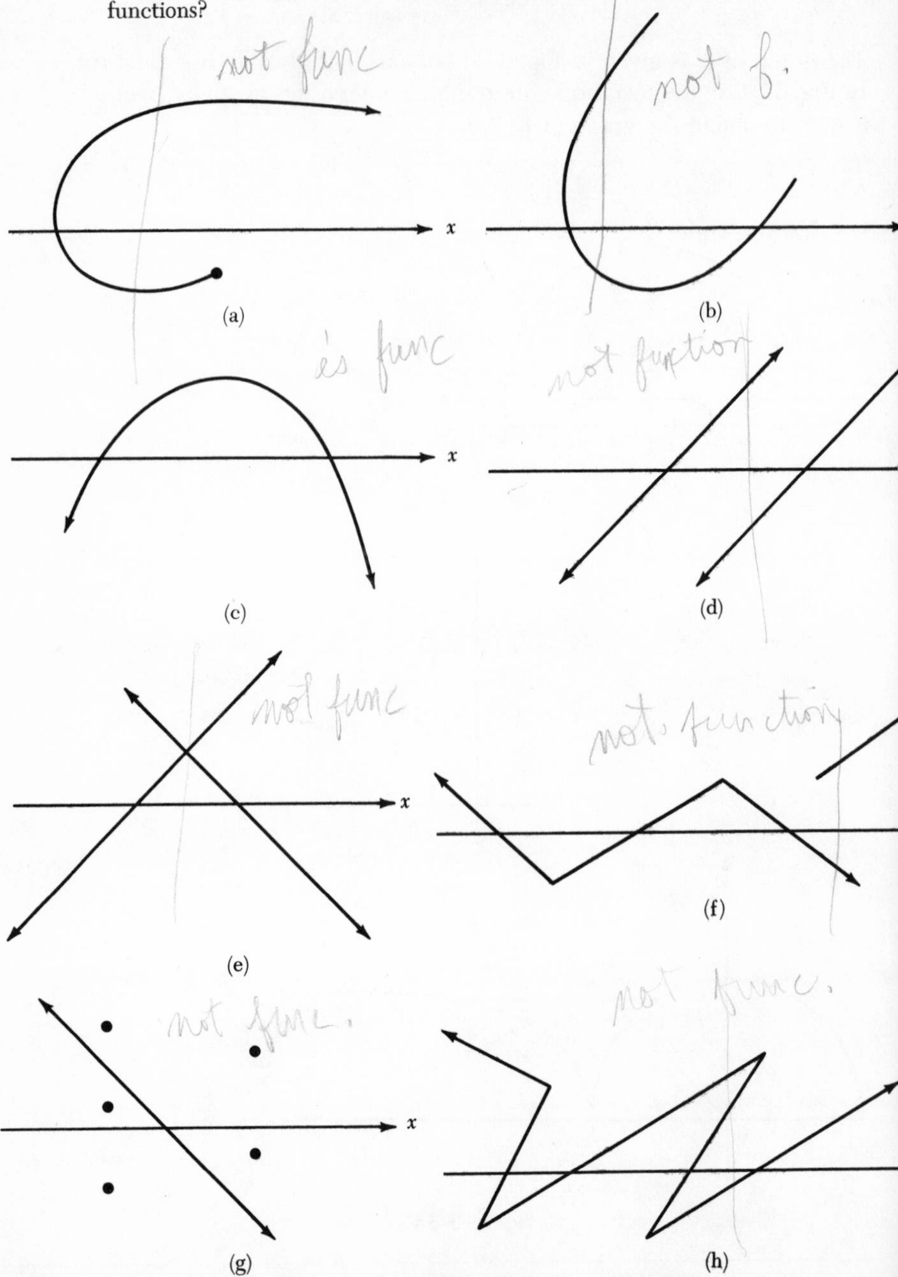

Figure 3-35

21. Which of the relations of Exercises 15, 16, and 17 are functions?

22. Construct the graph of each of the following functions and give their domain and range.
(a) $\{(a, b) \mid b = a^2 + 1\}$.
(b) $\{(x, y) \mid y = x^2 - 5,\ x \in [-6, -5]\}$.
(c) $\{(c, d) \mid d = \sqrt{c}\}$.
(d) $\{(p, q) \mid q = \sqrt{8 - c}\}$.

23. Write each of the functions of Exercise 22 above in the $f(x)$-notation.

24. Let f be the function defined by

$$f(x) = 8x^2 + 7x - 1.$$

Find:
(a) $f(1)$.
(b) $f(0)$.
(c) $f(-1)$.
(d) $f(1/8)$.
(e) $f(5t)$.
(f) $f(\sqrt{2})$.
(g) $f(a/b)$.
(h) $f(a - b)$.

25. Let G be the greatest integer function defined in Example 3-19. Calculate the following:
(a) $G(0)$.
(b) $G(7/2)$.
(c) $G(n)$, where $n \geq 0$ is an integer.

26. The greatest integer function defined in Example 3-19 has a domain restricted to the positive real numbers. This restriction is clearly not necessary for the definition of the function. Graph the following functions (the notation "[ ]" means the greatest integer function).
(a) $f(x) = [x]$ for $x \in [-1, 1]$.
(b) $f(x) = x + [x]$ for $x \in [-2, 1]$.
(c) $f(x) = 2[x]$ for $x \in [-8, 8]$.
(d) $f(x) = [|x|]$ for $x \in [-3, -1/2]$.

27. For each pair of functions f, g given below form the composite $f(g)$ and give the domain. Using the technique described on page 84, graph these composites.
(a) $f(x) = 2x + 1$
$g(x) = x - 1$.
(b) $f(x) = x^2 + 1$
$g(x) = 5x - 1$.
(c) $f(x) = [x]$
$g(x) = x^2$ for $x \in [-2, 2]$.
(d) $f(x) = [x]$
$g(x) = 1 + 1/x$ for $x \in (0, 10]$.

28. Prove the following properties of the greatest integer function.

(a) $[\sqrt{1 - x^2}] = 0$ if $|x| < 1, x \neq 0$

$= 1$ if $x = 0$.

(b) $[1/x] = 0$ for $x > 1$

$[1/x] \geq 1$ for $0 < x \leq 1$

(c) $[|x|/x] = 1$ for $x > 0$

$[|x|/x] = -1$ for $x < 0$

(d) $[x + 1] = [x] + 1$.

4

Polynomial Functions

4.1 Definitions

We have defined in the previous chapter the linear relation

$$f = \{(x, y) \mid Ax + By = C\},$$

where A, B, C are real numbers and not both A, B are zero. Since the graphs of these relations are straight lines, the only linear relations that are not functions are those having graphs which are lines parallel to the y-axis. The graphs are parallel to the y-axis if and only if $B = 0$ (see page 71).

Thus, if $B \neq 0$, f is a function and may be written

$$\{(x, y) \mid y = C/B - (A/B)x\}$$

or in the $f(x)$-notation $y = f(x) = C/B - (A/B)x$. In this case, f is an example of what is called a polynomial function of degree one.

DEFINITION. P is a *polynomial* function *of degree* n where $n \geq 0$ is an integer if and only if there are real numbers (called the *coefficients* of P) $a_0, a_1, a_2, \ldots, a_n$ with $a_n \neq 0$ such that

$$P(x) = a_0 + a_1x + a_2x^2 + \cdots + a_nx^n$$

for all x in the domain of P.

Example 4-1. In the linear function

$$f(x) = C/B - (A/B)x,$$
$$n = 1,\ a_0 = C/B, \text{ and } a_1 = -A/B.$$

Example 4-2. The polynomial functions

$$P(x) = a_0,\ a_0 \neq 0$$

of degree 0 are usually called *constant functions.* It should be noted that our definition of polynomial function does not include the constant function

$$Z(x) = 0.$$

We shall refer to this as a *zero function* or *polynomial function having no degree.*

Example 4-3. The function

$$f(x) = x^3 - 8x^2 - \sqrt{2}x + 9,\ x \in [1, 3]$$

is a polynomial function of degree 3.

Example 4-4. The absolute value function

$$A(x) = |x|,\ x \geq 0$$

is a polynomial function of degree 1, since in this case

$$A(x) = x.$$

However, if the domain is $[-2.5, 1]$ for

$$A(x) = |x|,$$

then this is *not* a polynomial function. On the other hand, since

$$\begin{aligned} A(x) &= |x| = -x && \text{for} \quad x \in [-2.5, 0] \\ A(x) &= |x| = x && \text{for} \quad x \in [0, 1] \end{aligned}$$

we might view this function as being composed of *pieces* of polynomial functions.

DEFINITION. Let q be a function and c a number in the domain of q. Then c is called *a zero of q* if and only if $q(c) = 0$.

Example 4-5. The non-zero constant polynomial functions

$$P(x) = a,\ a \neq 0$$

have no zeros (since $P(c) = 0$ for any number c implies $a = 0$). However, every number in the domain of a zero function is a zero of that function.

Example 4-6. If $Q(x) = x^2 - 2$, then

$$Q(\sqrt{2}) = (\sqrt{2})^2 - 2 = 2 - 2 = 0,$$

so that $\sqrt{2}$ is a zero of Q. Also $-\sqrt{2}$ is a zero of Q.

Example 4-7. Let

$$G(x) = [x],\ x \in [-2, 8].$$

Then for all x such that $0 \leq x < 1$,

$$G(x) = 0.$$

Conversely, if $x \notin [0, 1)$, then $G(x) \neq 0$. Hence, every number in the interval $[0, 1)$ is a zero of G, and there are no others.

The zeros (if any) of a function can be helpful when one is graphing the function; for each zero c of a function f determines a point $(c, f(c)) = (c, 0)$ where the graph of f crosses the x-axis. It therefore follows that in the case of a linear function

$$f(x) = a_0 + a_1x,$$

the x-intercept determines the only zero of the function. Since $a_1 \neq 0$, we have

$$f\left(-\frac{a_0}{a_1}\right) = a_0 + a_1\left(-\frac{a_0}{a_1}\right)$$
$$= a_0 - a_0 = 0.$$

Then the x-intercept is the point $\left(-\frac{a_0}{a_1}, 0\right)$.

4.2 General Comments on Graphs

The polynomial functions of degree 2 are called quadratic functions:

$$Q(x) = a_0 + a_1x + a_2x^2.$$

We shall consider these polynomials in some detail in this chapter.

We have seen the quadratic

$$f(x) = x^2$$

in the previous chapter; this has a graph as in Fig. 4-1 and only one zero,

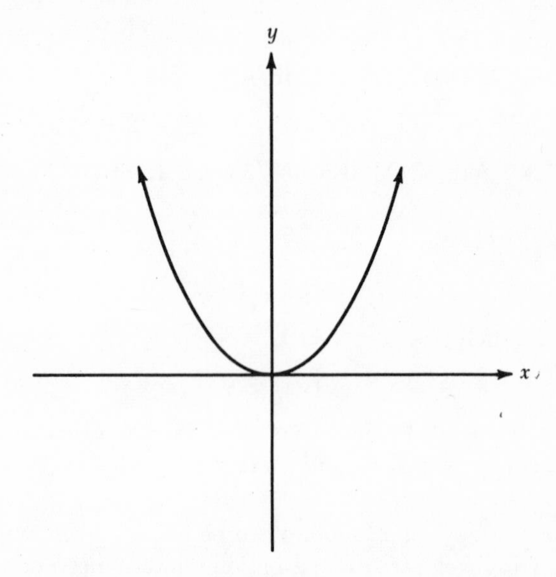

Figure 4-1

which is 0: $f(0) = 0^2 = 0$. The reader will have observed that the general appearance of this graph has not been justified; the tools at our disposal now are too limited to justify some aspects of the graphs of polynomials. For example, how do we know that the graph of $f(x) = x^2$ is *smooth*—as in Fig. 4-1—and has no *holes* or *gaps*? Generally, the graphs of polynomial functions are smooth with no jumps *as long as the domain is without gaps.* The graph of $f(x) = x^2$, for all real x, is as in Fig. 4-1; for $f(x) = x^2$, $x \in [-1, 1]$, the graph is as in Fig. 4-2. For the

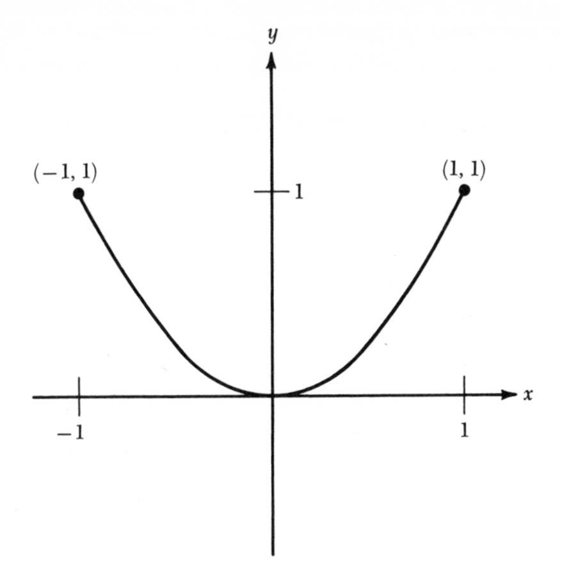

Figure 4-2

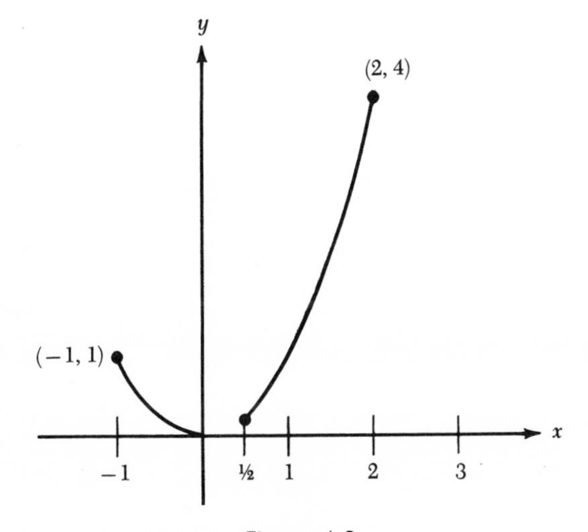

Figure 4-3

first of these, the domain is the set of all real numbers; and for the second, the set $[-1, 1]$. Neither of these domains have breaks or gaps. However, we get breaks and gaps in the graph if we make breaks or gaps in the domain. Fig. 4-3 indicates this situation for the function

$$f(x) = x^2, x \in [-1, 0] \cup [\tfrac{1}{2}, 2].$$

The break in the domain of this function between 0 and ½ produces the break in the curve. To construct the graph of a polynomial function, we may proceed by calculating enough points on the curve until we get a good idea of its general shape. We then connect the points thus obtained with a smooth line and hope for the best.

Example 4-8. Sketch the graph of

$$P(x) = 1 - 5x + x^5.$$

Solution. We calculate the points of the graph corresponding to -2, -1, $-\frac{1}{2}$, 0, ½, 1, 2. We have

$$\begin{aligned}
&P(-2) = 1 - 5(-2) + (-2)^5 = 1 + 10 - 32 = -21\\
&P(-1) = 1 - 5(-1) + (-1)^5 = 1 + 5 - 1 = 5\\
&P(-\tfrac{1}{2}) = 1 - 5(-\tfrac{1}{2}) + (-\tfrac{1}{2})^5 = 1 + \tfrac{5}{2} - \tfrac{1}{32} = 3 + \tfrac{15}{32}\\
&P(0) = 1 - 5(0) + (0)^5 = 1\\
&P(\tfrac{1}{2}) = 1 - 5(\tfrac{1}{2}) + (\tfrac{1}{2})^5 = 1 - \tfrac{5}{2} + \tfrac{1}{32} = -\tfrac{47}{32}\\
&P(1) = 1 - 5(1) + (1)^5 = 1 - 5 + 1 = -3\\
&P(2) = 1 - 5(2) + (2)^5 = 1 - 10 + 32 = 23
\end{aligned}$$

We now plot the points

$$\begin{aligned}
&(-2, P(-2)) = (-2, -21)\\
&(-1, P(-1)) = (-1, 5)\\
&(-\tfrac{1}{2}, P(-{}^{1}{}_{2})) = (-\tfrac{1}{2}, 3 + \tfrac{15}{32})\\
&(0, P(0)) = (0, 1)\\
&(\tfrac{1}{2}, P(\tfrac{1}{2})) = (\tfrac{1}{2}, -\tfrac{47}{32})\\
&(1, P(1)) = (1, -3)\\
&(2, P(2)) = (2, 23)
\end{aligned}$$

as shown in Fig. 4-4. In this figure we have indicated the general shape of the graph with the line through the plotted points.

4.3 Graphs of Quadratics

Returning now to the general quadratic function

$$Q(x) = c + bx + ax^2 \qquad a \neq 0,$$

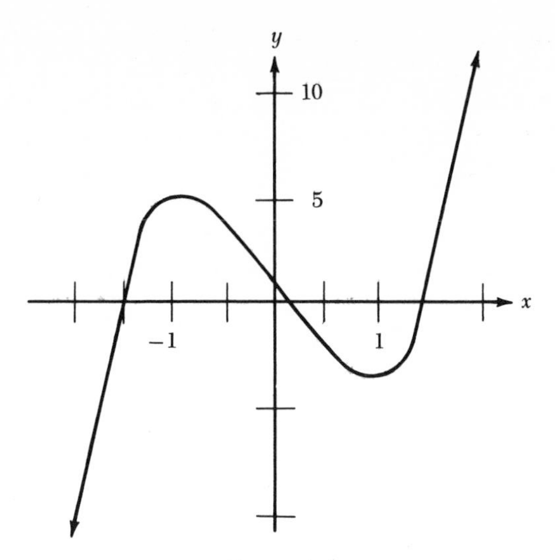

Figure 4-4

we will investigate the graphs of these. We may write

$$\begin{aligned} Q(x) &= ax^2 + bx + c \\ &= a(x^2 + (b/a)x) + c \\ &= a(x^2 + (b/a)x + b^2/4a^2) + c - b^2/4a \\ &= a(x + b/2a)^2 + \frac{(4ac - b^2)}{4a}. \end{aligned}$$

Now, for all x

$$(x + b/2a)^2 \geq 0,$$

and if $a > 0$,

$$a(x + b/2a)^2 \geq 0,$$

so that

$$a(x + b/2a)^2 + \frac{4ac - b^2}{4a} \geq \frac{4ac - b^2}{4a}.$$

We thus conclude that if $a > 0$,

$$Q(x) \geq \frac{4ac - b^2}{4a}$$

for all x. In constructing the graph of Q, we will be plotting points $(x, Q(x))$ where the second coordinate, $Q(x)$, is never smaller than

$(4ac - b^2)/4a$. This tells us that no part of the graph of Q lies below the line $y = (4ac - b^2)/4a$. (See Fig. 4-5.)

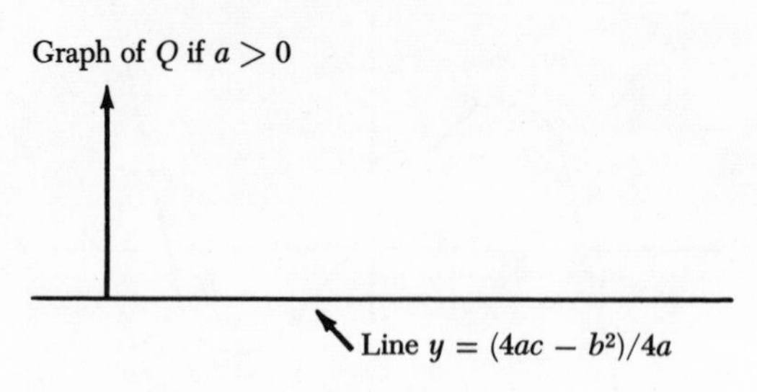

Figure 4-5

Example 4-9. If $Q(x) = 1 + x + x^2$, we have $a = 1$, $b = 1$, $c = 1$ and

$$\frac{4ac - b^2}{4a} = \frac{4 \cdot 1 \cdot 1 - 1^2}{4 \cdot 1} = \frac{3}{4}.$$

Thus, the graph of Q is nowhere below the line $y = 3/4$. We may, of course, conclude from this that Q has no zeros.

In case $a < 0$, the situation is similar:

$$a(x + b/2a)^2 \leq 0$$

and

$$a(x + b/2a)^2 + (4ac - b^2)/4a \leq (4ac - b^2)/4a,$$

or

$$Q(x) \leq (4ac - b^2)/4a$$

for all x. This gives rise to the conclusion that the graph of Q is nowhere above the line $y = (4ac - b^2)/4a$.

Since for all x

$$Q(x) = a(x + b/2a)^2 + \frac{4ac - b^2}{4a},$$

we have

$$\begin{aligned} Q(-b/2a) &= a \cdot 0 + (4ac - b^2)/4a \\ &= (4ac - b^2)/4a. \end{aligned}$$

Therefore, the graph of Q meets the line $y = (4ac - b^2)/4a$ since the point

$$(-b/2a, Q(-b/2a))$$

is on this line. Also, this is the only point of Q which is on this line since

$$a(x + b/2a)^2 = 0$$

only if $x = -b/2a$.

Consider the case when $a > 0$ and the number $(4ac - b^2)/4a < 0$. (See Fig. 4-6.) Let $x_1 < x_2$ be two numbers to the right of $-b/2a$ as shown in Fig. 4-6. Since $a > 0$, we know that both points $(x_1, Q(x_1))$ and

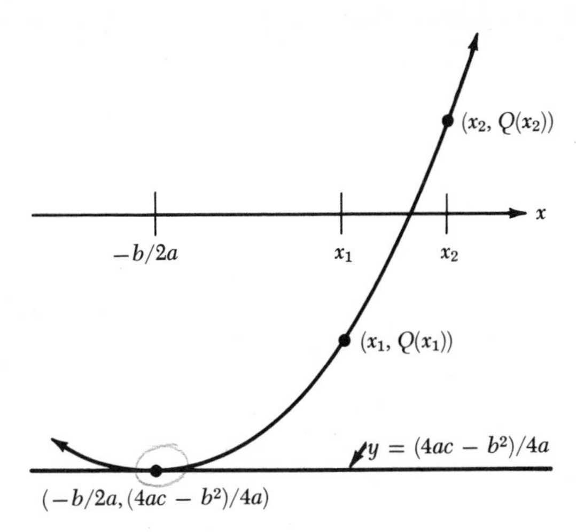

Figure 4-6

$(x_2, Q(x2))$ are above the line L. We also have

$$-b/2a < x_1 < x_2$$

so that

$$0 < x_1 + b/2a < x_2 + b/2a$$

and so

$$(x_1 + b/2a)^2 < (x_2 + b/2a)^2.$$

Finally,

$$(x_1 + b/2a)^2 + (4ac - b^2)/4a < (x_2 + b/2a)^2 + (4ac - b^2)/4a$$

or

$$Q(x_1) < Q(x_2).$$

It thus is seen that the point $(x_1, Q(x_1))$ is *below* the point $(x_2, Q(x_2))$. The relative positions of these points is shown in Fig. 4-6.

Similar considerations show that if $x_1 < x_2 < -b/2a$, then

$$Q(x_1) > Q(x_2),$$

and that $(x_1, Q(x_1))$ is *above* $(x_2, Q(x_2))$. This information may be summarized as follows:

(a) If $a > 0$ for the quadratic

$$Q(x) = c + bx + ax^2,$$

the graph of Q rises as x increases to the right of the number $-b/2a$, and the graph of Q rises as x decreases to the left of $-b/2a$. The graph of Q, therefore, has the general appearance given in Fig. 4-7.

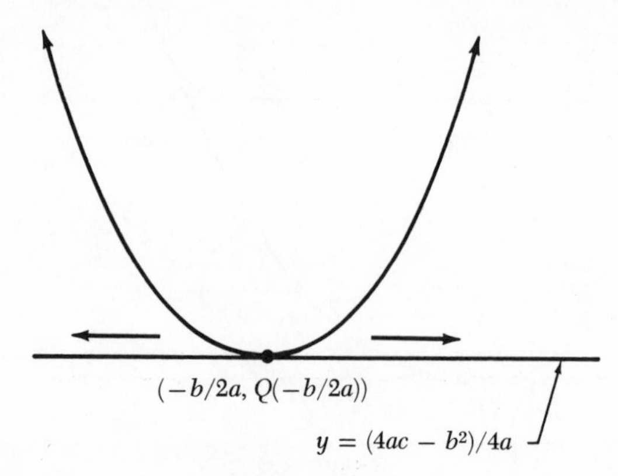

Figure 4-7

(b) If $a < 0$ for the quadratic

$$Q(x) = c + bx + ax^2,$$

the graph of Q falls as x increases to the right of the number $-b/2a$, and the graph of Q falls as x decreases to the left of $-b/2a$. The graph of Q therefore has the general appearance given in Fig. 4-8.

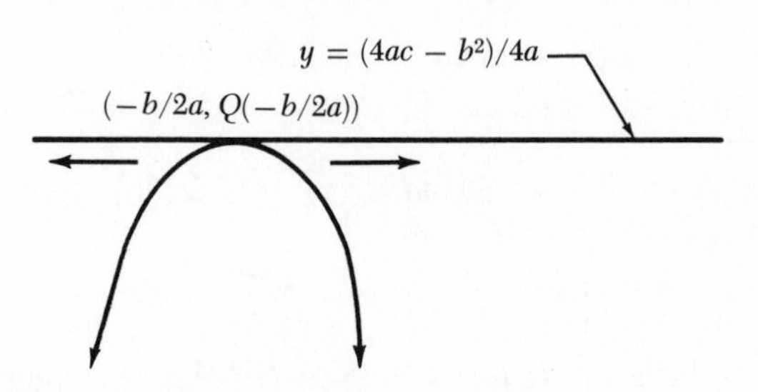

Figure 4-8

Example 4-10. We have seen above that the graph of

$$Q(x) = 1 + x + x^2$$

is nowhere below the line $y = \frac{3}{4}$.

Also, $-b/2a = -\frac{1}{2}$;

$$\begin{aligned} Q(-\tfrac{1}{2}) &= \tfrac{3}{4} \\ Q(-1) &= 1 \\ Q(0) &= 1 \\ Q(1) &= 3. \end{aligned}$$

(See Fig. 4-9 for the graph of Q.)

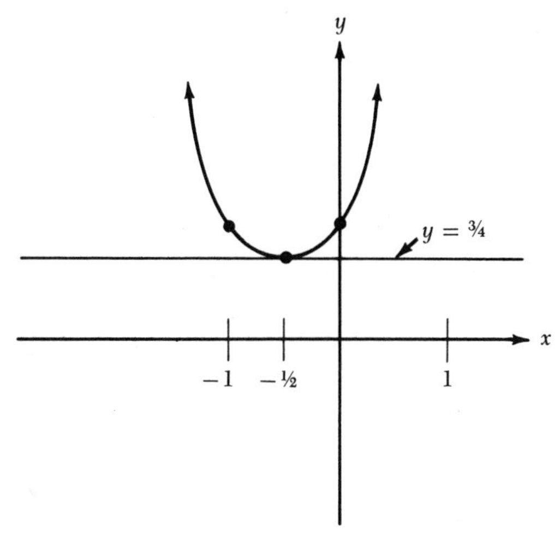

Figure 4-9

Exercises

1. Determine whether the following are polynomial functions. If a function is a polynomial function, give its degree.
   (a) $f(x) = \sqrt{2x}$.
   (b) $g(x) = (x + 2)(x - 2)$.
   (c) $h(x) = [x]$.
   (d) $p(x) = [x], x \in (0, 1)$.
   (e) $R(x) = 7x^5 - 4x + \sqrt{7}x^3 - x^9 - 8$.
   (f) $f(x) = \begin{cases} x^2 + 2x + 5 & \text{if} \quad x \in [-1, 0] \\ -x^2 + 2x + 5 & \text{if} \quad x \in [0, 1]. \end{cases}$
   (g) $g(x) = \begin{cases} x^2 + 2 & \text{if} \quad x \leq 0 \\ x + 2 & \text{if} \quad x > 0. \end{cases}$

2. Graph the functions (a), (b), (c), (d), (f), and (g) in Exercise 1.

3. Graph the following functions:

(a) $g(x) = x^3$.
(b) $s(x) = x^4$.
(c) $s(x) = x^4 + x^3$. [*Hint:* Use the graphs of (a) and (b).]
(d) $s(x) = x^4 + x^3 + x^2$.
(e) $s(x) = x^4 + x^3 + x^2 + x$.
(f) $s(x) = x^4 + x^3 + x^2 + x + 1$.

4. For each of the following quadratic functions determine

(a) the line $y = (4ac - b^2)/4a$.
(b) whether the graph is above or below the line $y = (4ac - b^2)/4a$.
(c) the coordinates of the *high* or *low* point of the graph. [*Hint:* $(-b/2a, Q(-b/2a))$ is the high or low point.] Then graph the function.

(i) $Q(x) = x^2$
(ii) $Q(x) = -x^2$
(iii) $Q(x) = x^2 - x$
(iv) $Q(x) = (1/2)x^2$
(v) $Q(x) = 10x^2$
(vi) $Q(x) = -3x^2 + x - 5$
(vii) $Q(x) = x^2 + x$
(viii) $Q(x) = -x^2 + (1/2)x + 1$

5. (a) Is it possible for the graph of

$$P(x) = 1 + 2kx + x^2$$

to be nowhere above the line $y = 101$ for some number k? If so, find such a k.

(b) Repeat (a) if

$$P(x) = 1 + 2kx - x^2.$$

(c) Is it possible for the graph of

$$P(x) = 4kx + 4x^2$$

to be nowhere above the line $y = 25$ for some number k? If so, find such a k.

(d) Repeat (c) if

$$P(x) = 4kx - 4x^2.$$

4.4 Zeros of Quadratic Functions

If Q is a quadratic given by

$$Q(x) = c + bx + ax^2, \ a \neq 0,$$

we have seen in Sec. 4-3 that

$$Q(x) = a(x + b/2a)^2 + \frac{4ac - b^2}{4a}.$$

A number $d \in \mathcal{D}(Q)$ is a zero of Q if and only if $Q(d) = 0$ or

$$a(d + b/2a)^2 + \frac{4ac - b^2}{4a} = 0.$$

From this we may conclude

$$(^*)\ 4a^2(d + b/2a)^2 = b^2 - 4ac.$$

For every real number d,

$$4a^2(d + b/2a)^2 \geq 0;$$

and hence, if $b^2 - 4ac < 0$, there can be no real number d such that $(^*)$ is true. If $b^2 - 4ac < 0$, the quadratic Q has no zeros.

If $b^2 - 4ac \geq 0$, $(^*)$ may be written

$$(d + b/2a)^2 = \frac{b^2 - 4ac}{4a^2}.$$

Therefore, since $\dfrac{b^2 - 4ac}{4a^2} \geq 0$,

$$d + b/2a = \pm\sqrt{\frac{b^2 - 4ac}{4a^2}} = \pm\frac{\sqrt{b^2 - 4ac}}{|2a|}$$

and

$$d = -b/2a \pm \frac{\sqrt{b^2 - 4ac}}{2a} = \frac{-b \pm \sqrt{b^2 - 4ac}}{2a}.$$

[Notice that $\pm(\sqrt{b^2 - 4ac})/|2a| = \pm(\sqrt{b^2 - 4ac})/2a$ by the definition of absolute value.]

In this case, if Q has any zeros at all, they must be one of the numbers

$$\frac{-b + \sqrt{b^2 - 4ac}}{2a}, \quad \text{or} \quad \frac{-b - \sqrt{b^2 - 4ac}}{2a}.$$

It is easy to show that these numbers actually are zeros of Q (if they are in the domain of Q); for example

$$Q\left(\frac{-b + \sqrt{b^2 - 4ac}}{2a}\right)$$

$$= a\left(\frac{-b + \sqrt{b^2 - 4ac}}{2a}\right)^2 + b\left(\frac{-b + \sqrt{b^2 - 4ac}}{2a}\right) + c$$

$$= a \cdot \frac{b^2 - 2b\sqrt{b^2 - 4ac} + (b^2 - 4ac)}{4a^2} + \frac{-b^2 + b\sqrt{b^2 - 4ac}}{2a} + c$$

$$= \frac{2b^2 - 2b\sqrt{b^2 - 4ac} - 4ac}{4a} + \frac{-b^2 + b\sqrt{b^2 - 4ac}}{2a} + c$$

$$= \frac{b^2 - b\sqrt{b^2 - 4ac} - 2ac}{2a} + \frac{-b^2 + b\sqrt{b^2 - 4ac}}{2a} + c$$

$$= -c + c = 0.$$

Thus,

$$Q\left(\frac{-b + \sqrt{b^2 - 4ac}}{2a}\right) = 0, \text{ and similarly, } Q\left(\frac{-b - \sqrt{b^2 - 4ac}}{2a}\right) = 0.$$

It may, of course, happen that the numbers

$$\frac{-b + \sqrt{b^2 - 4ac}}{2a} \quad \text{and} \quad \frac{b - \sqrt{b^2 - 4ac}}{2a}$$

are not different; i.e.,

$$\frac{-b + \sqrt{b^2 - 4ac}}{2a} = \frac{-b - \sqrt{b^2 - 4ac}}{2a}.$$

This is the case if and only if $b_2 - 4ac = 0$ as the following shows:

$$-b + \sqrt{b^2 - 4ac} = -b - \sqrt{b^2 - 4ac},$$

and

$$2\sqrt{b^2 - 4ac} = 0$$
$$b^2 - 4ac = 0.$$

In this case, then Q can have at most one zero.

These results may be summarized as follows for the quadratic function

$$Q(x) = c + bx + ax^2, a \neq 0:$$

1. *If the number $b^2 - 4ac < 0$, then Q has no real zeros.*
2. *If the number $b^2 - 4ac = 0$, then Q has no more than one real zero.*
3. *If the number $b^2 - 4ac > 0$, then Q has no more than two real zeros.*

Example 4-11. If $Q(x) = 1 + x + x^2$, then $a = 1$, $b = 1$, $c = 1$ and

$$b^2 - 4ac = 1 - 4 = -3 < 0$$

so that Q has no real zeros.

Example 4-12. If $Q(x) = 1 + 2x + x^2$, then $a = 1$, $b = 2$, $c = 1$ and

$$b^2 - 4ac = 4 - 4 = 0$$

so that Q can have no more than one zero and this must be the number

$$\frac{-b}{2a} = \frac{-2}{2} = -1.$$

Since -1 is in the domain of Q, -1 is a zero and the only zero of Q: $Q(-1) = 1 + 2(-1) + (-1)^2 = 0$.

Example 4-13. If $Q(x) = 1 + 2x + x^2$ for $x \in [0, 3]$, then Q has no zeros; for the only possible zero is -1 and this is not in the domain of Q.

Example 4-14. If $P(x) = 7 - x - x^2$ for $x \in [-10, 10]$, then $a = -1$, $b = -1$, $c = 7$ and $b^2 - 4ac = (-1)^2 - 4(-1)(7) = 1 + 28 = 29$. Therefore, the two numbers

$$\frac{1 + \sqrt{29}}{-2} \quad \text{and} \quad \frac{1 - \sqrt{29}}{-2}$$

are zeros of $P(x)$ if they are in the domain of P. We have

$$5 < \sqrt{29} < 6$$
$$6 < 1 + \sqrt{29} < 7$$

and

$$\frac{7}{-2} < \frac{1 + \sqrt{29}}{-2} < \frac{6}{-2} = -3$$

or

$$-3\tfrac{1}{2} < \frac{1 + \sqrt{29}}{-2} < -3$$

so that $\dfrac{1 + \sqrt{29}}{-2}$ is in the domain of P and is thus a zero. Similarly, $\dfrac{1 - \sqrt{29}}{-2}$ is a zero, so that P has two zeros.

The possibilities for the zeros of the quadratic

$$Q(x) = c + bx + ax^2, a \neq 0$$

may be seen clearly by considering the graph of Q. Consider the case in which $b^2 - 4ac < 0$ (this implies Q has no real zeros). Then $4ac - b^2 > 0$; and

(a) if $a > 0$, $(4ac - b^2)/4a > 0$.
(b) if $a < 0$, $(4ac - b^2)/4a < 0$.

For convenience we let $(4ac - b^2)/4a = L$. In case (a) we know by our previous considerations that the graph of Q can be nowhere below the

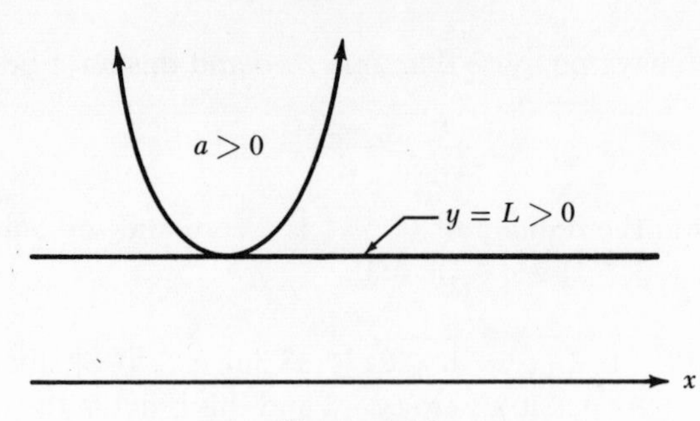

Figure 4-10

line $y = L$. But since $L > 0$, we have a situation as indicated in Fig. 4-10.
This clearly shows that the graph of Q cannot cross the x-axis and Q has no zeros. In case (b) $a < 0$ and $L < 0$ giving rise to a graphical situation as indicated in Fig. 4-11. Again, the graph does not cross the x-axis and Q cannot have zeros.

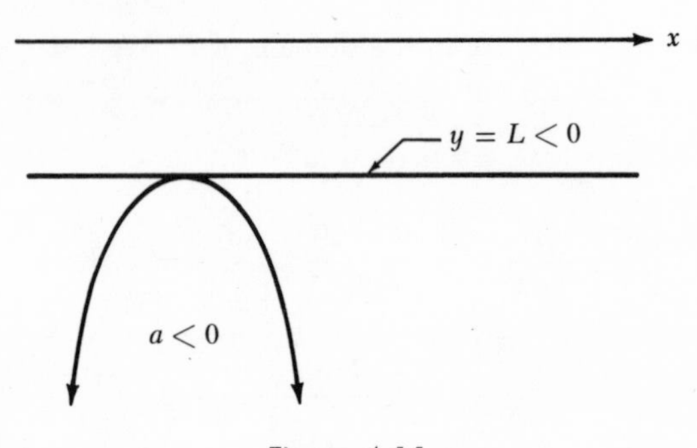

Figure 4-11

In case $L = 0$, the line $y = L$ is the x-axis; so the graph of Q may *touch* the x-axis once as indicated in Fig. 4-12, but cannot cross it twice.

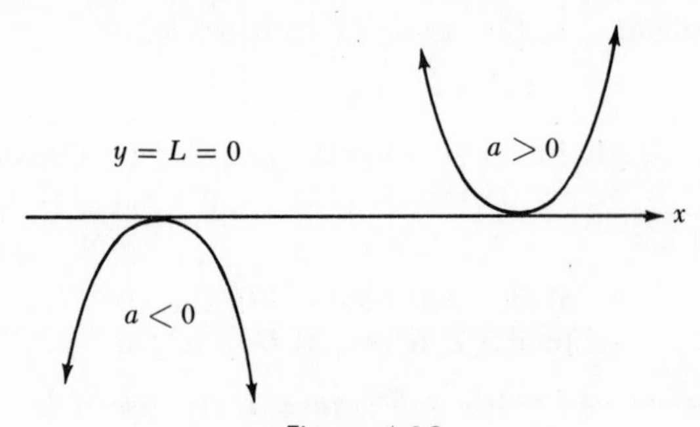

Figure 4-12

We leave as an exercise for the student the graphical consideration of the case $b^2 - 4ac > 0$.

Exercises

6. For each of the quadratic functions of Exercise 4, determine its zeros.

7. The number $b^2 - 4ac$ associated with the quadratic function

$$Q(x) = c + bx + ax^2,\ a \neq 0$$

is called the *discriminant* of the quadratic. Calculate the discriminant of each of the following quadratic functions and use this number to discuss the zeros of the functions.

(a) $Q(x) = 1 + x^2 + x$.
(b) $Q(x) = \frac{1}{2} + 2x + \sqrt{2}x^2$.
(c) $Q(x) = -3x^2 + (\frac{1}{2})x + 1$.
(d) $Q(x) = (\frac{5}{2})x^2 + \sqrt{5}x + 2$.

8. (a) Discuss the zeros of $Q(x) = 1 + x + x^2$ in each of the domains below:
(i) $[-1, 1]$.
(ii) The set of rational numbers.
(iii) The set of irrational numbers.
(iv) $[10, 101]$.
(v) The set of real numbers.

(b) Same question as (a) above except that

$$Q(x) = -3x^2 + (\tfrac{1}{2})x + 1.$$

(c) Same question as (a) above except that

$$Q(x) = (\tfrac{5}{2})x^2 + \sqrt{5}x + 2.$$

(d) Same question as (a) above except that

$$Q(x) = \tfrac{1}{2} + 2x + \sqrt{2}x^2.$$

(e) Same question as (a) above except that

$$Q(x) = (1 + \sqrt{2})x^2 - (10 + 11\sqrt{2})x - 11.$$

9. If the domain of the quadratic function

$$Q(x) = 3x^2 - 6x + k$$

is the set of all real numbers, what value of k will insure that Q has exactly one real zero?

10. Let r, s, t be rational numbers. Show that the zeros of the quadratic

$$R(x) = x^2 - 2rx + r^2 - s^2 + 2st - t^2$$

must be rational numbers.

11. If the quadratic function

$$F(x) = x^2 + 2(1 + t)x + t^2$$

has exactly one zero, what number is t?

4.5 More About the Zeros of a Quadratic Function

Let the number e be a zero of the quadratic polynomial

$$Q(x) = c + bx + ax^2$$

where $a \neq 0$. Then, by the definition of a zero,

$$Q(e) = c + be + ae^2 = 0.$$

Using the distributive law, we may write the last equation as

$$c + be + ae^2 = [c/a + (b/a)e + e^2]a = 0.$$

It is possible now to conclude that $c/a + (b/a)e + e^2 = 0$ since $a \neq 0$. This shows that the number e is also a zero of the quadratic

$$P(x) = c/a + (b/a)x + x^2$$

and that *the zeros of Q and P are the same.* It is possible, therefore, to study the zeros of Q by studying the zeros of P.

Suppose that $Q(x) = c + bx + ax^2$ has as zeros the real numbers z_1 and z_2. As we have seen already, this implies that the discriminant $d = b^2 - 4ac \geq 0$. We also know that

$$z_1 = \frac{-b + \sqrt{d}}{2a} \quad \text{and} \quad z_2 = \frac{-b - \sqrt{d}}{2a}.$$

Then,

$$z_1 + z_2 = (-2b)/(2a) = -(b/a)$$

and

$$z_1 \cdot z_2 = (b^2 - d)/4a^2 = [b^2 - (b^2 - 4ac)]/4a^2 = c/a.$$

This demonstrates that the sum of the zeros of Q is the additive inverse of the coefficient of x in $P(x)$ and that the product of the zeros of Q is the constant term of $P(x)$.

Example 4-15. Without finding the zeros of the quadratic function $Q(x) = 1 + 2x - 5x^2$, determine the sum and product of its zeros.

Solution. According to the above considerations, we may solve this problem by considering the quadratic

$$P(x) = (1/-5) + (2/-5)x + x^2.$$

The sum of the zeros of Q is $2/5$ and their product is $-1/5$.

Example 4-16. Find a quadratic which has the numbers $1 + \sqrt{2}$ and $1 - \sqrt{2}$ as zeros.

Solution. Since $(1 + \sqrt{2}) + (1 - \sqrt{2}) = 2$ and $(1 + \sqrt{2})(1 - \sqrt{2}) = 1 - 2 = -1$, we have that the quadratic

$$-1 - 2x + x^2$$

has $1 + \sqrt{2}$ and $1 - \sqrt{2}$ as zeros. There are, of course, other possibilities; for example, $-3 - 6x + 3x^2$.

The information just obtained concerning the zeros of a quadratic function may be used to factor the quadratic if it can be factored at all. If $Q(x) = c + bx + ax^2, a \neq 0$, has zeros z_1, z_2, then $z_1 + z_2 = -(b/a)$ and $z_1 \cdot z_2 = c/a$. Hence,

$$\begin{aligned} Q(x) &= ax^2 + bx + c \\ &= a[x^2 + (b/a)x + (c/a)] \\ &= a[x^2 - (z_1 + z_2)x + z_1 \cdot z_2] \\ &= a(x - z_1)(x - z_2). \end{aligned}$$

Example 4-17. Factor the quadratic $5x^2 - x - 1$.

Solution. First, we calculate the zeros:

$$z_1 = \frac{1 + \sqrt{1 - (4)(5)(-1)}}{2(5)} = \frac{1 + \sqrt{21}}{10}.$$

$$z_2 = \frac{1 - \sqrt{21}}{10}.$$

Then, the quadratic may be factored:

$$5x^2 - x - 1 = 5[x - (1 + \sqrt{21})/10][x - (1 - \sqrt{21})/10].$$

If the quadratic $Q(x) = c + bx + ax^2$ can be factored as

$$Q(x) = a(x - z_1)(x - z_2),$$

then $Q(z_1) = Q(z_2) = 0$ and consequently z_1, z_2 are zeros of Q. This shows that if Q can be factored, then Q has zeros. If the discriminant of Q is negative $(b^2 - 4ac < 0)$, Q has no real zeros. Hence, *if the dis-*

criminant of Q is negative, Q cannot be factored as the product of two real linear factors.

Example 4-18. The quadratic $x^2 + x + 1$ cannot be factored since the discriminant is $1^2 - 4 \cdot 1 \cdot 1 = -3 < 0$.

Example 4-19. The quadratic $3x^2 + 4x + \sqrt{6}$ cannot be factored since the discriminant is $16 - 4 \cdot 3 \cdot \sqrt{6} = 4(4 - 3\sqrt{6}) < 0$.

Example 4-20. Let the function F be defined by

$$F(x) = x/(x^2 - 5x + 9).$$

Determine the range of F.

Solution. Suppose that c is a number in the range of F, i.e., $c \in \mathcal{R}(F)$. Then, by definition of range, there is a number, say t, in the domain of F such that

$$F(t) = t/(t^2 - 5t + 9) = c.$$

Therefore,

$$t = c(t^2 - 5t + 9) = ct^2 - 5ct + 9c$$

and

$$ct^2 - (5c + 1)t + 9c = 0.$$

This equation shows that t is a zero of the quadratic

$$cx^2 - (5c + 1)x + 9c.$$

But the quadratic cannot have real zeros unless its discriminant is positive or zero. Hence,

$$(5c + 1)^2 - 4 \cdot c \cdot 9c \geq 0,$$

or

$$25c^2 + 10c + 1 - 36c^2 \geq 0,$$

or

$$1 + 10c - 11c^2 \geq 0.$$

Thus c is a number for which the quadratic $Q(x) \geq 0$, where

$$Q(x) = 1 + 10x - 11x^2 = (1 + 11x)(1 - x).$$

This quadratic may be shown to be non-negative between its zeros: $-1/11$, 1. We conclude that $\mathcal{R}(F) \subseteq [-1/11, 1]$. This argument may be reversed to show that $[-1/11, 1] \subseteq \mathcal{R}(F)$, and therefore that the range of F is the closed interval $[-1/11, 1]$.

Example 4-21. Factor the polynomial function $x^4 - 2x^2 - 3$.

Solution. If we write $x^4 - 2x^2 - 3 = (x^2)^2 - 2x^2 - 3$, the given polynomial may be considered a quadratic "in x^2." Consider the quadratic $y^2 - 2y - 3$. This has the zeros $-1, 3$ so that

$$y^2 - 2y - 3 = (y - 3)(y + 1).$$

Then,

$$\begin{aligned} x^4 - 2x^2 - 3 &= (x^2 - 3)(x^2 + 1) \\ &= (x + \sqrt{3})(x - \sqrt{3})(x^2 + 1). \end{aligned}$$

No further factorization is possible since $x^2 + 1$ has no zeros.

Exercises

12. Without computing the zeros, determine the sum and product of the zeros of the following quadratics:

(a) $x^2 - x + \frac{1}{4}$.
(b) $4x^2 - 4x + 1$.
(c) $x^2 + \sqrt{2}x + \frac{1}{4}$.
(d) $4x^2 + 4\sqrt{2}x + 1$
(e) $x^2 + 3x + 1$.
(f) $8x^2 + 24x + 8$.
(g) $x^2 - 4x + \frac{1}{2}\sqrt{2}$
(h) $2x^2 - 8x + \sqrt{2}$.

13. Find a quadratic which has the given numbers as zeros.

(a) $1, -2$.
(b) $8, -1$.
(c) $2 + \sqrt{3}, 2 - \sqrt{3}$.
(d) $\frac{1}{8}, -\frac{1}{2}$.
(e) $\frac{1}{2} + \sqrt{5}, -\frac{1}{2} + \sqrt{5}$.

14. Factor the polynomial functions of Exercise 12.

15. Determine all the numbers k so that the quadratic

$$x^2 + 2(k + 2)x + 9k$$

can be factored.

16. Show that if a, b are any real numbers, the quadratic

$$x^2 - 2ax + a^2 - b^2$$

can be factored.

17. If a, b, c are any real numbers, show that the quadratic

$$(a - b + c)x^2 + 2(a - b)x + (a - b - c)$$

can be factored if $c \neq b - a$.

18. Let $a \neq 0$ be a real number. Determine all numbers m such that the quadratic

$$2a^2x^2 + 2amx + m^2 - 2$$

can be factored.

19. Determine the range of the function F defined by

$$F(x) = (x^2 - x + 1)/(x^2 + 2x + 1).$$

20. Factor the following:
(a) $2x^4 - 10x^2 - 7$.
(b) $3x^4 - 29x^2 + 18$.
(c) $x^4 - 6x^3 + 8x^2 + 3x - 2$.

4.6 Synthetic Division

If we are given a function f and a number c in the domain of f, the determination of the number $f(c)$ can sometimes be very difficult. In case f is a polynomial function, the calculation of $f(c)$ involves only addition and multiplication; but even so, if the degree of f is large, the calculation can be quite tedious. A technique—applicable to polynomial functions only—known as synthetic division can be used to advantage to aid in these computations. To illustrate the process let

$$P(x) = a_0 + a_1x + a_2x^2 + a_3x^3$$

and suppose c is a number in the domain of P. Then

$$\begin{aligned} P(c) &= a_0 + a_1c + a_2c^2 + a_3c^3 \\ &= a_0 + (a_1 + a_2c + a_3c^2)c \\ &= a_0 + (a_1 + [a_2 + a_3c]c)c. \end{aligned}$$

Notice from this that $P(c)$ may be obtained by the following sequence of steps:

Multiply a_3 by c to obtain a_3c; then add a_2 to this to obtain $a_2 + a_3c$. Next multiply $(a_2 + a_3c)$ by c to obtain $(a_2 + a_3c)c$; then add to this a_1 to obtain $a_1 + (a_2 + a_3c)c$. The final step is to multiply by c and add a_0.

It will be obvious to the reader that the pattern is simply one of multiplying by c and adding the coefficients successively. If we wish to arrive at $P(c)$ in this fashion, the problem is one of hardly more than bookkeeping proportions. Consider then the schematic process for keeping track of the appropriate numbers as given in Table (a). In Table (a), the first row simply consists of the coefficients of P written in the appropriate order. It should be evident that this process can be carried out on a polynomial of any degree.

Example 4-22. For the polynomial function

$$f(x) = 3x^7 - x^6 + 31x^4 + 22x + 5$$

we calculate $f(-2)$. By the process just described, we write the coefficients in the first row and proceed as before [see Table (b)]. Notice that zeros are written for missing terms of the polynomial. The -2 is placed at the far right simply to remind us what to multiply by. Thus,

$$f(-2) = 9.$$

Example 4-23. Calculate $P(-5)$ if

$$P(x) = 3x^5 + 11x^4 + 90x^2 - 19x + 53.$$

Solution:

3	11	0	90	−19	53	−5
	−15	20	−100	50	−155	
3	−4	20	−10	31	−102	

Therefore, $P(-5) = -102$.

Example 4-24. If $P(x) = 5x^5 - x^3 + x + 2$, compute $P(3)$.

Solution:

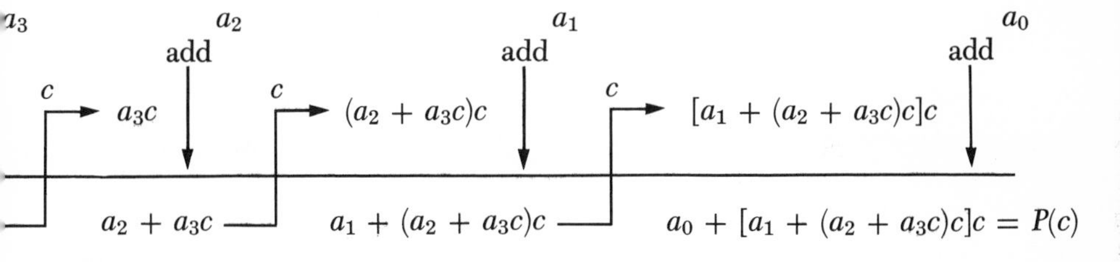

Table (a)

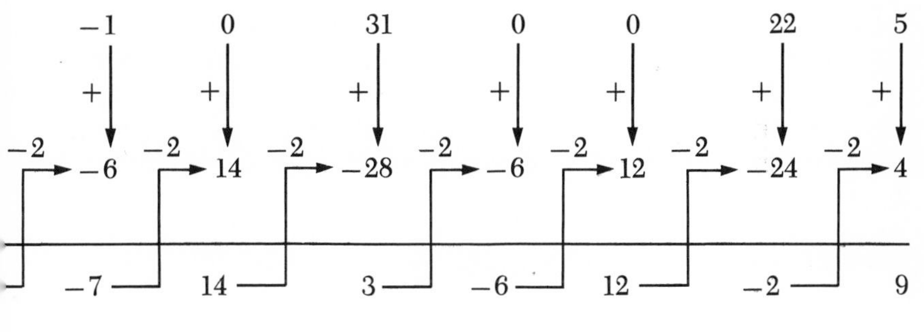

Table (b)

Hence, $P(3) = 1193$.

5	0	−1	0	1	2	3
	15	45	132	396	1191	
5	15	44	132	397	1193	

It may have occurred to the student that synthetic division *seems* to be a more efficient way of calculating $P(c)$ as opposed to the obvious straightforward way. Is this actually the case or does it just seem so? And, if this process is really advantageous, to what is the advantage attributable? To answer this question, let us consider our starting point. We illustrate again with the polynomial

$$P(x) = a_0 + a_1x + a_3x^2 + a_3x^3.$$

The original problem was to calculate $P(c)$, and to do this we wrote

$$\begin{aligned} P(c) &= a_0 + a_1c + a_2c^2 + a_3c^3 \\ &= a_0 + (a_1c + [a_2 + a_3c]c)c. \end{aligned}$$

This is possible by making repeated use of the distributive law:

$$a(b + d) = a \cdot b + a \cdot d.$$

Notice that on the left side of this equation there are 2 operations (one multiplication and one addition) and on the right-hand side there are 3 operations (two multiplications and one addition). Therefore, in expressing $P(c)$ as

$$a_0 + (a_1c + [a_2 + a_3c]c)c$$

we have replaced expressions of the form $a \cdot b + a \cdot d$ by ones of the form $a(b + d)$ and saved one operation each time. There is, then, a real advantage in using the synthetic division process, and the advantage stems from the distributive law.

Exercises

21. If $f(x) = 2x^3 + x^2 - 5x + 3$, use synthetic division to find $f(1), f(2), f(5), f(-1), f(-3), f(-6)$.

22. Compute $f(3)$ if

$$f(x) = 5x^5 - 6x^4 - 8x^3 + 7x^2 + 6x + 2.$$

23. Compute $f(a)$ if

$$f(x) = x^3 - (a + b + c)x^2 + (ab + ac + bc)x - abc.$$

24. If $P(x) = x^3 + mx^2 - 20x + 6$, determine m so that 3 is a zero of P. [*Hint:* Use synthetic division.]

25. If $C(x) = 2x^3 - x^2 + kx + n$, choose k and n so that $C(-2) = 0$ and $C(4) = 0$.

4.7 The Factor and Remainder Theorem

The reader is no doubt familiar with the usual process of dividing one polynomial function $P(x)$ by another, $D(x)$, to obtain a quotient and a remainder. This division is justified by the following theorem; the proof of this will not be given.

> **Theorem 22** (The Division Algorithm). Let $P(x)$ be a polynomial of degree n and let $D(x)$ be a polynomial of degree m. Then, there are unique polynomials $R(x)$ and $Q(x)$ such that
>
> $$P(x) = D(x) \cdot Q(x) + R(x), \text{ for all } x \in \mathfrak{D}(P)$$
>
> and $R(x)$ is either the zero polynomial or has a degree less than m. (Q is called the *quotient* and R the *remainder*.)

It is convenient to say that $D(x)$ *divides* $P(x)$ or is a factor of $P(x)$ in case

$$P(x) = D(x) \cdot Q(x)$$

for some polynomial $Q(x)$.

Let us consider the above theorem applied to polynomials $P(x)$ and $D(x) = x - c$, for some $c \in \mathfrak{D}(P)$. Then, by the theorem, there is $Q(x)$, $R(x)$ such that

$$P(x) = (x - c) \cdot Q(x) + R(x).$$

And in addition $R(x)$ is either the zero polynomial or has degree less than the degree of $(x - c)$; i.e., $R(x)$ is either the zero polynomial or a constant polynomial: $R(x) = a$ for all $x \in \mathfrak{D}(R)$. Since the above is true for all $x \in \mathfrak{D}(P)$, it is in particular true for c:

$$\begin{aligned} P(c) &= (c - c) \cdot Q(c) + R(c) \\ &= 0 \cdot Q(c) + R(c) \\ &= R(c). \end{aligned}$$

Therefore, $R(x)$ is the constant $P(c)$: $R(x) = P(c)$ for all $x \in \mathfrak{D}(R)$. Hence, for any polynomial function $P(x)$ and any $c \in \mathfrak{D}(P)$ we may write

$$(*)\ \ P(x) = (x - c) \cdot Q(x) + P(c)$$

for some Q.

THEOREM 23. The number $c \in \mathcal{D}(P)$ is a zero of $P(x)$ if and only if $x - c$ divides $P(x)$.

Proof: If $c \in \mathcal{D}(P)$ is a zero of $P(x)$, then $P(c) = 0$ and from (*) above

$$P(x) = (x - c) \cdot Q(x)$$

so that $(x - c)$ divides $P(x)$.

Now suppose that $(x - c)$ divides $P(x)$. Then by definition

$$P(x) = (x - c) \cdot L(x)$$

for some $L(x)$. Then we have an instance of the Division Algorithm

$$P(x) = (x - c) \cdot L(x) + 0$$

with quotient $L(x)$ and remainder 0. But since the quotient and remainder are unique, and (*) states that the remainder is always $P(c)$, we must have $P(c) = 0$ so that c is a zero of P.

The synthetic division process is extremely useful in writing a polynomial $P(x)$ in the form given in (*):

$$P(x) = (x - c) \cdot Q(x) + P(c)$$

where $c \in \mathcal{D}(P)$. We illustrate with

$$P(x) = a_0 + a_1x + a_2x^2 + a_3x^3.$$

First, we compute $P(c)$ by synthetic division:

$$\begin{array}{ccccc|c}
a_3 & a_2 & a_1 & a_0 & & c \\
 & a_3c & (a_2 + a_3c)c & [a_1 + (a_2 + a_3c)c]c & & \\
\hline
a_3 & a_2 + a_3c & a_1 + (a_2 + a_3c)c & a_0 + [a_1 + (a_2 + a_3c)c]c = P(c) & &
\end{array}$$

Now take the first three numbers in the last row as the coefficients of a new polynomial:

$$a_3x^2 + (a_2 + a_3c)x + [a_1 + (a_2 + a_3c)c].$$

It turns out that this new polynomial is the $Q(x)$ that we desire in (*):

$$\begin{aligned}
&(x - c) \cdot \{a_3x^2 + (a_2 + a_3c)x + [a_1 + (a_2 + a_3c)c]\} \\
&= \{a_3x^2 + (a_2 + a_3c)x + [a_1 + (a_2 + a_3c)c]\} \cdot x \\
&\quad - \{a_3x^2 + (a_2 + a_3c)x + [a_1 + (a_2 + a_3c)c]\} \cdot c \\
&= a_3x^3 + (a_2 + a_3c)x^2 + [a_1 + (a_3c)c]x \\
&\quad - a_3cx^2 - (a_2 + a_3c)cx - [a_1 + (a_2 + a_3c)c]c \\
&= a_3x^3 + a_2x^2 + a_1x - [a_1 + (a_2 + a_3c)c]c \\
&= a_3x^3 + a_2x^2 + a_1x + a_0 - a_0 - [a_1 + (a_2 + a_3c)c]c \\
&= P(x) - P(c).
\end{aligned}$$

Therefore, we have

$$\begin{aligned} P(x) &= (x - c) \cdot \{a_3x^2 + (a_2 + a_3c)x + [a_1 + (a_2 + a_3c)c]\} + P(c) \\ &= (x - c) \cdot Q(x) + P(c). \end{aligned}$$

The general situation for polynomials of degree different from 3 presents no new difficulties.

Example 4-25. To divide $P(x) = 5x^5 - x^3 + x + 2$ by $x - 3$ we first compute $P(3)$ by synthetic division thus obtaining the remainder $P(3)$. And the numbers (except the last) in the third row will be the coefficients of the quotient:

5	0	−1	0	1	2	3
	15	45	132	396	1191	
5	15	44	132	397	1193	$= P(3)$

$$5x^4 + 15x^3 + 44x^2 + 132x + 397 = Q(x)$$

Thus,

$$5x^5 - x^3 + x + 2 = (x - 3) \cdot (5x^4 + 15x^3 + 4x^2 + 132x + 397) + 1193.$$

Example 4-26. Divide $3x^7 - x^6 + 31x^4 + 22x + 5$ by $x + 2$ and obtain the quotient and remainder.

Solution. Notice that we are dividing by $x + 2 = x - (-2)$ so that we must use -2 in the synthetic division:

3	−1	0	31	0	0	22	5	−2
	−6	14	−28	−6	12	−24	4	
3	−7	14	3	−6	12	−2	9	$= P(-2)$

The remainder is therefore $P(-2) = 9$ and the quotient is

$$3x^6 - 7x^5 + 14x^4 + 3x^3 - 6x^2 + 12x - 2.$$

Exercises

26. Find the quotient and remainder if:
(a) $f(x) = x^2 - x + 1$ is divided by $x + 1$.
(b) $g(x) = 3x^3 - x^2 + 10x - 1$ is divided by $x - 1$.

(c) $m(x) = x^5 - 4x^3 - 3x^2 - 8$ is divided by $x + 3$
(d) $n(x) = x^4 - 8x^2 - x + 3/2$ is divided by $x + 1$
(e) $r(x) = 5x^3 - 3x^2 + 7x - 1$ is divided by $x - 2$.
(f) $g(x) = 3x^4 - 2x^3 + x$ is divided by $3x + 7$. [*Hint:* First divide by $x + 7/3$.]

27. Let b be a number, not zero. Show that if n is an odd integer $x + b$ is a factor of $x^n + b^n$ and is not a factor if n is even.

4.8 Partial Fractions

In the previous chapter we defined the function f/g of two given functions f, g with $g(x) \neq 0$ for all $x \in \mathfrak{D}(f) \cap \mathfrak{D}(g)$. If f and g are polynomial functions, the function f/g is called a *rational* function. It is possible to show that a *rational function can always be obtained as a sum of rational functions of the form*

$$(*) \qquad P(x), \qquad \frac{A}{(x-a)^k} \qquad \text{and} \qquad \frac{Ax+B}{(x^2+cx+d)^t}$$

where $P(x)$ is a polynomial, a, A, B, c, d are numbers, and k, t are positive integers. Writing a rational function in this fashion affects a simplification relative to certain problems which arise in calculus. We shall not attempt to prove this result here, but rather describe a technique for writing a rational function as a sum of functions of the form given in (*).

It first may be observed that if in the rational function P/Q, P has a degree greater than or equal to the degree of Q, we may find polynomials F and R such that

$$(1) \quad P/Q = F + R/Q,$$

and the degree of R is *less* than the degree of Q (if $R \neq 0$). This follows from the Division Algorithm: For the polynomials P, Q there are polynomials F and R such that

$$P(x) = Q(x) \cdot F(x) + R(x),$$

and $R(x)$ is either zero or has degree less than the degree of $Q(x)$. Then dividing by $Q(x)$ gives (1).

Every rational function R/Q, where R has degree less than the degree of Q is a sum of terms of the form

$$\frac{A}{(x-a)^k} \qquad \text{and} \qquad \frac{Ax+B}{(x^2+cx+d)^t}.$$

These terms are usually referred to as *partial fractions*. The problem then is to determine the partial fractions

$$\frac{A}{(x-a)^k} \quad \text{and} \quad \frac{Ax+B}{(x^2+cx+d)^t}$$

that we need to express a given function R/Q. This is done by factoring the polynomial Q. It can be shown that every polynomial with real number coefficients can be factored as a constant multiplied by a product of terms of the form

$$(x-a)^k \quad \text{and} \quad (x^2+cx+d)^t$$

where $c^2 - 4d < 0$. Once this factorization has been determined, the terms

$$\frac{A}{(x-a)^k} \quad \text{and} \quad \frac{Bx+C}{(x^2+cx+d)^t}$$

needed to obtain R/Q as a sum may be determined. This determination is made as follows:

(a) If $(x-a)^k$ is a factor of Q and this is the highest power of $(x-a)$ that occurs as a factor of Q, then to obtain R/Q as a sum we need one each of the following summands:

$$\frac{A_1}{x-a}, \frac{A_2}{(x-a)^2}, \frac{A_3}{(x-a)^3}, \ldots, \frac{A_k}{(x-a)^k}$$

where $A_1, A_2, \ldots, A_k$ are numbers to be determined.

(b) If $(x^2+cx-d)^t$ is a factor of Q with $c^2-4d<0$ and this is the highest power of (x^2+cx+d) that occurs as a factor of Q, then to obtain R/Q as a sum we need one each of the following summands:

$$\frac{B_1x+C_1}{x^2+cx+d}, \frac{B_2x+C_2}{(x^2+cx+d)^2}, \ldots, \frac{B_tx+C_t}{(x^2+cx+d)^t}$$

where $B_1, C_1, B_2, C_2, \ldots, B_t, C_t$ are numbers to be determined.

Example 4-27. Express $\dfrac{x^4}{x^3+2x^2+2x+1}$ as a sum of a polynomial and partial fractions.

Solution. By dividing x^4 by x^3+2x^2+2x+1,

$$x^4 = (x-2)(x^3+2x^2+2x+1) + (2x^2+3x+2)$$

so that

$$\frac{x^4}{x^3 + 2x^2 + 2x + 1} = (x - 2) + \frac{2x^2 + 3x + 2}{x^3 + 2x^2 + 2x + 1}.$$

Next, $x^3 + 2x^2 + 2x + 1 = (x + 1) \cdot (x^2 + x + 1)$.

(Note that we cannot take the factorization any further since the discriminant of $x^2 + x + 1$ is negative.) Then

$$\frac{2x^2 + 3x + 2}{x^3 + 2x^2 + 2x + 1} = \frac{2x^2 + 3x + 2}{(x + 1) \cdot (x^2 + x + 1)} = \frac{A}{x + 1} + \frac{Bx + C}{x^2 + x + 1}.$$

The task now is to determine the numbers A, B, C.

$$\frac{A}{x + 1} + \frac{Bx + C}{x^2 + x + 1} = \frac{A(x^2 + x + 1) + (Bx + C)(x + 1)}{(x + 1)(x^2 + x + 1)} = \frac{(A + B)x^2 + (A + B + C)x + A + C}{(x + 1)(x^2 + x + 1)}$$

so that

$$\frac{2x^2 + 3x + 2}{(x + 1)(x^2 + x + 1)} = \frac{(A + B)x^2 + (A + B + C)x + A + C}{(x + 1)(x^2 + x + 1)},$$

and it follows that

$$2x^2 + 3x + 2 = (A + B)x^2 + (A + B + C)x + A + C.$$

Since this is true for *all* x we get

(1) $2 = A + C$ if $x = 0$
(2) $7 = 3A + 2B + 2C$ if $x = 1$
(3) $1 = A$ if $x = -1$.

Therefore, from (1) and (3) $C = 1$ and from (2)

$$7 = 3 + 2B + 2$$
$$7 = 5 + 2B$$
$$2 = 2B$$

or

$$B = 1.$$

Thus, we conclude that $A = B = C = 1$.

As a check we add $\dfrac{1}{x+1}$ and $\dfrac{x+1}{x^2+x+1}$

$$\frac{1}{x+1}+\frac{x+1}{x^2+x+1}=\frac{(x^2+x+1)+(x+1)^2}{(x+1)(x^2+x+1)}$$
$$=\frac{2x^2+3x+2}{(x+1)(x^2+x+1)}.$$

Hence,

$$\frac{x^4}{x^3+2x^2+2x+1}=(x-2)+\frac{1}{x+1}+\frac{x+1}{x^2+x+1}.$$

Example 4-28. Express $\dfrac{x+1}{x^2(x-1)(x^2-x+1)}$ as a sum of partial fractions.

Solution. We need to find numbers A, B, C, D, E such that

$$\frac{x+1}{x^2(x-1)(x^2-x+1)}=\frac{A}{x}+\frac{B}{x^2}+\frac{C}{x-1}+\frac{Dx+E}{x^2-x+1}.$$

From

$$\frac{A}{x}+\frac{B}{x^2}+\frac{C}{x-1}+\frac{Dx+E}{x^2-x+1}$$
$$=\frac{Ax+B}{x^2}+\frac{C}{x-1}+\frac{Dx+E}{x^2-x+1}$$
$$=\frac{(A+C)x^2+(B-A)x-B}{x^2(x-1)}+\frac{Dx+E}{x^2-x+1}$$
$$=\frac{(A+C+D)x^4+(B-2A-C+E-D)x^3+(2A-2B+C-E)x^2+(2B-A)x-B}{x^2(x-1)(x^2-x+1)},$$

we conclude that

$$(A+C+D)x^4+(B-2A-C+E-D)x^3+(2A-2B+C-E)x^2 + (2B-A)x-B=x+1.$$

Since this must be true for all x, we choose $x=0$, $x=1$, $x=-1$, $x=2$, $x=-2$ and obtain the following equations:

For $x=0$, $-B=1$ or $B=-1$.
For $x=1$, $C=2$.
For $x=-1$, $6A+3C+2D-6B-2E=0$.
For $x=2$, $6A+3B+12C+8D+4E=3$.
For $x=-2$, $42A-21B+28C+24D-12E=-1$.

Using the two values for B and C ($B = -1$, $C = 2$) in the last three equations gives:

$$(1)\ 6A + 2D - 2E + 12 = 0.$$
$$(2)\ 6A + 8D + 4E + 21 = 3.$$
$$(3)\ 42A + 24D - 12E + 77 = -1.$$

Subtracting Eq. (1) from (2):

$$6D + 6E + 9 = 3 \qquad \text{or} \qquad D + E = -1.$$

Now, multiplying Eq. (2) by 7:

$$42A + 56D + 28E + 147 = 21,$$

and subtracting this from Eq. (3):

$$-32D - 40E - 70 = -22 \qquad \text{or} \qquad -32D - 40\text{E} = 48.$$

Dividing this last equation by 8 gives:

$$-4D - 5E = 6.$$

Since we already have that $D + E = -1$, we may substitute $D = -1 - E$ in the last equation to obtain

$$-4(-1 - E) - 5E = 6$$
$$4 + 4E - 5E = 6$$
$$-E = 2 \qquad \text{or} \qquad E = -2.$$

Then

$$D = -1 - (-2) = -1 + 2 = 1.$$

We have thus obtained

$$B = -1, C = 2, D = 1, E = -2.$$

It only remains to determine A, and this can be done from Eq. (1) now that we have $D = 1$ and $E = -2$:

$$6A + 2(1) - 2(-2) + 12 = 0$$
$$6A + 18 = 0$$
$$A + 3 = 0$$
$$A = -3.$$

It is easy to verify that these values for A, B, C, D, E work. Hence,

$$\frac{-3}{x} + \frac{-1}{x^2} + \frac{2}{x - 1} + \frac{x - 2}{x^2 - x + 1} = \frac{x + 1}{x^2(x - 1)(x^2 - x + 1)}.$$

Example 4-29. Express $\dfrac{x + 1}{2x^2((½)x - ½)(3x^2 - 3x + 3)}$ as a sum of partial fractions.

Solution.

$$\frac{x+1}{2x^2((½)x - ½)(3x^2 - 3x + 3)} = \frac{x+1}{x^2(x-1)(3x^2-3x+3)}$$
$$= \frac{x+1}{3x^2(x-1)(x^2-x+1)}$$
$$= \frac{1}{3} \cdot \frac{x+1}{x^2(x-1)(x^2-x+1)}.$$

Thus, the problem is reduced to Example 4-28 above:

$$\frac{1}{3} \cdot \frac{x+1}{x^2(x-1)(x^2-x+1)} = \frac{1}{3}\left[\frac{-3}{x} + \frac{-1}{x^2} + \frac{2}{x-1} + \frac{x-2}{x^2-x+1}\right]$$
$$= \frac{-1}{x} + \frac{-1}{3x^2} + \frac{2}{3x-3} + \frac{x-2}{3x^2-3x+3}.$$

Example 4-30. Express $\dfrac{x+1}{x^2(x-1)^3(x^2-x+1)^2}$ as a sum of partial fractions.

Solution. Numbers $A_1, A_2, A_3, A_4, A_5, A_6, A_7, A_8, A_9$ must be determined so that

$$\frac{A_1}{x} + \frac{A_2}{x^2} + \frac{A_3}{x-1} + \frac{A_4}{(x-1)^2} + \frac{A_5}{(x-1)^3} + \frac{A_6 x + A_7}{x^2-x+1}$$
$$+ \frac{A_8 x + A_9}{(x^2-x+1)^2} = \frac{x+1}{x^2(x-1)^3(x^2-x+1)^2}.$$

The procedure is similar to that in Example 4-28 except that the calculations are much more involved and tedious. We leave the details to the reader.

Exercises

Express each of the following rational functions as the sum of a polynomial and/or partial fractions.

28. $\dfrac{1}{x(x+1)}.$

29. $\dfrac{x}{(x+1)(x-1)}.$

30. $\dfrac{4x+1}{2x^2+4x-6}.$

31. $\dfrac{x^2}{(x^2-1)}.$

32. $\dfrac{2x+1}{x^3+1}.$

33. $\dfrac{x^3+x^2+x-1}{(2x+1)(x^2+1)^2}.$

4.9 Inequalities Involving Polynomials

It is convenient at this point to consider inequalities again in the light of our considerations concerning polynomial functions. In Chapter 2 inequalities of the type

$$x^2 - x - 6 \geq 0$$

were studied. This is obviously an instance of an inequality of the kind

$$P(x) \geq 0$$

where $P(x)$ is a quadratic function. Here the domains of our polynomial functions will always be the set of all real numbers. The problem is to describe all those numbers x for which it is true that

$$P(x) \geq 0.$$

We were able to solve the inequality

$$x^2 - x - 6 \geq 0,$$

by factoring

$$(x - 3)(x + 2) \geq 0$$

and then reasoning that this product is non-negative only if

$$\text{(a) } x - 3 \geq 0 \quad \text{and} \quad x + 2 \geq 0$$

or

$$\text{(b) } x - 3 \leq 0 \quad \text{and} \quad x + 2 \leq 0.$$

From (a)

$$x \geq 3 \quad \text{and} \quad x \geq -2$$

and from (b)

$$x \leq 3 \quad \text{and} \quad x \leq -2.$$

Condition (a) is met if $x \geq 3$ and condition (b) is met if $x \leq -2$. These

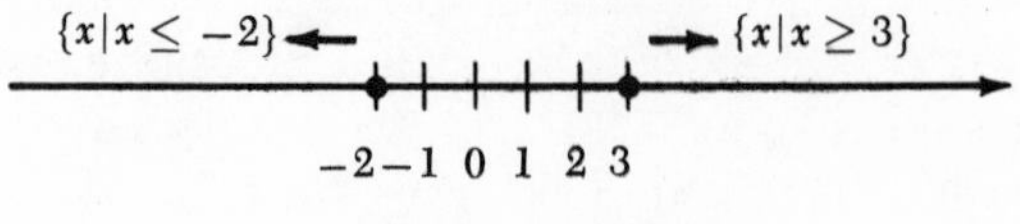

$\{x|x \leq -2\}$ ← → $\{x|x \geq 3\}$

−2 −1 0 1 2 3

Figure 4-13

two conditions are pictured in Fig. 4-13. Consider now the graph of

$$Q(x) = x^2 - x - 6.$$

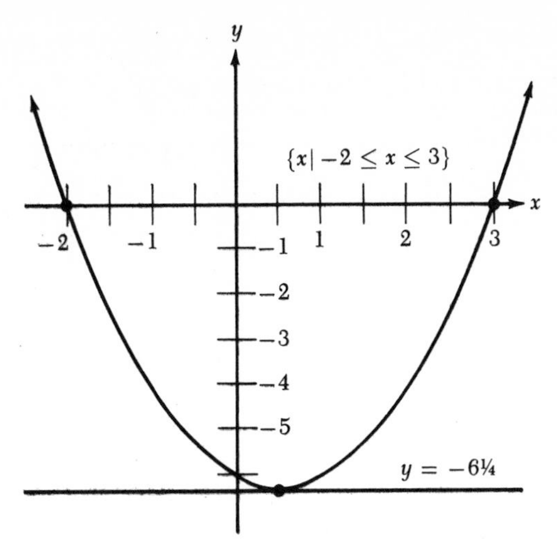

Figure 4-14

This is given in Fig. 4-14. It is quite clear from Fig. 4-14 why we reached the solution indicated in Fig. 4-13. In fact, we can also immediately see that the inequality

$$x^2 - x - 6 \leq 0$$

has the solution set $[-2, 3]$.

The solution sets for both inequalities

$$Q(x) \geq 0 \qquad \text{and} \qquad Q(x) \leq 0$$

are described in terms of the two numbers -2, 3; and these are the zeros of the function $Q(x)$.

Because of the knowledge we now have of the graphs of quadratic functions, inequalities of the form $Q(x) \geq 0$ and $Q(x) \leq 0$ can be solved simply by investigating the discriminant and zeros. In the case above,

$$Q(x) = x^2 - x - 6$$

has a discriminant of $(-1)^2 - 4 \cdot 1(-6) = 25$ and hence two zeros: -2 and 3. Also, the graph of Q has its low point (the coefficient of x^2 is positive) on the line $y = -25/4 = -6\frac{1}{4}$ and rises above this line to cross the x-axis at $(-2, 0)$ and $(3, 0)$. Thus, for $x \in [-2, 3]$ the graph of Q lies between the lines $y = -6\frac{1}{4}$ and $y = 0$; i.e.,

$$-6\tfrac{1}{4} \leq Q(x) \leq 0 \text{ for all } x \in [-2, 3].$$

(See Fig. 4-14.)

I.

Theorem 24. Let $Q(x) = c + bx + ax^2$, $a \neq 0$, and let $d = b^2 - 4ac$ be its discriminant.

(a) If $a > 0$ and $d < 0$, then the solution set for the inequality $Q(x) \leq 0$ is $\varnothing$ and the solution set for the inequality $Q(x) > 0$ is **R** (all real numbers).

(b) If $a > 0$ and $d > 0$, then the solution set for the inequality $Q(x) \leq 0$ is $[z_1, z_2]$, where $z_1 < z_2$ are the zeros of Q, and the solution set for the inequality $Q(x) \geq 0$ is $\{x \mid x \leq z_1\} \cup \{x \mid x \geq z_2\}$.

(c) If $a < 0$ and $d < 0$, then the solution set for $Q(x) < 0$ is **R** and the solution set for $Q(x) \geq 0$ is $\varnothing$.

(d) If $a < 0$ and $d > 0$, then the solution set for $Q(x) \leq 0$ is $\{x \mid x \leq z_1\} \cup \{x \mid x \geq z_2\}$ where $z_1 < z_2$ and these are the zeros of Q. The solution set for $Q(x) \geq 0$ is $[z_1, z_2]$.

Proof: We prove statement (d) and leave the others for the student. With $d > 0$, we know that Q has two distinct zeros, say, $z_1 < z_2$. Since $a < 0$, the graph of Q falls from its high point and crosses the x-axis at $(z_1, 0)$ and $(z_2, 0)$. (See Fig. 4-15.) The solution sets of the two inequalities are then clearly the ones given.

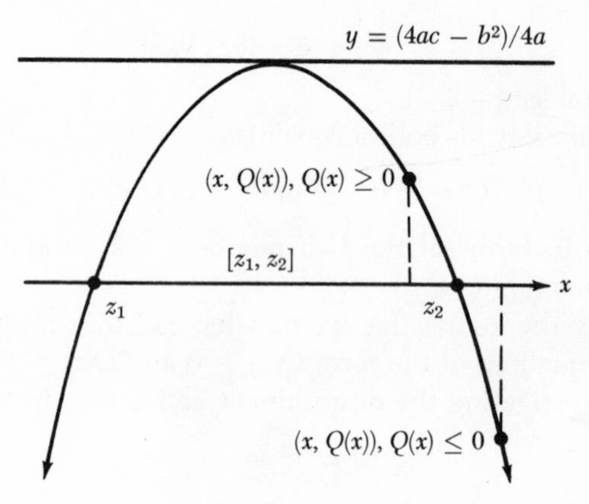

Figure 4-15

a > 0
d < 0

Example 4-31. Find the solution set for $x^2 - x + 1 > 0$.

Solution. $d = (-1)^2 - 4(1)(1) = 1 - 4 = -3 < 0$ and $a = 1 > 0$. Hence, $x^2 - x + 1 > 0$ for all real numbers.

Example 4-32. Find the solution set for $-x^2 - x + 1 \geq 0$.

Solution. $d = (-1)^2 - 4(-1)(1) = 1 + 4 = 5$ and $a = -1 < 0$. The zeros of the function are

$$\frac{1+\sqrt{5}}{-2} = -\tfrac{1}{2} - \tfrac{1}{2}\sqrt{5}$$

and

$$\frac{1-\sqrt{5}}{-2} = -\tfrac{1}{2} + \tfrac{1}{2}\sqrt{5}.$$

The solution set is then

$$[-\tfrac{1}{2} - \tfrac{1}{2}\sqrt{5}, -\tfrac{1}{2} + \tfrac{1}{2}\sqrt{5}].$$

Example 4-33. Obtain the solution set of $x < x^2$.

Solution. This is equivalent to

$$x^2 - x > 0,$$

and the quadratic $x^2 - x$ has a discriminant $d = (-1)^2 - 4(1) \cdot 0 = 1 > 0$ and $a = 1$. The zeros are 0 and 1 so that the solution set is

$$\{x \mid x > 1\} \cup \{x \mid x < 0\}.$$

Example 4-34. Find the solution set for $x^2 \leq 1$.

Solution. This is equivalent to $x^2 - 1 \leq 0$; the quadratic $x^2 - 1$ has the two zeros $1, -1$ so $[-1, 1]$ is the solution set.

We consider now a type of inequality which involves rational functions. Suppose, for example, that we wish to find the solution set of

$$\frac{3x+1}{(x-1)(x+7)} > 0 \quad \text{or} \quad \frac{3x+1}{(2-1)(x+7)} < 0.$$

We observe the following:

(i) $3x + 1 = 3(x + \tfrac{1}{3}) > 0$ for $x > -\tfrac{1}{3}$
$3x + 1 < 0$ for $x < -\tfrac{1}{3}$.

(ii) $x - 1 > 0$ for $x > 1$
$x - 1 < 0$ for $x < 1$.

(iii) $x + 7 > 0$ for $x > -7$
$x + 7 < 0$ for $x < -7$.

Taking now the numbers $-\tfrac{1}{3}$, 1, and -7 in order, we make the following table:

If . . . ,	then . . .			
$x < -7$	$x + 7 < 0$	$x - 1 < 0$	$3x + 1 < 0$	$\frac{3x + 1}{(x - 1)(x + 7)} < 0$
$-7 < x < -\frac{1}{3}$	$x + 7 > 0$	$x - 1 < 0$	$3x + 1 < 0$	$\frac{3x + 1}{(x - 1)(x + 7)} > 0$
$-\frac{1}{3} < x < 1$	$x + 7 > 0$	$x - 1 < 0$	$3x + 1 > 0$	$\frac{3x + 1}{(x - 1)(x + 7)} < 0$
$1 < x$	$x + 7 > 0$	$x - 1 > 0$	$3x + 1 > 0$	$\frac{3x + 1}{(x - 1)(x + 7)} > 0$

The information in the above table is pictured graphically in Fig. 4-16.

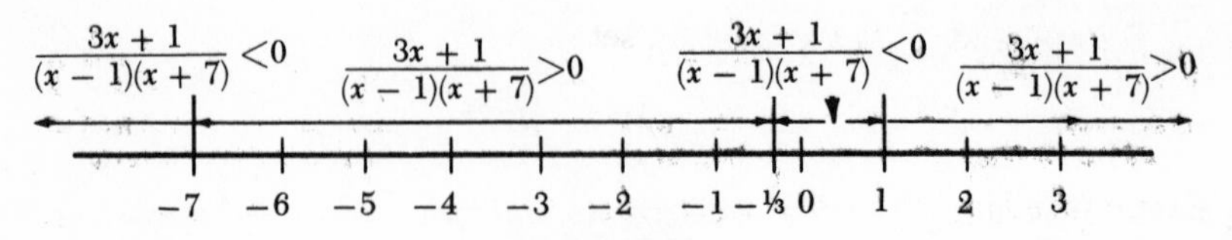

Figure 4-16

The information obtained for the rational function

$$\frac{3x + 1}{(x - 1)(x + 7)}$$

made use of the fact that it is a quotient of linear factors, and that linear functions are positive on one side of their zero and negative on the other side.

Example 4-35. Obtain the solution set of

$$\frac{x^2 + x + 6}{x^2 - 4} > 0.$$

Solution. $x^2 + x + 6 > 0$ for all x since $a = 1 > 0$ and $d = 1^2 - 4(1)(6) = -23 < 0$. Therefore,

$$\frac{x^2 + x + 6}{x^2 - 4} > 0 \text{ if and only if } x^2 - 4 > 0.$$

But the solution set for $x^2 - 4 > 0$ is $\{x | x < -2\} \cup \{x | x > 2\}$. Hence, the solution set for

$$\frac{x^2 + x + 6}{x^2 - 4} > 0 \quad \text{is} \quad \{x | x < -2\} \cup \{x | x > 2\}.$$

Example 4-36. Find the solution set for

$$\frac{P(x)}{Q(x)} = \frac{(7x - 1)((2/3)x - 1)}{(5x + 2)(x - 8)} < 0.$$

Solution. Since the zeros of the linear factors involved are $1/7$, $3/2$, $-2/5$, and 8 we have

If . . . ,	then . . .				
$x < -2/5$	$7x - 1 < 0$	$(2/3)x - 1 < 0$	$5x + 2 < 0$	$x - 8 < 0$	$P(x)/Q(x) > 0$
$-2/5 < x < 1/7$	$7x - 1 < 0$	$(2/3)x - 1 < 0$	$5x + 2 > 0$	$x - 8 < 0$	$P(x)/Q(x) < 0$
$1/7 < x < 3/2$	$7x - 1 > 0$	$(2/3)x - 1 < 0$	$5x + 2 > 0$	$x - 8 < 0$	$P(x)/Q(x) > 0$
$3/2 < x < 8$	$7x - 1 > 0$	$(2/3)x - 1 > 0$	$5x + 2 > 0$	$x - 8 < 0$	$P(x)/Q(x) < 0$
$8 < x$	$7x - 1 > 0$	$(2/3)x - 1 > 0$	$5x + 2 > 0$	$x - 8 > 0$	$P(x)/Q(x) > 0$

We conclude that the solution set of

$$P(x)/Q(x) < 0 \qquad \text{is} \qquad (-2/5, 1/7) \cup (3/2, 8).$$

Example 4-37. Show that

$$\frac{1}{x - 1} + \frac{1}{x + 1} < 0$$

for $x \in (0, 1)$.

Solution. Since

$$\frac{1}{x - 1} + \frac{1}{x + 1} = \frac{2x}{(x - 1)(x + 1)} = \frac{P(x)}{Q(x)},$$

we have

$$\frac{P(x)}{Q(x)} < 0 \qquad \text{for} \qquad x < -1,$$

$$\frac{P(x)}{Q(x)} > 0 \qquad \text{for} \qquad -1 < x < 0,$$

$$\frac{P(x)}{Q(x)} < 0 \qquad \text{for} \qquad 0 < x < 1,$$

$$\frac{P(x)}{Q(x)} > 0 \qquad \text{for} \qquad 1 < x.$$

Exercises

34. Obtain the solution set of each of the following inequalities: refer to page 124
(a) $2x^2 - 8x + 1 \geq 0$.
(b) $(2/3)x^2 + x - 1 \leq 0$.

(c) $x^2 + \sqrt{2}x + \sqrt{3} < 0$.
(d) $-x^2 + \sqrt{2}x + \sqrt{3} < 0$.
(e) $x^2 - x \leq 0$.
(f) $x + 2 > 5x^2$.
(g) $(1 + \sqrt{2})x^2 \geq (10 + 11\sqrt{2})x + 11$.

35. Prove the (a), (b), (c) parts of Theorem 23.

36. Find the solution sets for the following:

(a) $\dfrac{x + 1}{x - 4} < 0$.

(b) $\dfrac{x + 1}{(x - 4)(x + 5)} > 0$.

(c) $\dfrac{2}{3x + 1} < \dfrac{1}{5x - 8}$.

(d) $\dfrac{1}{x - 2} < \dfrac{1}{x^2 - x - 6}$.

(e) $\dfrac{2}{-2x^2 + 5} \geq \dfrac{1}{-x^2 + \frac{1}{2}}$.

(f) $\dfrac{-x^2 + 2x + 3}{x^2 - x - 6} < 0$.

5

The Trigonometric Functions

A very important class of real functions is the so-called trigonometric functions. A thorough understanding of these functions is vital in the study of calculus and certain of its applications.

5.1 The Definition of the Trigonometric Functions

There are several ways of defining the trigonometric functions; the method which will be used here makes use of the unit circle and *assumes* that it is possible to measure arcs along the unit circle. (This assumption is justified in more advanced courses.)

We start with the unit circle

$$\mathcal{C} = \{(x, y) \mid x^2 + y^2 = 1\}$$

whose graph is given in Fig. 5-1. If t is a real number, an arc of the circle

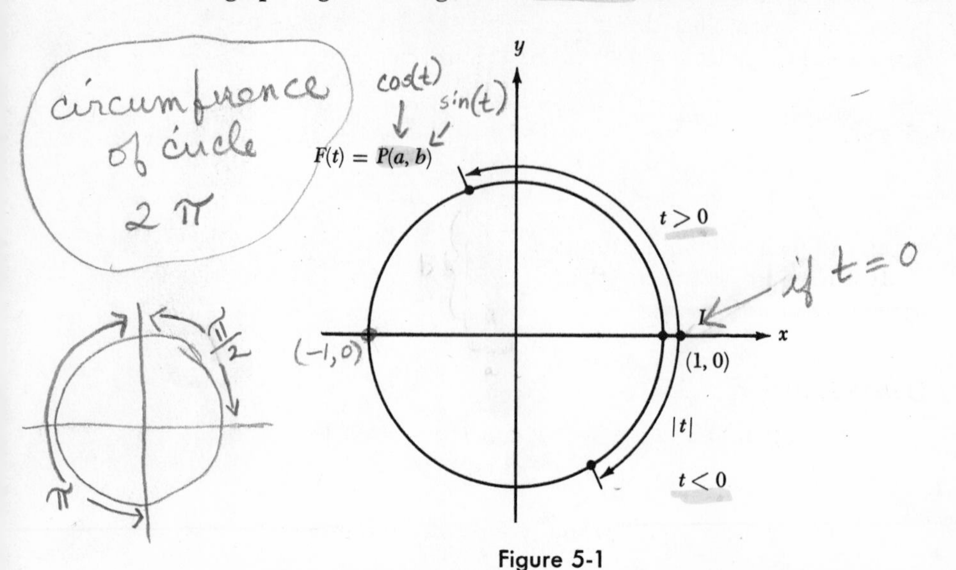

Figure 5-1

$\mathcal{C}$ is measured from the point $I(1, 0)$ having a length $|t|$; the arc is measured in the counter-clockwise direction from I if $t \geq 0$ and is measured in the clockwise direction if $t < 0$. (See Fig. 5-1.) This gives us a method of associating with each real number t a point $P(a, b)$ (the end point of the arc opposite I) of the circle $\mathcal{C}$. In other words, a function F has been defined whose domain is the set of all real numbers and whose range is the set of all points of $\mathcal{C}$:

$$F = \{(t, P(a, b)) \mid t \in \mathbf{R} \text{ and } P \text{ is obtained as described above}\}.$$

We also may write

$$F(t) = P(a, b).$$

For $t = 0$,

$$F(0) = I(1, 0),$$

and since the circumference of the circle is 2π,

$$F(2\pi) = I(1, 0)$$

and

$$F(-2\pi) = I(1, 0).$$

Suppose that $F(t) = P(a, b)$, that n is an integer and that we wish to compute $F(t + 2n\pi)$. The point on the circle associated with the number $t + 2n\pi$ may be obtained by first finding $F(t) = P(a, b)$ and then measuring from this point an arc having length $2n\pi$. But since n is an integer, it is clear that the end point of the arc associated with $2n\pi$, when we measure from $P(a, b)$, is just $P(a, b)$. Hence,

$$F(t + 2n\pi) = P(a, b)$$

or, since

$$F(t) = P(a, b),$$

$$(*) \quad F(t + 2n\pi) = F(t)$$

for all real numbers t and integers n.

It is now possible to use the function F to define the trigonometric functions *sine* and *cosine*.

DEFINITION.

1. Sine $= \{(t, b) \mid t \in \mathbf{R} \text{ and } F(t) = P(a, b)\}$.
2. Cosine $= \{(t, a) \mid t \in \mathbf{R} \text{ and } F(t) = P(a, b)\}$.

The names "sine" and "cosine" are usually abbreviated to "sin" and

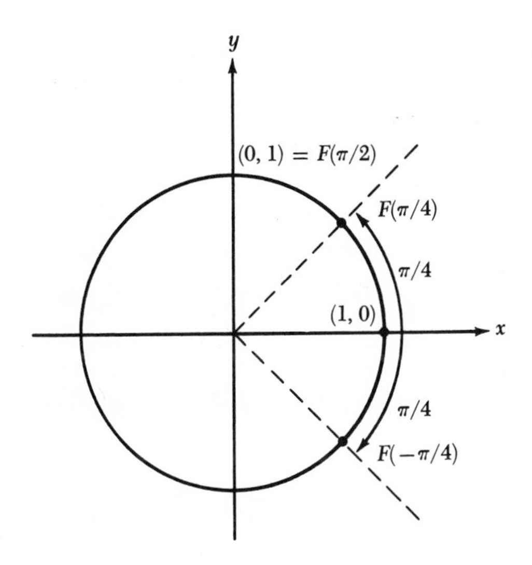

Figure 5-2

"cos" so that in the $f(t)$-notation

$$\sin(t) = b$$
$$\cos(t) = a.$$

Observe that $\sin(t)$ and $\cos(t)$ are the second and first coordinates of the point

$$F(t) = P(a, b)$$

on the unit circle. (See Fig. 5-2.)

Example 5-1. Find $\cos(\pi/2)$.

Solution. We start at $I(1, 0)$ and proceed $\pi/2$ units counterclockwise along the circle. Since $\pi/2$ is ¼ the total circumference 2π, we stop ¼ of the way around the circle. That is,

$$F(\pi/2) = P(0, 1).$$

Therefore,

$$\cos(\pi/2) = 0.$$

Example 5-2. Find $\sin \pi/4$ and $\cos \pi/4$.

Solution. To calculate $F(\pi/4)$ our arc from $I(1, 0)$ is in the same direction as the arc for $F(\pi/2)$ and ½ as long. Hence the point $F(\pi/4)$ is on the line bisecting the first quadrant. (See Fig. 5-2.) Thus, if

$$F(\pi/4) = P(a, b),$$

$a = b$. But $P(a, a)$ is on the circle $\mathcal{C}$:

$$a^2 + a^2 = 1$$

or

$$2a^2 = 1$$
$$a^2 = ½$$

and

$$a = 1/\sqrt{2}.$$

(Note that $a = 1/\sqrt{2}$ and not $-1/\sqrt{2}$ since the point is in the first quadrant.) Therefore,

$$\sin(\pi/4) = 1/\sqrt{2}$$
$$\cos(\pi/4) = 1/\sqrt{2}.$$

Example 5-3. Calculate $\sin(-\pi/4)$ and $\cos(-\pi/4)$.

Solution. Referring to Fig. 5-2 it is evident that

$$F(-\pi/4) = P(1/\sqrt{2}, -1/\sqrt{2})$$

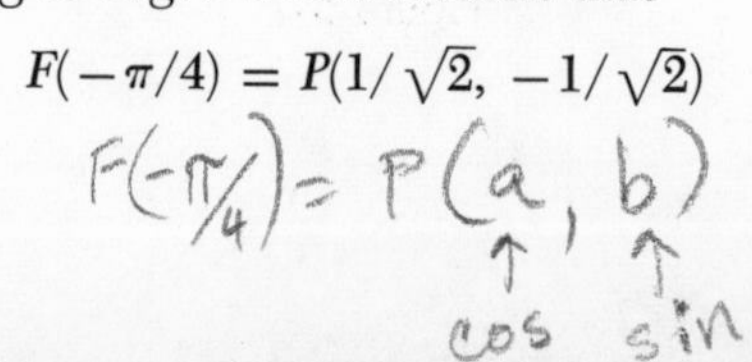

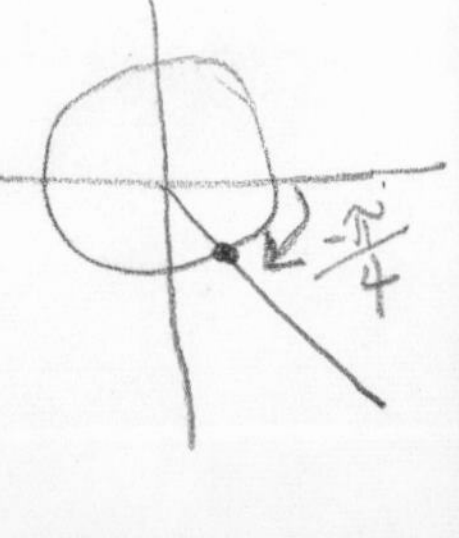

and therefore,

$$\sin(-\pi/4) = -1/\sqrt{2} \qquad \text{and} \qquad \cos(-\pi/4) = 1/\sqrt{2}.$$

Example 5-4. Calculate $\sin(\pi/3)$ and $\cos(\pi/3)$.

Solution. To calculate $F(\pi/3)$, we observe that $\pi/3 = \frac{2}{3}(\pi/2)$, and hence the arc from $I(1, 0)$ to $F(\pi/3)$ is $\frac{2}{3}$ the length of the arc from $I(1, 0)$ to $F(\pi/2)$. Now using Fig. 5-3 and elementary geometry, the triangle OFI is seen to be equilateral so that the length of the segment

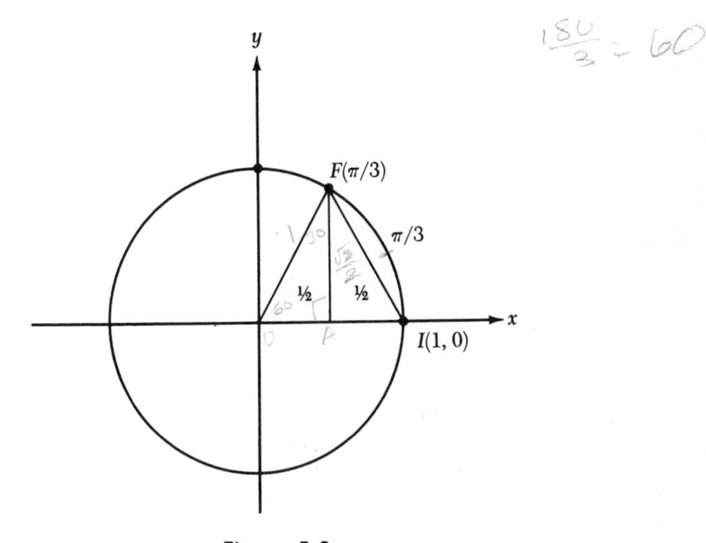

Figure 5-3

OA is ½. Therefore, the first coordinate of $F(\pi/3)$ is ½. If $F(\pi/3) = P(\frac{1}{2}, b)$, then

$$(\tfrac{1}{2})^2 + b^2 = 1$$

and

$$b = \tfrac{1}{2}\sqrt{3}.$$

We then conclude that

$$\sin(\pi/3) = \tfrac{1}{2}\sqrt{3} \qquad \text{and} \qquad \cos(\pi/3) = \tfrac{1}{2}.$$

Example 5-5. Find $\cos(3\pi)$.

Solution. From the relationship

$$F(t + 2n\pi) = F(t),$$

we have for $n = 1$

$$F(3\pi) = F(\pi + 2\pi) = F(\pi) = P(-1, 0).$$

Thus,

$$\cos(3\pi) = -1.$$

(See Fig. 5-4.)

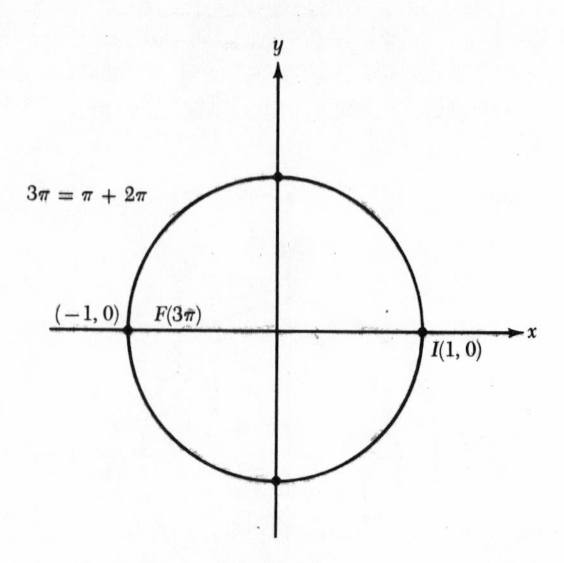

Figure 5-4

In Example 5-5, we used the equation

$$F(t + 2n\pi) = F(t)$$

to find $\cos(3\pi)$. This equation gives rise to the following very important property of the sine and cosine functions:

$$\sin(t + 2n\pi) = \sin(t)$$
$$\cos(t + 2n\pi) = \cos(t)$$

for all real numbers t and integers n.

If $n = 1$ in these equations, we have

$$\sin(t + 2\pi) = \sin(t)$$
$$\cos(t + 2\pi) = \cos(t)$$

for all real numbers t. This shows that the sine and cosine are examples of *periodic* functions.

DEFINITION. A function f is said to be *periodic* if and only if there is some positive number a such that

$$f(t + a) = f(t)$$

for all numbers t and $t + a$ in the domain of f.

It has just been observed that sine and cosine are both *periodic* functions. Now consider

$$f(x) = x - [x].$$

Using the property that

$$[x + 1] = [x] + 1$$

(see Exercise 28(d) in Chapter 3), we have

$$\begin{aligned} f(x + 1) &= (x + 1) - [x + 1] \\ &= (x + 1) - ([x] + 1) \\ &= x - [x] \\ &= f(x). \end{aligned}$$

This then shows that

$$f(x + 1) = f(x)$$

for all x and that $f(x) = x - [x]$ is periodic.

Exercises

1. By using Fig. 5-5, obtain the coordinates of the following points:

(a) $F(0)$.	(i) $F(3\pi/2)$.	(q) $F(11\pi/6)$.
(b) $F(-2\pi)$.	(j) $F(2\pi/3)$.	(r) $F(-3\pi/2)$.
(c) $F(\pi/6)$.	(k) $F(5\pi/6)$.	(s) $F(-2\pi/3)$.
(d) $F(-\pi/6)$.	(l) $F(\pi)$.	(t) $F(-5\pi/6)$.
(e) $F(\pi/4)$.	(m) $F(5\pi/4)$.	(u) $F(-\pi)$.
(f) $F(-\pi/3)$.	(n) $F(7\pi/6)$.	(v) $F(-5\pi/4)$.
(g) $F(\pi/2)$.	(o) $F(4\pi/3)$.	(w) $F(-7\pi/6)$.
(h) $F(-\pi/2)$.	(p) $F(5\pi/3)$.	(x) $F(-5\pi/3)$.

2. Use the information obtained in 1 above to determine $\sin t$ and $\cos t$ for the following values of t.

(a) 0.	(e) $\pi/4$.	(i) $3\pi/2$.
(b) -2π.	(f) $-\pi/3$.	(j) $2\pi/3$.
(c) $\pi/6$.	(g) $\pi/2$.	(k) $5\pi/6$.
(d) $-\pi/6$	(h) $-\pi/2$.	(l) π.

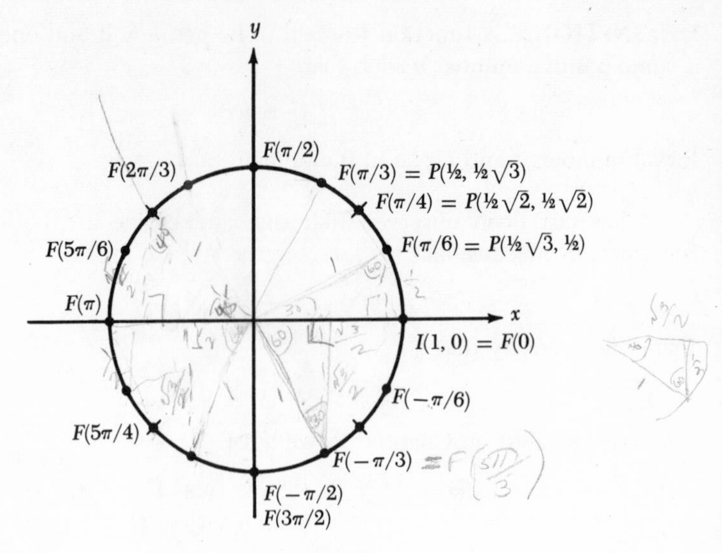

Figure 5-5

(m) $5\pi/4$.
(n) $7\pi/6$.
(o) $4\pi/3$.
(p) $5\pi/3$.
(q) $-3\pi/2$.
(r) $-2\pi/3$.
(s) $-5\pi/6$.
(t) $-\pi$.
(u) $-5\pi/4$.
(v) $-7\pi/6$.
(w) $-5\pi/3$.
(x) $11\pi/6$.

3. Find:
(a) $\cos(9\pi/2)$.
(b) $\sin(25\pi/6)$.
(c) $\cos(10\pi/3)$.
(d) $\sin(-7\pi/3)$.
(e) $\sin(11\pi/4)$.
(f) $\cos(-5\pi)$.

4. Show that the following are periodic functions and draw their graphs.
(a) $f(x) = 2$.
(b) $g(x) = [x] + 1 - x$. [*Hint:* Compute $g(x + 1)$.]
(c) $N(x) = \begin{cases} x - [x] \text{ if } x \leq [x] + \frac{1}{2} \\ [x] + 1 - x \text{ if } x > [x] + \frac{1}{2}. \end{cases}$
(d) $T(x) = (x - [x])^2$.
(e) $L(x) = \begin{cases} (x - [x])^2 \text{ if } [x] \text{ is even} \\ -([x] + 1 - x)^2 \text{ if } [x] \text{ is odd.} \end{cases}$

5.2 Some Trigonometric Identities

There are four trigonometric functions other than sine and cosine; *tangent, cotangent, secant* and *cosecant.* These are defined in terms of sine and cosine as follows:

(a) tangent $= \left\{\left(t, \dfrac{\sin t}{\cos t}\right) \middle| \, t \in \mathbf{R} \text{ and } \cos t \neq 0\right\}.$

(b) cotangent $= \left\{\left(t, \dfrac{\cos t}{\sin t}\right) \middle| \, t \in \mathbf{R} \text{ and } \sin t \neq 0\right\}.$

(c) secant $= \left\{\left(t, \dfrac{1}{\cos t}\right) \middle| \, t \in \mathbf{R} \text{ and } \cos t \neq 0\right\}.$

(d) cosecant $= \left\{\left(t, \dfrac{1}{\sin t}\right) \middle| \, t \in \mathbf{R} \text{ and } \sin t \neq 0\right\}.$

These are usually abbreviated respectively as follows: "tan", "cot", "sec", "csc." Then in the $f(t)$-notation:

(a′) $\tan(t) = \dfrac{\sin t}{\cos t}.$ (c′) $\sec(t) = \dfrac{1}{\cos t}.$

(b′) $\cot(t) = \dfrac{\cos t}{\sin t}.$ (d′) $\csc(t) = \dfrac{1}{\sin t}.$

In the definition of the tangent function, no real number t such that $\cos t = 0$ is allowed. Let us determine those real numbers t such that $\cos t = 0$. By definition, $\cos t$ is the first coordinate of the point $F(t)$ on the unit circle $\mathcal{C}$. Since there are only two points on the unit circle with first coordinate zero,

$$F(t) = P(0, 1)$$

or

$$F(t) = P(0, -1).$$

The first of these is obviously satisfied by $t = \pi/2$; and from the equation

$$F(t + 2n\pi) = F(t),$$

when $t = \pi/2$,

$$F(\pi/2 + 2n\pi) = F(\pi/2) = P(0, 1).$$

For any number t, if $F(t) = P(0, 1)$, the point $(0, 1)$ has been reached as the end point of an arc measured *from* $I(1, 0)$; and hence, $t = \pi/2 + 2n\pi$ for some integer n. Also if $F(t) = P(0, -1)$, $t = (3\pi)/2 + 2n\pi$ for some integer n. But we may write:

$$\begin{aligned}(3\pi)/2 + 2n\pi &= (\pi/2 + \pi) + 2n\pi \\ &= \pi/2 + (2n + 1)\pi.\end{aligned}$$

Therefore, if $F(t) = P(0, \pm 1)$, then

$$t = \pi/2 + 2n\pi \qquad \text{or} \qquad t = \pi/2 + (2n + 1)\pi$$

for some integer n. Notice that in the first case we add *even* multiples of π to $\pi/2$, and in the second case we add *odd* multiples of π to $\pi/2$. Since every integer is either even or odd, we have

$$F(t) = P(0, \pm 1) \text{ if and only if } t = \pi/2 + k\pi$$

for some integer k. Hence,

$$\cos(t) = 0 \text{ if and only if } t \in \{\pi/2 + k\pi \mid k \text{ is an integer}\}.$$

The domain of the tangent function is then the set of all real numbers t *except* those of the set $\{\pi/2 + k\pi \mid k \text{ is an integer}\}$; i.e.,

$$\mathfrak{D}(\tan) = \mathbf{R} \sqcap \{\pi/2 + k\pi \mid k \text{ is an integer}\}.$$

In a similar manner, one shows that

$$\mathfrak{D}(\cot) = \mathbf{R} \sqcap \{k\pi \mid k \text{ is an integer}\}.$$

Let us consider now the range of the sine and cosine. If t is a real number,

$$F(t) = P(a, b)$$

for some numbers a, b. By definition

$$\sin(t) = b \qquad \text{and} \qquad \cos(t) = a.$$

Since $P(a, b)$ is a point on the unit circle $\mathcal{C}$,

$$a^2 + b^2 = 1$$

or

$$(\cos t)^2 + (\sin t)^2 = 1.$$

It is customary to write $\cos^2 t$ for $(\cos t)^2$ so that the last equation above may be expressed as

$$\cos^2 t + \sin^2 t = 1. \tag{5-1}$$

Hence, from Eq. (5-1) we have

$$0 \leq \sin^2 t = 1 - \cos^2 t \leq 1$$

and

$$0 \leq \cos^2 t = 1 - \sin^2 t \leq 1.$$

Therefore (see Example 4-27),

$$-1 \leq \sin t \leq 1$$

and

$$-1 \leq \cos t \leq 1.$$

We conclude from this that the range of both the sine and cosine is contained in $[-1, 1]$. As a matter of fact, the range of these functions is exactly the set $[-1, 1]$, but we cannot at this stage offer a proof of the fact that for any number $z \in [-1, 1]$ there are numbers t_1, t_2 such that

$$\sin(t_1) = z \qquad \text{and} \qquad \cos(t_2) = z.$$

For convenience of reference we list in the table below the domain and range of the trigonometric functions. $\mathbf{R}$ denotes the set of real numbers.

FUNCTION	DOMAIN	RANGE
sine	$\mathbf{R}$	$[-1, 1]$
cosine	$\mathbf{R}$	$[-1, 1]$
tangent	$\mathbf{R} \cap \{\pi/2 + k\pi\}$	$\mathbf{R}$
cotangent	$\mathbf{R} \cap \{k\pi\}$	$\mathbf{R}$
secant	$\mathbf{R} \cap \{\pi/2 + k\pi\}$	$\{x \mid x \geq 1\} \cup \{x \mid x \leq -1\}$
cosecant	$\mathbf{R} \cap \{k\pi\}$	$\{x \mid x \geq 1\} \cup \{x \mid x \leq -1\}$

We have just seen that for all real numbers t,

$$\sin^2 t + \cos^2 t = 1.$$

If $\cos t \neq 0$, we may divide the above and obtain

$$\frac{\sin^2 t}{\cos^2 t} + 1 = \frac{1}{\cos^2 t}$$

or

$$\left(\frac{\sin t}{\cos t}\right)^2 + 1 = \left(\frac{1}{\cos t}\right)^2.$$

Then, using the definition of tan and sec,

$$\tan^2 t + 1 = \sec^2 t. \tag{5-2}$$

In a similar manner, if we divide Eq. (5-1) by $\sin^2 t$ and use the definition of csc and cot, we obtain

$$\cot^2 t + 1 = \csc^2 t. \tag{5-3}$$

Equations (5-1), (5-2), (5-3) are true for all real numbers t for which the functions involved are defined and for this reason are referred to as *identities.*

We now derive an identity which allows one to compute $\cos(t - s)$ in terms of $\sin t$, $\sin s$, $\cos t$, $\cos s$. In fact, we have the identity

$$\cos(t - s) = (\cos t)(\cos s) + (\sin t)(\sin s) \tag{5-4}$$

for all real numbers t, s. In order to prove this we refer to Fig. 5-6 where the point $F(s)$ is in the first quadrant and $F(t)$ is in the third quadrant. These particular positions of $F(s)$ and $F(t)$ are not necessary to the proof of (5-4), but do clearly indicate the essential element in the proof, which

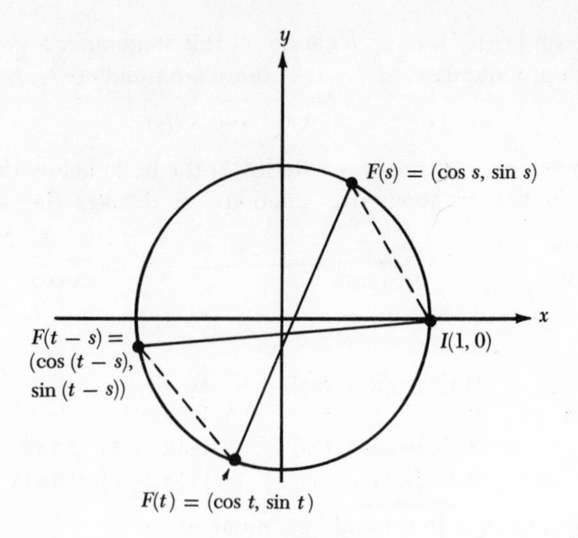

Figure 5-6

is that the cords $F(t)F(s)$* and $F(t - s)I(1, 0)$ are equal in length. This being so, the distance formula gives

$$\sqrt{[\cos (t - s) - 1]^2 + [\sin (t - s) - 0]^2} = \sqrt{(\cos t - \cos s)^2 + (\sin t - \sin s)^2}.$$

If we square the above, we get

$$\cos^2(t - s) - 2\cos (t - s) + 1 + \sin^2(t - s) = \cos^2 t - 2\cos t \cdot \cos s + \cos^2 s + \sin^2 t - 2\sin t \cdot \sin s + \sin^2 s.$$

This reduces to

$$2 - 2\cos (t - s) = 2 - 2(\cos t \cdot \cos s + \sin t \cdot \sin s),$$

and this last equation is equivalent to Eq. (5-4). It should be observed in the above manipulations that we have used identity Eq. (5-1) three times, to replace

$$\cos^2(t - s) + \sin^2(t - s)$$
$$\cos^2 t + \sin^2 t$$
$$\cos^2 s + \sin^2 s$$

each by 1.

Now we use identity Eq. (5-4) to derive several other identities.

* The notation *AB* means the cord or line segment connecting the points *A*, *B*.

Choose $t = 0$ in Eq. (5-4):

$$\begin{aligned}\cos(-s) = \cos(0 - s) &= \cos 0 \cdot \cos s + \sin 0 \cdot \sin s \\ &= 1 \cdot \cos s + 0 \cdot \sin s \\ &= \cos s.\end{aligned}$$

Hence, for all real numbers s,

$$\cos(-s) = \cos s. \tag{5-5}$$

In Eq. (5-4) take $t = \pi/2$:

$$\begin{aligned}\cos(\pi/2 - s) &= \cos \pi/2 \cdot \cos s + \sin \pi/2 \sin s \\ &= 0 \cdot \cos s + 1 \cdot \sin s \\ &= \sin s.\end{aligned}$$

Therefore, for all real numbers s,

$$\cos(\pi/2 - s) = \sin s. \tag{5-6}$$

Taking $t = -\pi/2$ in (5-4), gives

$$\begin{aligned}\cos(-\pi/2 - s) &= \cos(-\pi/2) \cdot \cos s + \sin(-\pi/2) \cdot \sin s \\ &= 0 \cdot \cos s + (-1) \cdot \sin s = -\sin s.\end{aligned}$$

This gives (a) $\cos(-\pi/2 - s) = -\sin s$. But also, by (5-4),

$$\begin{aligned}\cos(\pi/2 + s) = \cos(\pi/2 - (-s)) &= \cos \pi/2 \cdot \cos(-s) + \sin \pi/2 \cdot \sin(-s) \\ &= 0 \cdot \cos(-s) + 1 \cdot \sin(-s) \\ &= \sin(-s).\end{aligned}$$

Therefore, (b) $\cos(\pi/2 + s) = \sin(-s)$. From (5-5),

$$\cos(-\pi/2 - s) = \cos[-(\pi/2 + s)] = \cos(\pi/2 + s).$$

We then have from (a) and (b)

$$\sin(-s) = -\sin s \tag{5-7}$$

for all real numbers s.

By writing $t + s = t - (-s)$ and using Eq. (5-4) and (5-7), we have that for all real numbers s, t,

$$\cos(t + s) = \cos t \cdot \cos s - \sin t \cdot \sin s. \tag{5-8}$$

In Eq. (5-6) take $s = \pi/2 - t$:

$$\cos[\pi/2 - (\pi/2 - t)] = \sin(\pi/2 - t)$$

or

$$\cos t = \sin(\pi/2 - t) \tag{5-9}$$

for all real numbers t.

Now using Eq. (5-9), (5-6) and (5-4),

$$\begin{aligned}\sin(s+t) &= \cos[\pi/2 - (s+t)] \\ &= \cos[(\pi/2 - s) - t] \\ &= \cos(\pi/2 - s)\cdot\cos t + \sin(\pi/2 - s)\cdot\sin t \\ &= \sin s\cdot\cos t + \cos s\cdot\sin t.\end{aligned}$$

Therefore, for all real numbers s, t,

$$\sin(s+t) = \sin s\cdot\cos t + \cos s\cdot\sin t. \tag{5-10}$$

We list below several other important trigonometric identities, the proofs of which will be left to the student.

For all real numbers a, t for which the functions involved are defined,

$$\sin(t-s) = \sin t\cdot\cos s - \cos t\cdot\sin s \tag{5-11}$$

$$\tan(t+s) = \frac{\tan t + \tan s}{1 - (\tan t)\cdot(\tan s)} \tag{5-12}$$

$$\tan(t-s) = \frac{\tan t - \tan s}{1 + (\tan t)\cdot(\tan s)} \tag{5-13}$$

$$\sin(2t) = 2\sin t\cdot\cos t \tag{5-14}$$

$$\begin{aligned}\cos(2t) &= \cos^2 t - \sin^2 t \\ &= 2\cos^2 t - 1 \\ &= 1 - 2\sin^2 t.\end{aligned} \tag{5-15}$$

$$\sin(t/2) = \pm\sqrt{\frac{1-\cos t}{2}} \tag{5-16}$$

$$\cos(t/2) = \pm\sqrt{\frac{1+\cos t}{2}} \tag{5-17}$$

$$\begin{aligned}\sin t\cdot\cos s &= (\tfrac{1}{2})[\sin(t+s) + \sin(t-s)] \\ &= (\tfrac{1}{2})[\sin(s+t) - \sin(s-t)]\end{aligned} \tag{5-18}$$

$$(\tfrac{1}{2})[\sin t + \sin s] = \left[\sin\left(\frac{t+s}{2}\right)\right]\left[\cos\left(\frac{t-s}{2}\right)\right]. \tag{5-19}$$

Example 5-6. Show that for all real numbers t for which the functions are defined,

$$\cos t + \csc t = \frac{\sin t}{1 - \cos t}.$$

Solution. By definition of cot and csc,

$$\cot t + \csc t = \frac{\cos t}{\sin t} + \frac{1}{\sin t} = \frac{\cos t + 1}{\sin t} = \frac{(1-\cos t)(1+\cos t)}{(1-\cos t)\cdot\sin t}$$

$$= \frac{1 - \cos^2 t}{(1 - \cos t) \cdot \sin t} = \frac{\sin^2 t}{(1 - \cos t) \cdot \sin t} \quad \text{by Eq. (5-1)}$$

$$= \frac{\sin t}{1 - \cos t}.$$

This proves the identity.

Example 5-7. Compute $\sin(5\pi/12)$.

Solution. Since $5\pi/12 = \pi/6 + \pi/4$, we have by Eq. (5-10),

$$\begin{aligned}\sin(5\pi/12) &= \sin(\pi/6 + \pi/4) = \sin \pi/6 \cdot \cos \pi/4 + \cos \pi/6 \cdot \sin \pi/4 \\ &= (\tfrac{1}{2})(1/\sqrt{2}) + (\tfrac{1}{2})\sqrt{3} \cdot (1/\sqrt{2}) = (\sqrt{2}/4)(1 + \sqrt{3}).\end{aligned}$$

Exercises

5. Complete the proof of Eq. (5-8).

6. Prove Eq. (5-11) by using Eq. (5-10).

7. Prove Eq. (5-12) by using Eq. (5-9) and Eq. (5-10).

8. Prove Eq. (5-13).

9. Prove Eq. (5-14) by using Eq. (5-10).

10. Prove Eq. (5-15).

11. Prove Eq. (5-16) by taking $t/2$ for t in Eq. (5-15). Also discuss the $\pm$ sign in this identity; i.e., discuss the conditions under which the $+$ is appropriate and the conditions under which the sign should be $-$.

12. Prove Eq. (5-17). Discuss the $\pm$ sign in this identity.

13. Prove Eq. (5-18) by computing $\sin(t + s)$ and $\sin(t - s)$.

14. Prove Eq. (5-19) by using Eq. (5-18).

15. (a) Show that if $\sec t$ is defined for the number t, then

$$\sec t \geq 1 \quad \text{or} \quad \sec t \leq -1.$$

(b) Show that if $\csc t$ is defined for the number t, then

$$\csc t \geq 1 \quad \text{or} \quad \csc t \leq -1.$$

16. Prove the following identities:

(a) $\cos t = -\sin (3\pi/2 + t)$.
(b) $\tan x + \cot x = (\sec x)(\csc x)$.
(c) $(\sec t + \tan t)(1 - \sin t) = \cos t$.
(d) $(\sec t - \tan t)^{-1} = \sec t + \tan t$.
(e) $(1 + \cot^2 t) = (\csc^2 t - 1)(\tan^2 t + 1)$.
(f) $\sin^4 t - \cos^4 t = 2 \sin^2 t - 1$.

5.3 Generalized Trigonometric Functions and Their Graphs

In considering the graph of one of the trigonometric functions, say cosine for example, we naturally need information about its domain and range. Knowing that the range of cosine is $[-1, 1]$ tells us that its graph will lie between the lines $y = 1$ and $y = -1$. Just as important, however, is the fact that the cosine is a periodic function. If we graph the cosine function on the interval $[-\pi, \pi]$ for instance, the graph at *any* other number t can be obtained. If we wish to obtain the graph of cosine on the interval $[\pi, 3\pi]$, we reason that $t \in [-\pi, \pi]$ if and only if $t + 2\pi \in [\pi, 3\pi]$. But $\cos (t + 2\pi) = \cos t$. Consequently, the graph of cosine on $[\pi, 3\pi]$ is just a repetition of its graph on $[-\pi, \pi]$. In a similar fashion we can extend the graph of the cosine function along the x-axis in either direction from the interval $[-\pi, \pi]$ as far as we like.

To construct the graph of cosine on the interval $[-\pi, \pi]$, we first plot some points $(t, \cos t)$ for a few convenient values of t. These numbers t and their corresponding numbers $\cos t$ we may obtain from Exercise 2. The following table summarizes this information. In the fourth column of this table we use 3.12 as an approximation for π. Having plotted the points indicated, we connect these with a smooth curve to obtain the graph of cosine on $[-\pi, \pi]$ as given in Fig. 5-7.

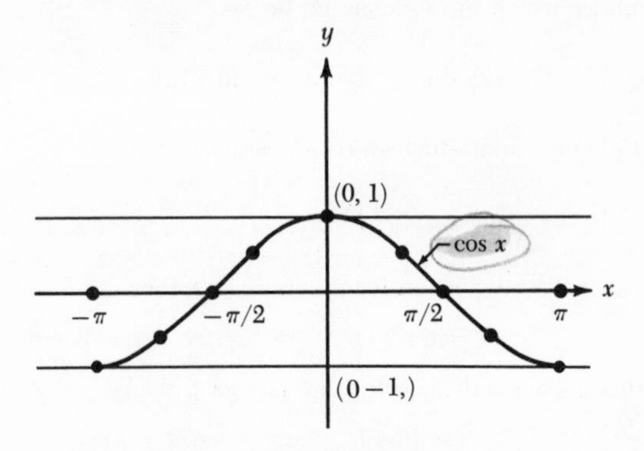

Figure 5-7

t	$\cos t$	Point $(t, \cos t)$ on graph	Approximate point to plot
$-\pi$	-1	$(-\pi, -1)$	$(-3.12, -1)$
$-5\pi/6$	$-\tfrac{1}{2}\sqrt{3}$	$(-5\pi/6, -\tfrac{1}{2}\sqrt{3})$	$(-261, -0.86)$
$-3\pi/4$	$-1/\sqrt{2}$	$(-3\pi/4, -1/\sqrt{2})$	$(-2.33, -0.71)$
$-2\pi/3$	$-\tfrac{1}{2}$	$(-2\pi/3, -\tfrac{1}{2})$	$(-2.10, -0.50)$
$-\pi/2$	0	$(-\pi/2, 0)$	$(-1.57, 0)$
$-\pi/3$	$\tfrac{1}{2}$	$(-\pi/3, \tfrac{1}{2})$	$(-1.05, 0.50)$
$-\pi/4$	$1/\sqrt{2}$	$(-\pi/4, 1/\sqrt{2})$	$(-0.79, 0.71)$
$-\pi/6$	$\tfrac{1}{2}\sqrt{3}$	$(-\pi/6, \tfrac{1}{2}\sqrt{3})$	$(-0.52, 0.86)$
0	1	$(0, 1)$	$(0, 1)$
$\pi/6$	$\tfrac{1}{2}\sqrt{3}$	$(\pi/6, \tfrac{1}{2}\sqrt{3})$	$(0.52, 0.86)$
$\pi/4$	$1/\sqrt{2}$	$(\pi/4, 1/\sqrt{2})$	$(0.79, 0.71)$
$\pi/3$	$\tfrac{1}{2}$	$(\pi/3, \tfrac{1}{2})$	$(1.05, 0.50)$
$\pi/2$	0	$(\pi/2, 0)$	$(1.57, 0)$
$2\pi/3$	$-\tfrac{1}{2}$	$(2\pi/3, -\tfrac{1}{2})$	$(2.10, -0.50)$
$3\pi/4$	$-1/\sqrt{2}$	$(3\pi/4, -1/\sqrt{2})$	$(2.33, -0.71)$
$5\pi/6$	$-\tfrac{1}{2}\sqrt{3}$	$(5\pi/6, -\tfrac{1}{2}\sqrt{3})$	$(2.61, -0.86)$
π	-1	$(\pi, -1)$	$(3.12, -1)$

To obtain the graph of sine on $[-\pi, \pi]$, we may use the equation

$$\sin t = \cos (t - \pi/2)$$

which is immediately derivable from Eq. (5-4). This equation allows us to compute $\sin t$ for any number t simply by computing $\cos (t - \pi/2)$. Since we already have the graph of cosine, the graph of sine is obtained by shifting to the right by $(\tfrac{1}{2})\pi$. See Fig. 5-8.

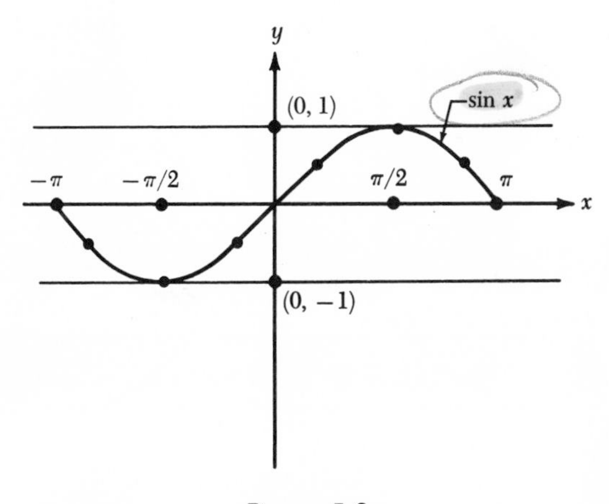

Figure 5-8

To graph the tangent function we recall that

$$\tan(t + \pi) = \tan t$$

for all numbers in the domain of tangent. Using this fact we may graph tangent on $(-\pi/2, \pi/2)$ for example, and make extensions from this. Notice that the interval chosen above is open since tangent is not defined at the end points of $(-\pi/2, \pi/2)$. The graph of tangent on $(-\pi/2, \pi/2)$ is given in Fig. 5-9. [Compare the graph of tangent with the graph of

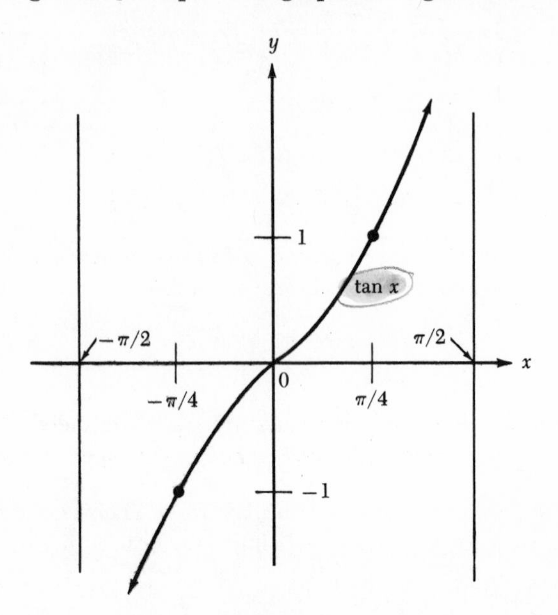

Figure 5-9

the function L given in Exercise 4(e).]

In certain applications of the trigonometric functions we are concerned with functions of the type

$$f(x) = A \sin(bx + c) \quad \text{and} \quad g(x) = A \cos(bx + c).$$

These are known as *generalized* trigonometric functions and are seen to be composite. Here A, b, c are real numbers and $A \neq 0$, $b \neq 0$.

Since for all real numbers x

$$-1 \leq \sin(bx + c) \leq 1,$$

we have, if $A > 0$,

$$-A < A \sin(bx + c) < A.$$

It is easy to see, then, that the range of both f and g is $[-A, A]$ if $A > 0$. This shows that the graph of f and g will lie between the lines

$$y = A \qquad \text{and} \qquad y = -A.$$

The number $|A|$ is called the *amplitude* of these functions.

The function f is periodic as the following computation shows:

$$\begin{aligned} f(x + 2\pi/|b|) &= A \sin [b(x + 2\pi/|b|) + c] \\ &= A \sin (bx \pm 2\pi + c) \\ &= A \sin [(bx + c) \pm 2\pi] \\ &= A \sin (bx + c) \\ &= f(x). \end{aligned}$$

And similarly,

$$g(x + 2\pi/|b|) = g(x) \qquad \text{for all } x.$$

The number $2\pi/|b|$ is called the *period* of these functions.

Since the generalized trigonometric functions

$$\begin{aligned} f(x) &= A \sin (bx + c) \\ g(x) &= A \cos (bx + c) \end{aligned}$$

are composite, we may construct their graph by the method described in 3-4. To study the graph of these functions a few special cases may be instructive.

Example 5-8. The graph of $f(x) = \cos (x + 1)$ is given in Fig. 5-10. The effect of adding 1 is evidently to "shift" the graph of cosine one unit to the left. Generally, for any $c > 0$ the graph of $\cos (x + c)$ will be "shifted" c units to the left from the graph of cosine. The shift will be to the right if $c < 0$.

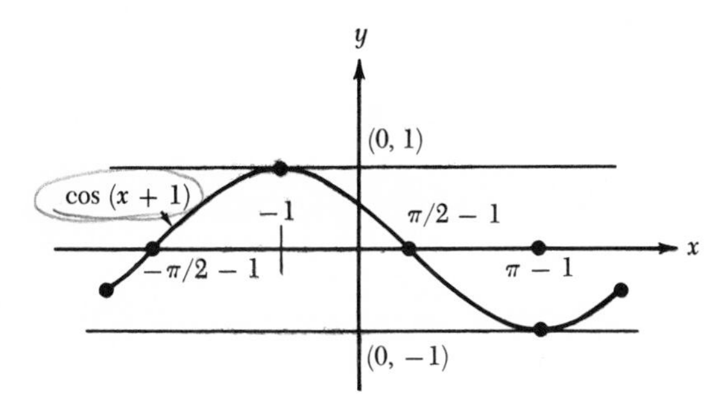

Figure 5-10

Example 5-9. The graph of $f(x) = \cos(½)x$ is given in Fig. 5-11. The effect here of the ½ is to "stretch" the cosine curve in the x-direction. This effect is also indicated by the equation

$$\begin{aligned} f(x + 4\pi) &= \cos[½(x + 4\pi)] \\ &= \cos[((½)x + 2\pi)] \\ &= \cos(½)x = f(x). \end{aligned}$$

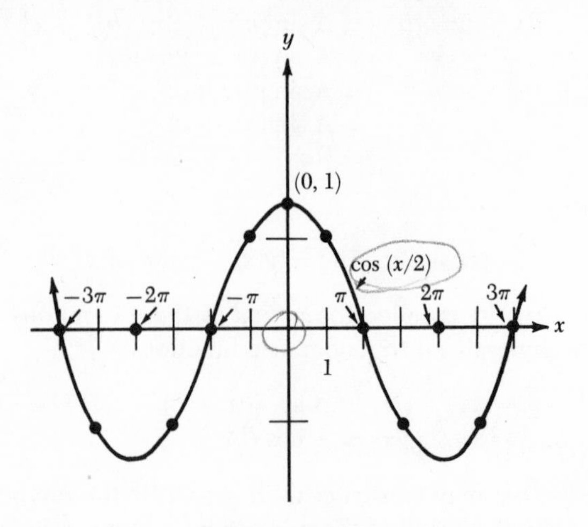

Figure 5-11

This suggests that the distance between the numbers at which $\cos(½)x$ repeats is $2(2\pi)$ rather than 2π as with $\cos x$. This situation is typical: if b is a positive number, then the graph of the function

$$f(x) = \cos(bx)$$

is stretched in the x-direction from the position of $\cos x$ if $b < 1$ and is "compressed" in the x-direction from the position of $\cos x$ if $b > 1$.

Example 5-10. As indicated in examples 5-8 and 5-9, the graph of

$$f(x) = \cos[(½)x + 1]$$

will be changed from that of $\cos x$ in two respects; there is both a stretching (from the ½) and a shifting (from the 1). This graph is given in Fig. 5-12. It should also be noted that the ½ has played a part in the shift. To see why this is so, we only have to remember that the graph of $f(x) = \cos(x + 1)$ meets the line $y = 1$ at $x = -1$, i.e., $f(-1) = \cos[(-1) + 1] = \cos 0 = 1$. But $\cos[½(-1) + 1] = \cos(½) \neq 1$. However, $\cos[½(-2) + 1] = \cos 0 = 1$. This indicates that the ½ has

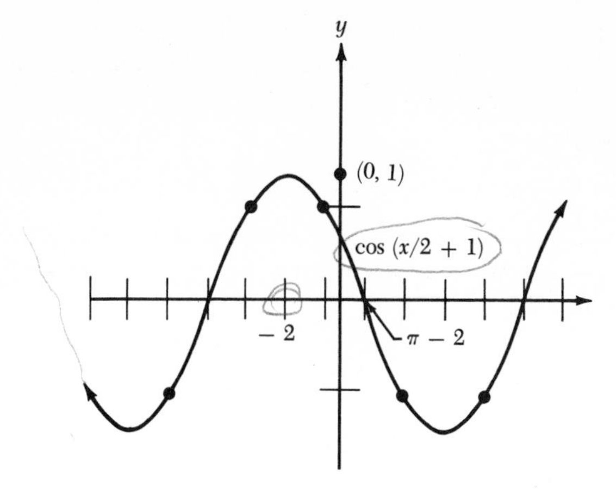

Figure 5-12

contributed to the shift and the graph of $f(x) = \cos[(\frac{1}{2})x + 1]$ is shifted 2 units from the graph of $f(x) = \cos(\frac{1}{2})x$ instead of only 1 unit as we might at first expect.

Example 5-11. The effect of multiplying the function $f(x) = \cos[(\frac{1}{2})x + 1]$ by a number $A > 0$ is a stretch in the y-direction if $A > 1$ and a compression in the y-direction is $A < 1$. This is illustrated in Fig. 5-13 which gives the graph of

$$f(x) = 3\cos[(\tfrac{1}{2})x + 1].$$

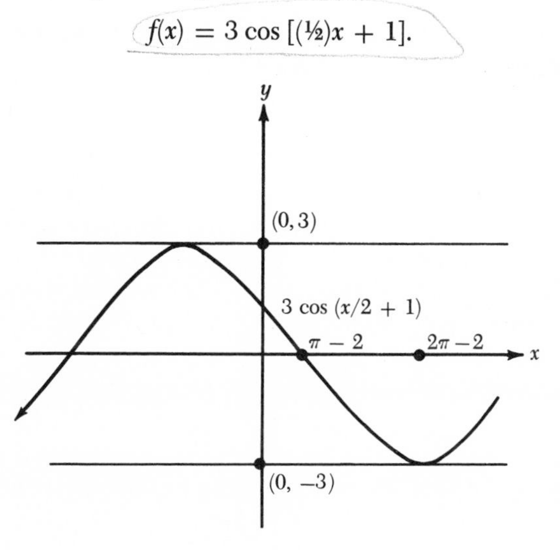

Figure 5-13

If we wish to graph one of the generalized trigonometric functions, it is helpful to begin by determining the amplitude and the period. If the amplitude is $|A|$, we have seen that the graph of the function lies between the lines

$$y = A \qquad \text{and} \qquad y = -A.$$

Next, if the graph is obtained over an interval which has length equal to the function's period, we may determine the behavior of the function over any other interval.

Exercises

17. Determine the amplitude and period of each of the following functions and graph each over an interval having a length equal to the period of the function.
(a) $f(x) = (1/3) \sin x$.
(b) $g(x) = \cos (\pi x)$.
(c) $f(x) = \sin (7x)$.
(d) $g(x) = -2 \cos x$.
(e) $f(x) = \sin (2x - 1)$.
(f) $g(x) = -2 \cos (\pi x + \pi/2)$.

18. Graph each of the following.
(a) $f(x) = \sin x - \cos x$.
(b) $g(x) = \tan x + 1$.
(c) $h(x) = \sec x$.
(d) $j(x) = \sec x - 1$.

19. Is the function $k(x) = \sin (x^2)$ periodic?

20. Is the function $p(x) = \cos |x|$ periodic? Graph this function and compare with the graph of the cosine function.

21. Let the function q be defined as follows:

$$q(x) = \sin ([x] + 1 - x).$$

Construct the graph of this function by using the technique described earlier for graphing composite functions.

5.4 Trigonometric Equations

The trigonometric equations which we shall consider here are easily solved by using the following results.

$$\text{(I)} \quad \sin t = \sin s \text{ if and only if} \quad \begin{cases} t = s + 2n\pi, \text{ for some integer } n \\ \quad \text{or} \\ t = -s + (2n + 1)\pi. \end{cases}$$

$$\text{(II)} \quad \sin t = -\sin s \text{ if and only if} \quad \begin{cases} t = -s + 2n\pi, \text{ for some integer } n \\ \quad \text{or} \\ t = s + (2n + 1)\pi. \end{cases}$$

(III) $\sin t = \cos s$ if and only if $\begin{cases} t = s + (4n + 1)\pi/2, \text{ for some integer } n \\ \quad\text{or} \\ t = -s + (4n + 1)\pi/2. \end{cases}$

(IV) $\cos t = \cos s$ if and only if $\begin{cases} t = s + 2n\pi, \text{ for some integer } n \\ \quad\text{or} \\ t = -s + 2n\pi. \end{cases}$

We will prove the first of these and leave the others for exercises. First, if $t = s + 2n\pi$ for some integer n, it is clear that $\sin t = \sin s$. Also if $t = -s + (2n + 1)\pi$,

$$\begin{aligned} \sin t &= \sin(-s + (2n + 1)\pi) \\ &= \sin(-s + 2n\pi + \pi) \\ &= \sin(-s + \pi) \\ &= \sin(\pi - s) \\ &= \sin(\pi)\cos s - \cos(\pi)\sin s \\ &= \sin s. \end{aligned}$$

Thus the first part of (I) is proved. To prove the second part, we start with the following identity [see Eq. (5-18)]:

$$\sin(x + y) - \sin(x - y) = 2\sin y \cdot \cos x.$$

In this identity, if we take

$$t = x + y \qquad \text{and} \qquad s = x - y,$$

we have

$$x = \tfrac{1}{2}(s + t) \qquad \text{and} \qquad y = \tfrac{1}{2}(t - s)$$

which gives the identity

$$\sin t - \sin s = 2\sin\left(\frac{t - s}{2}\right) \cdot \cos\left(\frac{t + s}{2}\right).$$

Now if $\sin t = \sin s$, $\sin t - \sin s = 0$ and this implies that

$$2\sin \tfrac{1}{2}(t - s) \cdot \cos \tfrac{1}{2}(t + s) = 0.$$

From this we conclude that

$$\sin \tfrac{1}{2}(t - s) = 0 \qquad \text{or} \qquad \cos \tfrac{1}{2}(t + s) = 0.$$

If $\sin \frac{1}{2}(t - s) = 0$, then $\frac{1}{2}(t - s) = n\pi$, for some integer n, and $t - s = 2n\pi$. This then gives

$$t = s + 2n\pi.$$

If $\cos \frac{1}{2}(t + s) = 0$, $\frac{1}{2}(t + s) = (2n + 1)\pi/2$ and this gives $t = -s + (2n + 1)\pi$, for some integer n.

Example 5-12. Solve the equation $2 \cos x - 1 = 0$; i.e., find all real numbers x such that $2 \cos x - 1 = 0$.

Solution. If x is a number such that $2 \cos x - 1 = 0$, then

$$\cos x = \tfrac{1}{2}.$$

But, $\cos (\pi/3) = \frac{1}{2}$, and so,

$$\cos x = \cos (\pi/3).$$

Then, from (IV) above,

$$x = \pi/3 + 2n\pi \qquad \text{or} \qquad x = -\pi/3 + 2n\pi$$

where n is an integer. It is clear that either choice of x is a solution to the equation. Therefore, the solution set of this equation is

$$\{\pi/3 + 2n\pi \,|\, n \text{ is an integer}\} \cup \{-\pi/3 + 2n\pi \,|\, n \text{ is an integer}\}.$$

Example 5-13. Solve the equation $\sin^2 x - 2 \sin x = 3$.

Solution. If x is a number such that $\sin^2 x - 2 \sin x = 3$, then

$$\sin^2 x - 2 \sin x - 3 = 0$$

or

$$(\sin x - 3)(\sin x + 1) = 0.$$

From this,

$$\sin x = 3 \qquad \text{or} \qquad \sin x = -1.$$

Since there is no number such that $\sin x = 3$, we conclude that $\sin x = -1$. But $\sin (-\frac{1}{2}\pi) = -1$ and by (I) above

$$x = -(\tfrac{1}{2})\pi + 2n\pi \qquad \text{or} \qquad \begin{aligned} x &= (\tfrac{1}{2})\pi + (2n + 1)\pi \\ &= (\tfrac{1}{2})\pi + \pi + 2n\pi \\ &= \tfrac{1}{2}(3\pi) + 2n\pi. \end{aligned}$$

In this case,

$$\{-(\tfrac{1}{2})\pi + 2n\pi\} = \{\tfrac{1}{2}(3\pi) + 2n\pi\}$$

and hence, the solution set for the equation is

$$\{-(\tfrac{1}{2})\pi + 2n\pi\} \cup \{\tfrac{1}{2}(3\pi) + 2n\pi\} = \{-(\tfrac{1}{2})\pi + 2n\pi\}.$$

Example 5-14. Solve the equation $\sin (3t) = \cos t$.

Solution. From (III)

$$3t = t + (4n + 1)\pi/2 \qquad \text{or} \qquad 3t = -t + (4n + 1)\pi/2.$$

Thus,

$$t = (4n + 1)\pi/4 = \pi/4 + n\pi$$

or

$$t = (4n + 1)\pi/8 = \pi/8 + \tfrac{1}{2}(n\pi).$$

The solution set is, therefore,

$$\{(\tfrac{1}{4})\pi + n\pi\} \cup \{\pi/8 + \tfrac{1}{2}(n\pi)\}.$$

Exercises

22. Prove that $\sin t = \sin s$ if and only if for some integer n

$$t = -s + 2n\pi \quad \text{or} \quad t = s + (2n + 1)\pi$$

23. Prove that $\sin t = \cos s$ if and only if for some integer n

$$t = s + (4n + 1)\pi/2 \quad \text{or} \quad t = -s + (4n + 1)\pi/2.$$

[*Hint:* Use the identity $\cos s = \sin [(\tfrac{1}{2})\pi - s]$ and (I).]

24. Prove that $\cos t = \cos s$ if, and only if, for some integer n

$$t = s + 2n\pi \quad \text{or} \quad t = -s + 2n\pi.$$

25. Solve the following equations:
(a) $2 \sin x - 1 = 0$.
(b) $2 \sin (x - 1) = 0$.
(c) $\cos^2 x + 3 \sin x - 3 = 0$. [*Hint:* write $\cos^2 x$ in terms of $\sin^2 x$ and factor—or use the quadratic formula.]
(d) $2 \cos x = -1$.
(e) $2 \sin x \cdot \cos x + \sin x = 0$.
(f) $\cos (2x) = -1$.

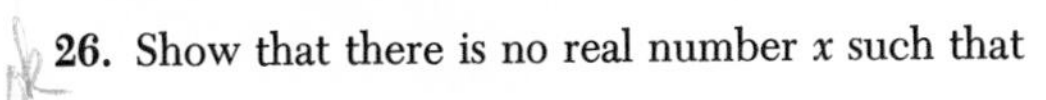

26. Show that there is no real number x such that

$$2 \sin^2 x + 4 \sin x + 3 = 0.$$

27. Solve the equations:
(a) $\sin (x/3) = \cos x$.
(b) $\cos (2x) = -\sin x$.
(c) $-\sin (2x) = \cos x$.
(d) $\sin (7t) = \sin (-5t)$.

28. Solve the equations:
(a) $\tan x \cdot \csc x - 1 = 0$.
(b) $2 \tan (x/2) = \cot (x/2)$.
(c) $\sin^4 y - \cos^4 y = 1$.
(d) $\sin s + \cos s = 1$.

5.5 Angles, Triangles and the Trigonometric Functions

It will be assumed that the reader is familiar with the geometric objects called "angles."

If an angle AOB is given, we may take a coordinate system with x-axis along one of its sides and origin at the vertex as shown in Fig. 5-14. If

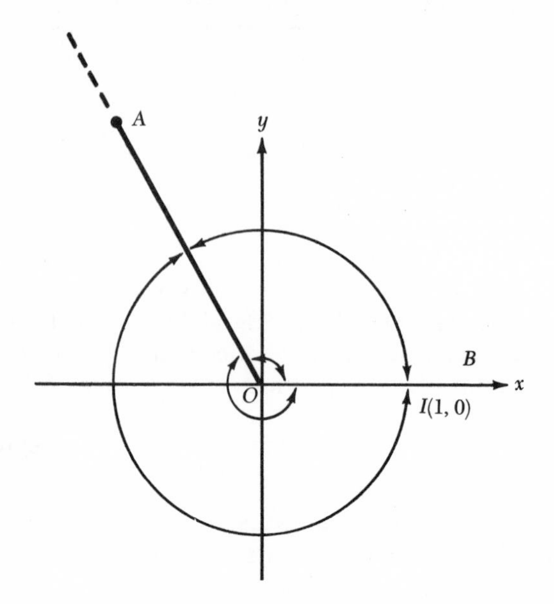

Figure 5-14

the unit circle is centered at the origin, the angle AOB determines two arcs on this circle. The two arcs in turn each have a length which can be used as a measure of the angle. This kind of angle measure is known as *radian* measure. It is common practice to use the word "angle" ambiguously to mean both the geometric figure and one of the two arc lengths associated with this geometric figure. We shall not argue with this practice here; usually our main concern will be with the numbers (or measures) associated with the angle and we will distinguish between the two numbers by drawing small arcs as in Fig. 5-14.

The student is no doubt familiar with degree measure for angles. It will be recalled that in degree measure, a right angle is 90; i.e., a right angle (as in Fig. 5-15) measures 90 degrees (90°). The radian measure of a right angle is by our definition ¼ of the length of the circumference

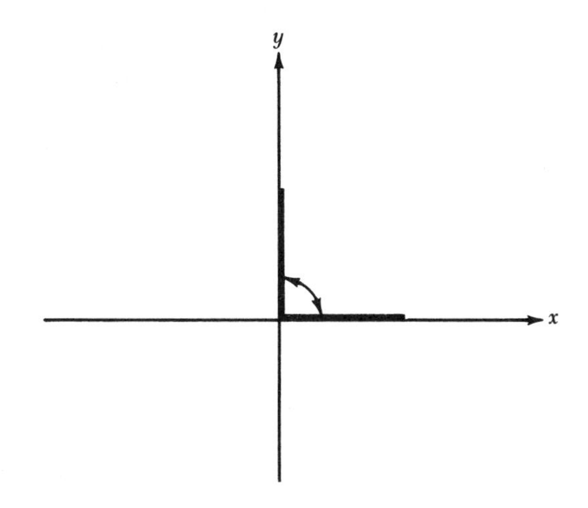

Figure 5-15

of the unit circle: $\frac{1}{4}(2\pi) = \frac{1}{2}\pi$. From this we may conclude that a straight angle measures 180° and π radians since a straight angle is twice as "large," and, hence, has measure twice that of a right angle. In like manner, we can arrive at the information given in the following table.

Angle	Radian measure	Degree measure
Right ⊾	$(\frac{1}{2})\pi$	90
$\frac{1}{2}$(Right)	$(\frac{1}{4})\pi\ (= \frac{1}{2}(\frac{1}{2})\pi)$	45 $[= \frac{1}{2}(90)]$
$(\frac{1}{3})$(Right)	$\pi/6\ [= (\frac{1}{3})(\frac{1}{2})\pi]$	30 $[= (\frac{1}{3})(90)]$
$(\frac{2}{5})$(Right)	$\pi/5\ [= (\frac{2}{5})(\frac{1}{2})\pi]$	36 $[= (\frac{2}{5})(90)]$
$(\frac{1}{90})$(Right)	$\pi/180$	1
$(2/\pi)$(Right)	1	$180/\pi$

From the table, one observes that if an angle measures 1°, its radian measure is $\pi/180$, and if an angle measures 1 radian, its degree measure is $180/\pi$. From this fact we obtain the following conversion rules.

= 180°

(I) TO CONVERT FROM RADIAN MEASURE TO DEGREE MEASURE: If an angle A has radian measure t, then A has degree measure

$$t \cdot (180/\pi).$$

(II) TO CONVERT FROM DEGREE MEASURE TO RADIAN MEASURE: If an angle A has degree measure t, then A has radian measure

$$t \cdot (\pi/180).$$

Example 5-15. Find the degree measure of an angle which measures 14 radians.

Solution. From the conversion rule I:

$$14(180/\pi) = 2520/\pi$$

is the degree measure.

Example 5-16. What is the sum of the interior angles of a triangle in radian measure?

Solution. From geometry, we know that the sum is as large as a straight angle; and a straight angle has radian measure π.

The use of degree measure of angles leads to new functions in terms of the trigonometric functions. If we are given a number t such that

$$0 \leq t \leq 360,$$

t is the degree measure of some angle; and by our conversion rule, this angle has radian measure

$$t \cdot (\pi/180).$$

Next, the number $t \cdot (\pi/180)$ measures a certain arc on the unit circle leading to the point

$$F(t \cdot (\pi/180)).$$

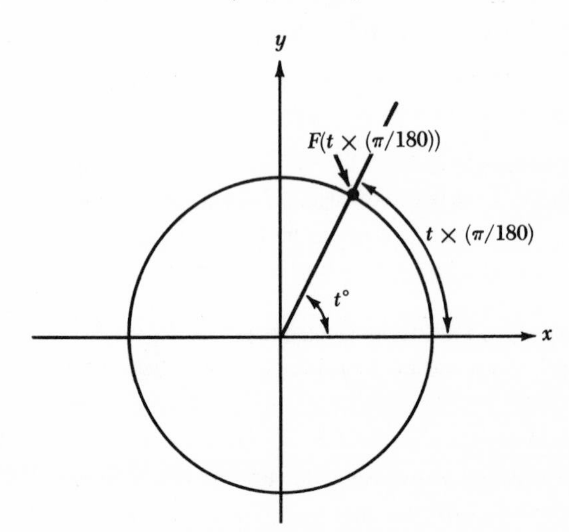

Figure 5-16

(See Fig. 5-16.) Now we may define

$$f(t) = \sin\big(t \cdot (\pi/180)\big) \qquad t \in [0, 360]$$
$$g(t) = \cos\big(t \cdot (\pi/180)\big) \qquad t \in [0, 360].$$

These functions usually are written

$$f(t) = \sin(t^\circ) \qquad g(t) = \cos(t^\circ),$$

that is,

$$\sin(t^\circ) = \sin\big(t \cdot (\pi/180)\big)$$
$$\cos(t^\circ) = \cos\big(t \cdot (\pi/180)\big).$$

It should be emphasized here that these two functions f, g are *not* the same functions sine and cosine as originally defined.

Example 5-17. Find $\sin(60^\circ)$.

Solution. By definition

$$\sin(60^\circ) = \sin(60 \cdot \pi/180) = \sin(\pi/3) = \tfrac{1}{2}\sqrt{3}.$$

Example 5-18. Find $\cos(270^\circ)$.

Solution. $\cos(270^\circ) = \cos(270 \cdot \pi/180) = \cos(3\pi/2) = 0.$

The reader has no doubt noticed that the connection the functions $\sin(t^\circ)$ and $\cos(t^\circ)$ have with angles is not essential since the functions

$$\sin(t \cdot \pi/180) \qquad \text{and} \qquad \cos(t \cdot \pi/180)$$

are defined for *all* real numbers t, and hence the restriction to the interval $[0, 360]$ is not necessary. We may, therefore, write

$$\sin(t^\circ) = \sin(t \cdot \pi/180) \qquad \text{and} \qquad \cos(t^\circ) = \cos(t \cdot \pi/180)$$

for all real numbers t.

The functional values of the trigonometric functions, which we have obtained up to this point, have been easy to calculate from the definition of these functions because they were computed at convenient multiples of 2π. For example, $\sin(\pi/4)$ is easy to compute because $\pi/4 = \tfrac{1}{8}(2\pi)$. Of course, the quite natural and practical question arises about these functional values at numbers t which are not so convenient. For instance, what is a more familiar name for the number $\sin(0.2)$? The answer is that a more familiar name for the number $\sin(0.2)$ is 0.1987—to four places of accuracy; that is,

$$\sin(0.2) \doteq 0.1987.$$

(Here the sign "$\doteq$" is used for "approximately equal to".) A detailed discussion of the answers to such questions cannot be given here. Suffice it to say at this point that one may refer to trigonometric tables to answer this kind of question. There are tables which give functional values for both $\sin t$ and $\sin (t°)$, $\cos t$ and $\cos (t°)$, etc. Reproduced below is a portion of such a table.

t (radian)	$\sin t$	$\cos t$	$\tan t$
0.96	0.8192	0.5735	1.428
0.97	0.8249	0.5653	1.459
0.98	0.8305	0.5570	1.491
0.99	0.8360	0.5487	1.524
1.00	0.8415	0.5403	1.557
1.01	0.8468	0.5319	1.592
1.02	0.8521	0.5234	1.628

$t°$	$\sin (t°)$	$\cos (t°)$	$\tan (t°)$
43	0.6820	0.7314	0.9325
44	0.6947	0.7193	0.9657
45	0.7071	0.7071	1.0000
46	0.7193	0.6947	1.036
47	0.7314	0.6820	1.072
48	0.7431	0.6691	1.111
49	0.7547	0.6561	1.150

Let us now consider a point $A(a, b)$ as in Fig. 5-17 (a). We let t be a measure of the angle AOI as shown. By the distance formula,

$$OA = \sqrt{a^2 + b^2}.$$

For convenience we let $\sqrt{a^2 + b^2} = r$. From the fact that the triangles ABO and PCO are similar, we have

$$\frac{b}{r} = \frac{\sin t}{1} \quad \text{and} \quad \frac{-a}{r} = \frac{-\cos t}{1}$$

or

$$b = r \sin t \quad \text{and} \quad a = r \cos t.$$

This says that the coordinates of a point A may be given in terms of the distance the point A is from the origin O and a measure t of the angle AOI. Fig. 5-17 (b) illustrates this situation with A in the first quadrant. In this case we may express $\sin t$ and $\cos t$ in terms of the length of the

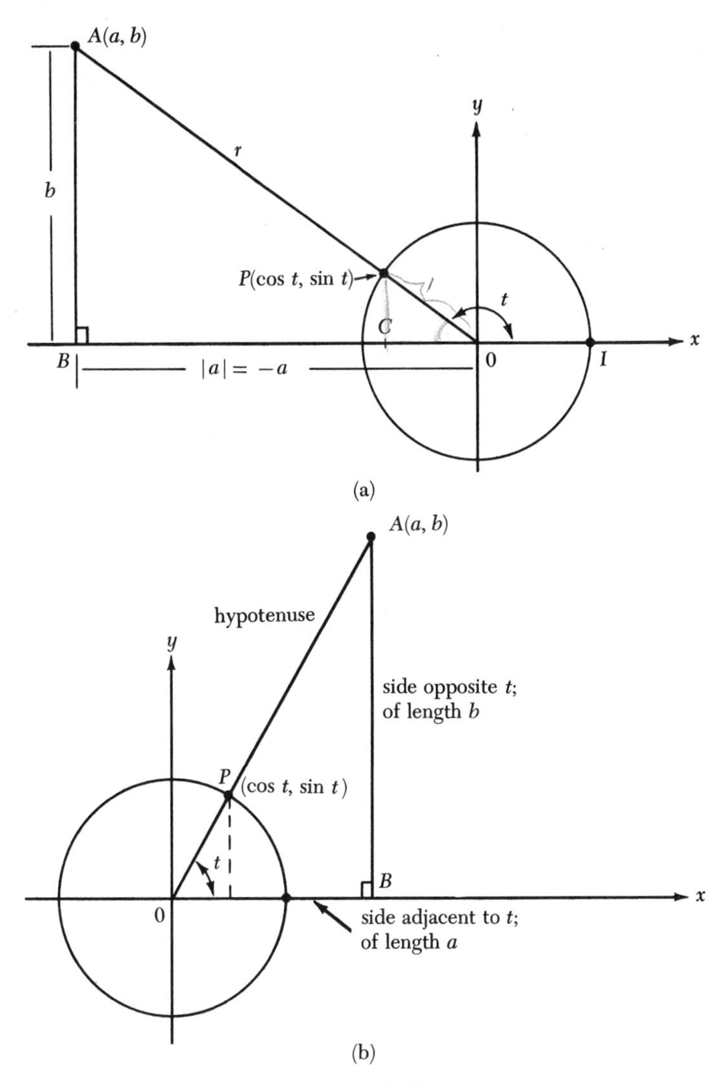

Figure 5-17

sides of the right triangle AOB:

$$\sin t = \frac{L(\text{opposite})}{L(\text{hypotenuse})} \qquad \cos t = \frac{L(\text{adjacent})}{L(\text{hypotenuse})}.$$

We have used $L(\ )$ here to mean "length of".

The information we have just obtained above may be applied to a triangle ABC to deduce the *law of sines*. Let $\triangle ABC$ be as in Fig. 5-18 (a),

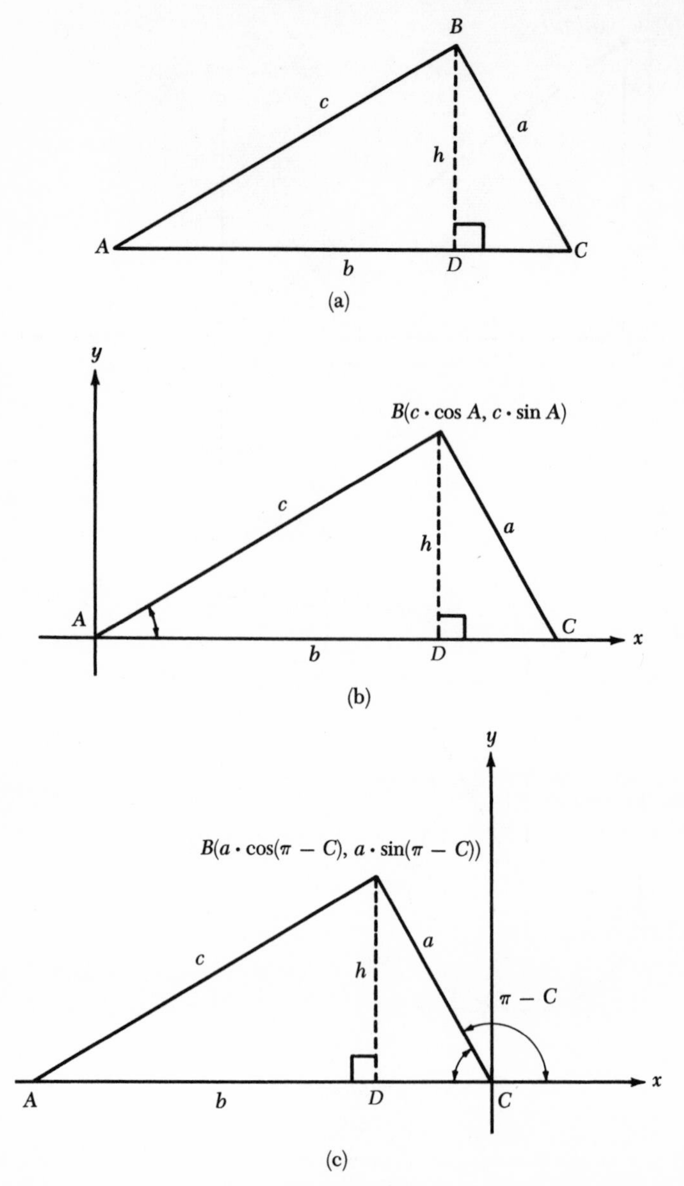

Figure 5-18

with height h. Then take a coordinate system with origin at A and x-axis along AC as in Fig. 5-18 (b). Next, take the origin at C as in Fig. 5-18 (c). In the first case

$$h = c \sin A,$$

and in the second

$$h = a \sin (\pi - C) = a \sin C.$$

Therefore,

$$\frac{\sin A}{a} = \frac{\sin C}{c}.$$

In like manner we prove that

$$\frac{\sin A}{a} = \frac{\sin B}{b},$$

so that

$$\frac{\sin A}{a} = \frac{\sin B}{b} = \frac{\sin C}{c}.$$

The equations above are known as the *law of sines.* Note that A, B, C have been used here to denote both vertices and angle measures.

Example 5-19. If a triangle ABC has $A = 43°$, $C = 49°$ and $b = 1$, find B, a, c.

Solution. First of all, since the sum of the interior angles of ABC is 180°,

$$\begin{aligned} B &= 180° - (43° + 49°) \\ &= 180° - 92° = 88°. \end{aligned}$$

By the law of sines,

$$\frac{\sin (43°)}{a} = \frac{\sin (88°)}{1} = \frac{\sin (49°)}{c}.$$

Then, using a table of trigonometric functions, we have

$$\begin{aligned} a &= (\sin 43°)/(\sin 88°) \doteq (.6820)/(.9994) = 0.685 \\ c &= (\sin 49°)/(\sin 88°) \doteq (.7547)/(.9994) = 0.755. \end{aligned}$$

Exercises

29. If each of the following numbers is the radian measure of an angle, find the corresponding degree measure.

(a) 2π. (b) 0. (c) $\pi/8$. (d) $11\pi/6$.

30. If each of the following numbers is the degree measure of an angle, find the corresponding radian measure.

(a) 4. (b) 0.59. (c) 1¾. (d) 0.32.

31. Compute the following:

(a) $\sin 30^\circ$ $\cos 30^\circ$.   (c) $\sin 135^\circ$ $\cos 135^\circ$.   (e) $\sin(-45)^\circ$ $\cos(-45)^\circ$.

(b) $\sin 90^\circ$ $\cos 90^\circ$.   (d) $\sin 225^\circ$ $\cos 225^\circ$.   (f) $\tan 180^\circ$ $\sec 180^\circ$.

32. Let ABC be a triangle as in Fig. 5-18 (a).

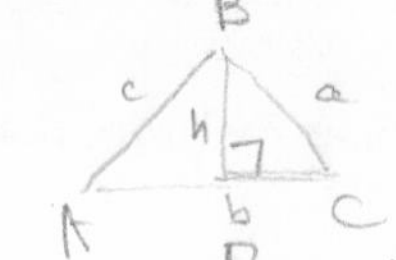

(a) Express DC in terms of a and C.
(b) Express AD in terms of b, a, C.
(c) Express h in terms of a, C.
(d) Prove that

$$c^2 = a^2 + b^2 - 2ab \cos C.$$

[*Hint:* Apply the Pythagorean Theorem to $\triangle ABD$ and use (b), (c).]

(e) Use similar techniques to show that

$$a^2 = b^2 + c^2 - 2bc \cos A$$

and

$$b^2 = a^2 + c^2 - 2ac \cos B.$$

The equations in (d), (e) are known as the *law of cosines.*

33. In a triangle ABC we are given that $b = 2$, $c = 2$ and $A = 60^\circ$. Use the law of cosines and the law of sines to find a, $\sin B$ and $\sin C$.

6

Inverse Functions

6.1 Functions and Their Inverses

If R is a relation, the inverse of R, R^{-1}, has been defined as follows:

$$R^{-1} = \{(a, b) \mid (b, a) \in R\}.$$

In other words, a relation R^{-1} is obtained from R by interchanging first and second elements in the ordered pairs of R. We will be concerned here with the real functions R which have the property that R^{-1} is also a function. It will be recalled from Chapter 1 that R^{-1} is a function if and only if R is a 1-1 function. By definition, R is a 1-1 function if and only if

$$(x_1, y) \in R \text{ and } (x_2, y) \in R \text{ implies that } x_1 = x_2.$$

In Fig. 6-1 the situation illustrated is that in which $x_1 \neq x_2$ and both

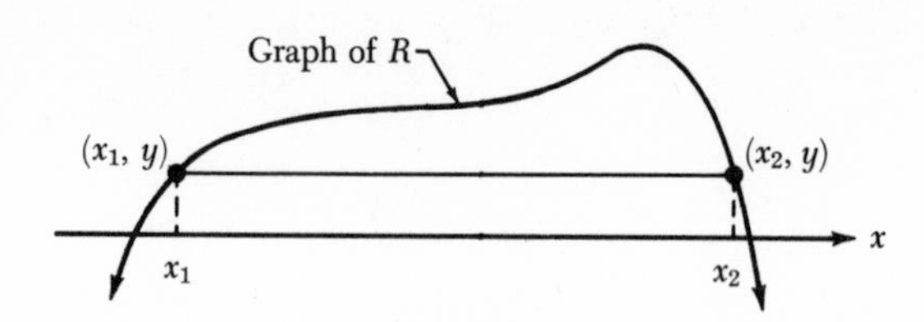

Figure 6-1

(x_1, y) and (x_2, y) are elements of R. Fig. 6-1 thus gives the graph of a function R which is not 1-1. It is evident from this illustration that the property of being 1-1 may be interpreted geometrically as follows:

> The function R is 1-1 if and only if every line which is parallel to the x-axis intersects the graph of R at most once.

Example 6-1. The graph of $f(x) = x^2$ on $[-1, 1]$ is given in Fig. 6-2. It is clear from this graph that f is not a 1-1 function since any line parallel to the x-axis and lying between the lines $y = 0$ and $y = 1$ will intersect the graph exactly twice. It also is evident from the definition that f is not 1-1 since $(1, 1) \in f$ and $(-1, 1) \in f$.

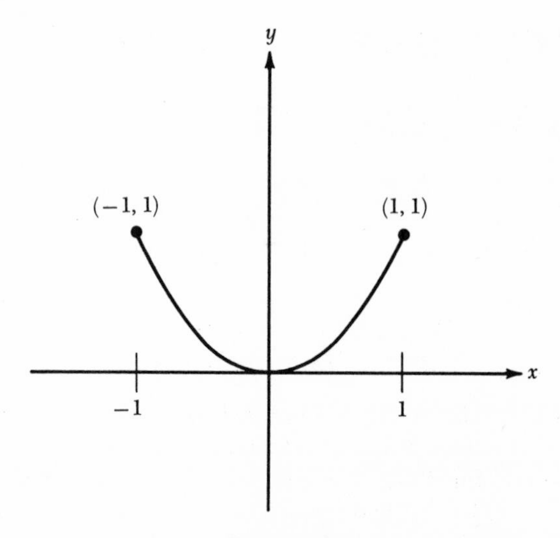

Figure 6-2

Example 6-2. Show that a linear function

$$f(x) = ax + b, a \neq 0$$

is 1-1.

Solution. Suppose that (x_1, y), (x_2, y) are both members of f; i.e.,

$$y = f(x_1) = ax_1 + b$$

and

$$y = f(x_2) = ax_2 + b.$$

Then

$$ax_1 + b = ax_2 + b.$$

Hence,

$$ax_1 = ax_2,$$

and since $a \neq 0$, $x_1 = x_2$. Therefore, by definition f is 1-1. It will be recalled that the graphs of linear functions are straight lines and so the result just obtained is obvious geometrically.

Example 6-3. Show that the function

$$Q(x) = x^3$$

is 1-1.

Solution. Assume that $(x_1, y) \in Q$ and $(x_2, y) \in Q$. Then $x_1^3 = x_2^3$. Since x_1, x_2 cannot have different signs in this situation, we have

$$x_1 \geq 0 \quad \text{and} \quad x_2 \geq 0$$

or

$$x_1 < 0 \quad \text{and} \quad x_2 < 0.$$

Clearly, if either x_1 or x_2 is zero, so is the other—and in that case, $x_1 = x_2$. Hence, suppose that $x_1 \neq 0$ and $x_2 \neq 0$. Therefore,

$$x_1 > 0 \quad \text{and} \quad x_2 > 0$$

or

$$x_1 < 0 \quad \text{and} \quad x_2 < 0.$$

In either case $x_1x_2 > 0$. Now from

$$x_1^3 = x_2^3,$$
$$x_1^3 - x_2^3 = 0;$$

and

$$(x_1 - x_2)(x_1^2 + x_1x_2 + x_2^2) = 0.$$

From this,

$$x_1 - x_2 = 0$$

or

$$x_1^2 + x_1x_2 + x_2^2 = 0.$$

We have just seen that $x_1x_2 > 0$, and hence,

$$x_1^2 + x_1x_2 + x_2^2 > 0,$$

so that

$$x_1 - x_2 = 0 \qquad \text{and} \qquad x_1 = x_2.$$

Therefore, $Q(x) = x^3$ is a 1-1 function by definition.

If we are given a relation T and wish to construct its inverse, we only need to interchange first and second members of the ordered pairs of T. If $T = \{(x, y) | y = 2x + 3\}$, then by definition

$$T^{-1} = \{(y, x) | y = 2x + 3\}.$$

This is an adequate description of T^{-1}, but it is customary to express the second members of ordered pairs—when possible—in terms of the first members. This is not done in this description of T^{-1}. But this may be accomplished from

$$y = 2x + 3$$

by solving for x in terms of y:

$$x = \tfrac{1}{2}(y - 3).$$

Then,

$$T^{-1} = \{(y, x) | x = \tfrac{1}{2}(y - 3)\}.$$

Everything is fine now except that we have violated the convention of calling first coordinates x and second coordinates y. Since it makes no difference what names we give these elements, we conform and write

$$T^{-1} = \{(x, y) | y = \tfrac{1}{2}(x - 3)\}.$$

In the $T(x)$-notation,

$$T(x) = 2x + 3$$

and

$$T^{-1}(x) = \tfrac{1}{2}(x - 3).$$

Let us compute the composites $T(T^{-1})$ and $T^{-1}(T)$:

$$\begin{aligned} T(T^{-1}(x)) &= T(\tfrac{1}{2}(x - 3)) \\ &= 2(\tfrac{1}{2}(x - 3)) + 3 \\ &= (x - 3) + 3 = x \end{aligned}$$

$$\begin{aligned} T^{-1}(T(x)) &= T^{-1}(2x + 3) \\ &= \tfrac{1}{2}(2x + 3 - 3) \\ &= x. \end{aligned}$$

Thus,

$$\begin{aligned} T(T^{-1}) &= \{(x, T(T^{-1}(x))) \mid x \in R\} \\ &= \{(x, x) \mid x \in R\}, \end{aligned}$$

and

$$\begin{aligned} T^{-1}(T) &= \{(x, T^{-1}(T(x))) \mid x \in R\} \\ &= \{(x, x) \mid x \in R\}. \end{aligned}$$

This shows that in this case both $T(T^{-1})$ and $T^{-1}(T)$ are functions which associate with each real number x the number x itself. A function J which associates the number x with each number x in the domain of J is called an *identity function*. In other words, if J is an identity function, then

$$J(x) = x$$

for all $x \in \mathfrak{D}(J)$.

The fact that $T(T^{-1})$ and $T^{-1}(T)$ are both identity functions is not peculiar to the above example. If T is any function such that T^{-1} is a function, we have $y = T(x)$ if and only if $x = T^{-1}(y)$. Therefore, by substitution,

$$y = T(T^{-1}(y)) \text{ and } x = T^{-1}(T(x)).$$

The above shows that $T(T^{-1})$ *and* $T^{-1}(T)$ *are identity functions for any* T *which is 1-1.*

This property may be used to compute inverses when only functions are involved. For the function

$$T(x) = 2x + 3,$$

for example, we know that $T(T^{-1}(x)) = x$ so that

$$x = T(T^{-1}(x)) = 2(T^{-1}(x)) + 3.$$

Then solving for $T^{-1}(x)$:

$$T^{-1}(x) = \tfrac{1}{2}(x - 3).$$

Exmple 6-4. Show that the function

$$f(x) = |x| \qquad \text{for} \qquad x \in [-1, 1]$$

is not 1-1.

Solution. $f(-\frac{1}{2}) = |-\frac{1}{2}| = \frac{1}{2}$ and $f(\frac{1}{2}) = |\frac{1}{2}| = \frac{1}{2}$.

Hence, f is not 1-1.

Example 6-5. Show that the function given below is 1-1:

$$g(x) = x^2 \qquad \text{for} \qquad x \geq 0.$$

Solution. Suppose that $g(x_1) = g(x_2)$. Then $x_1^2 = x_2^2$ and

$$x_1^2 - x_2^2 = 0,$$

or

$$(x_1 - x_2)(x_1 + x_2) = 0.$$

Therefore,

$$x_1 - x_2 = 0 \qquad \text{or} \qquad x_1 + x_2 = 0.$$

Since in this case $x_1 \geq 0$ and $x_2 \geq 0$,

$$x_1 + x_2 \neq 0$$

unless both x_1 and x_2 are zero—and in that case $x_1 = x_2$. So $x_1 - x_2 = 0$ and $x_1 = x_2$ which shows that g is 1-1.

Example 6-6. Describe the inverse of the function g above.

Solution. Since g is 1-1, g^{-1} is a function. We then may use composites to compute g^{-1}:

$$x = g(g^{-1}(x)) = (g^{-1}(x))^2.$$

Therefore, since $x \geq 0$,

$$g^{-1}(x) = \sqrt{x}.$$

Example 6-7. Show that the function

$$g(x) = \frac{x - 1}{x + 1}$$

is 1-1 and describe its inverse.

Solution. If x_1, x_2 are numbers such that

$$(x_1 - 1)/(x_1 + 1) = (x_2 - 1)/(x_2 + 1),$$

then

$$(x_1 - 1)(x_2 + 1) = (x_1 + 1)(x_2 - 1)$$

or

$$x_1x_2 - x_2 + x_1 - 1 = x_1x_2 + x_2 - x_1 - 1.$$

Therefore,

$$
\begin{aligned}
-x_2 + x_1 &= x_2 - x_1, \\
2(x_2 - x_1) &= 0, \\
x_2 - x_1 &= 0, \\
x_1 &= x_2
\end{aligned}
$$

and g is 1-1. To compute g^{-1}:

$$x = g(g^{-1}(x)) = (g^{-1}(x) - 1)/(g^{-1}(x) + 1).$$

Hence,

$$
\begin{aligned}
x(g^{-1}(x) + 1) &= g^{-1}(x) - 1 \\
xg^{-1}(x) - g^{-1}(x) &= -x - 1 \\
(x - 1)g^{-1}(x) &= -x - 1 \\
g^{-1}(x) &= (-x - 1)/(x - 1) = (1 + x)/(1 - x).
\end{aligned}
$$

Note that the domain of g is the set of all real numbers except -1 and that of g^{-1} is the set of all real numbers except 1.

It has been pointed out in Chapter 1 that the graph of T^{-1}, for a relation T, may be constructed as follows:

> For each point P of the graph of T plot the point Q which is symmetric to P with respect to the line $y = x$.

This means that through each point P of the graph of T we draw a line L perpendicular to the line D which bisects quadrants I and III. If

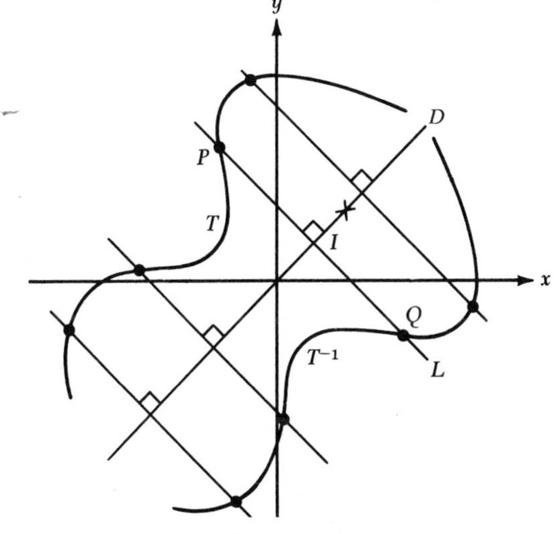

Figure 6-3

I is the point of D where L intersects, we choose Q on L opposite P such that $PI = IQ$. (See Fig. 6-3.)

Example 6-8. Construct the graph of

$$T^{-1}(x) = \tfrac{1}{2}(x - 3)$$

from the graph of

$$T(x) = 2x + 3.$$

Solution. Since T^{-1} is a linear function its graph will be determined by any two points on it. The graph is given in Fig. 6-4.

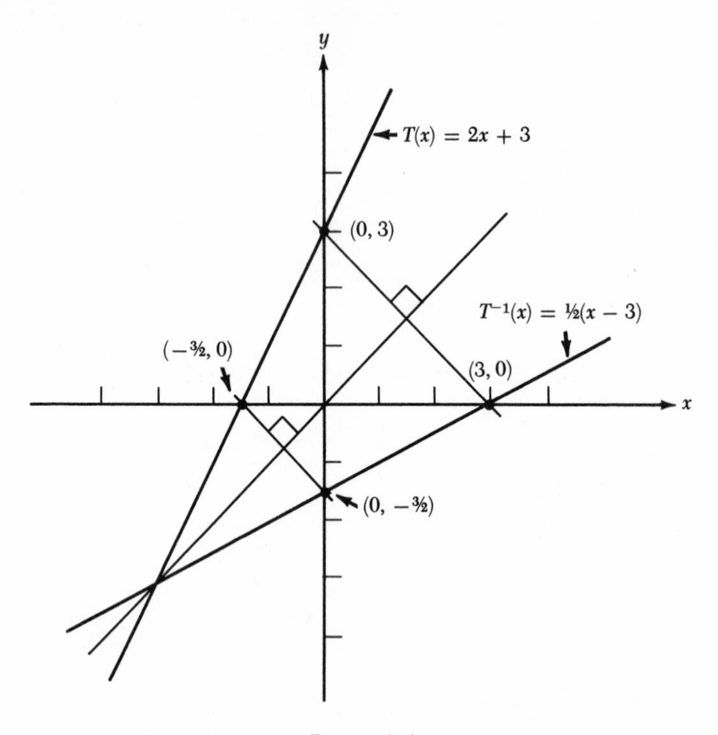

Figure 6-4

Example 6-9. The graphs of

$$f(x) = x^2, \qquad \text{for} \qquad x \geq 0$$

and

$$f^{-1}(x) = \sqrt{x}, \qquad \text{for} \qquad x \geq 0$$

have been constructed in Fig. 6-5.

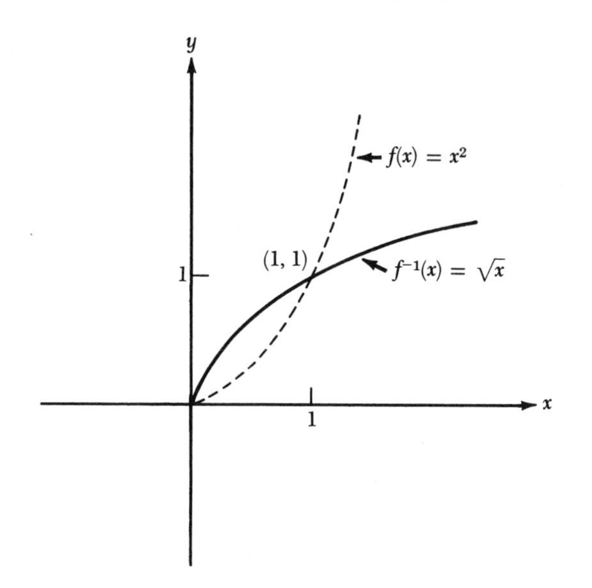

Figure 6-5

Exercises

1. In Fig. 6-6, which of the graphs are graphs of 1-1 functions?

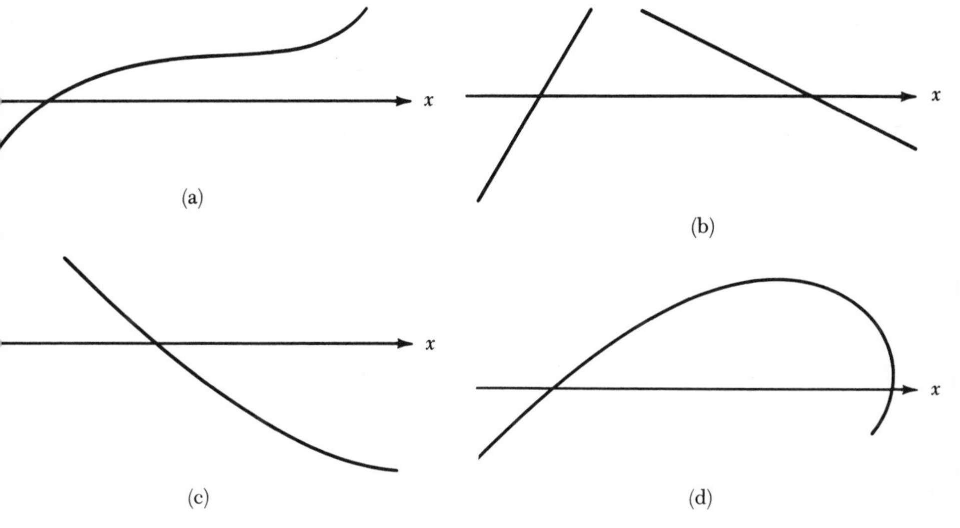

Figure 6-6

2. Use the graph of each of the following functions to determine if it is 1-1.
   (a) $f(x) = [x]$.
   (b) $g(x) = x - [x]$.
   (c) $T(x) = \cos x$.
   (d) $L(x) = 3 \sin (x + 1), x \in [0, 2\pi]$.
   (e) $g(x) = -x^2 + 1, x \in [-1, 0]$.
   (f) $g(x) = -x^2 + 1, x \in [-1, 1]$.

3. Graph each of the following functions. Then, construct the graph of the function's inverse geometrically.
   (a) $T(x) = -x^2, x \leq 0$.
   (b) $Q(x) = x^3 + 1, x \in [-1, 2]$.
   (c) $C(x) = \sqrt{2 - x^2}, x \in [0, \sqrt{2}]$.
   (d) $C(x) = \sqrt{2 - x^2}, x \in [-\sqrt{2}, \sqrt{2}]$.
   (e) $L(x) = x + 1$.
   (f) $K(x) = -x + 1$.
   (g) $M(x) = -(⅓)x - 6$.

4. For each of the functions f given below give a description of f^{-1} using the method of composites as described in Example 6-6.
   (a) $f(x) = 7 - 2x$.
   (b) $f(x) = \sqrt{1 - x^2}, x \in [-1, 0]$.
   (c) $f(x) = 1/x, x > 0$.
   (d) $f(x) = 3/(1 - x), x > 1$.
   (e) $f(x) = x/(x + 1), x < -1$.
   (f) $f(x) = x + \sqrt{x}$. [*Hint:* Solve the quadratic

$$x = (\sqrt{f^{-1}(x)})^2 + \sqrt{f^{-1}(x)} \quad \text{for} \quad \sqrt{f^{-1}(x)}].$$

   (g) $f(x) = \dfrac{ax + b}{cx + d}$, for $ad \neq bc$.

6.2 Exponential and Logarithmic Functions

The functions that we shall examine now are based upon the meaning of a^t, where t and a denote numbers and $a > 0$. We assume that the reader is to some extent familiar with this notation. For example, if $a = 2$ and $t = 3$, the usual meaning of 2^3 is 8, i.e., $2 \cdot 2 \cdot 2$. Generally, if t is a positive integer, a^t means

$$a \cdot a \cdot a \cdots a$$

with t factors, each of which is a. From this starting point, when t is a positive integer, it is possible to go further and give meaning to a^t for any real number t. This is accomplished in such a way that the following statements are true for all real numbers t, s:

1. $a^t \cdot a^s = a^{t+s}$.
2. $a^t/a^s = a^{t-s}$.
3. $(a^t)^s = a^{ts}$.
4. $(ab)^t = a^t \cdot b^t$.

We shall not at this point pursue the definition of a^t further. It is enough for our purposes to know that when $a > 0$, a^t means a number for each real number t such that 1, 2, 3, 4 above hold.*

If $a > 0$, a^t is a real number for each real number t and we may define a real function

$$\{(t, a^t) \mid t \text{ is a real number}\}.$$

This function we denote by E_a and call it the *exponential function of base a*. In our usual functional notation we have

$$E_a(t) = a^t \qquad \text{for all real } t.$$

As examples of members of E_a, we have

$$(0, a^0) = (0, 1) \in E_a \qquad \text{or} \qquad E_a(0) = 1.$$
$$(1, a^1) = (1, a) \in E_a \qquad \text{or} \qquad E_a(1) = a.$$
$$(-1, a^{-1}) = (-1, 1/a) \in E_a \qquad \text{or} \qquad E_a(-1) = 1/a.$$
$$(\sqrt[3]{5}, a^{\sqrt[3]{5}}) \in E_a \qquad \text{or} \qquad E_a(\sqrt[3]{5}) = a^{\sqrt[3]{5}}.$$

From 1, 2, 3, we have the following rules:

1′. $E_a(t + s) = E_a(t) \cdot E_a(s)$.
2′. $E_a(t - s) = E_a(t)/E_a(s)$.
3′. $E_a(ts) = [E_a(t)]^s = [E_a(s)]^t$.

We illustrate the graph of E_a for $a = 3$. Some convenient pairs belonging to E_3 are the following:

$$(0, 1) \in E_3.$$
$$(1, 3) \in E_3.$$
$$(-1, \tfrac{1}{3}) \in E_3.$$
$$(2, 9) \in E_3.$$
$$(-2, \tfrac{1}{9}) \in E_3, \text{ etc.}$$

Then, assuming that the graph of E_a is a smooth curve, we may obtain the graph of E_3 as in Fig. 6-7.

---

* The reader who is interested in the precise definition of a^t may consult *The Number System* by B. K. Youse, Dickenson Pub. Co., 1965.

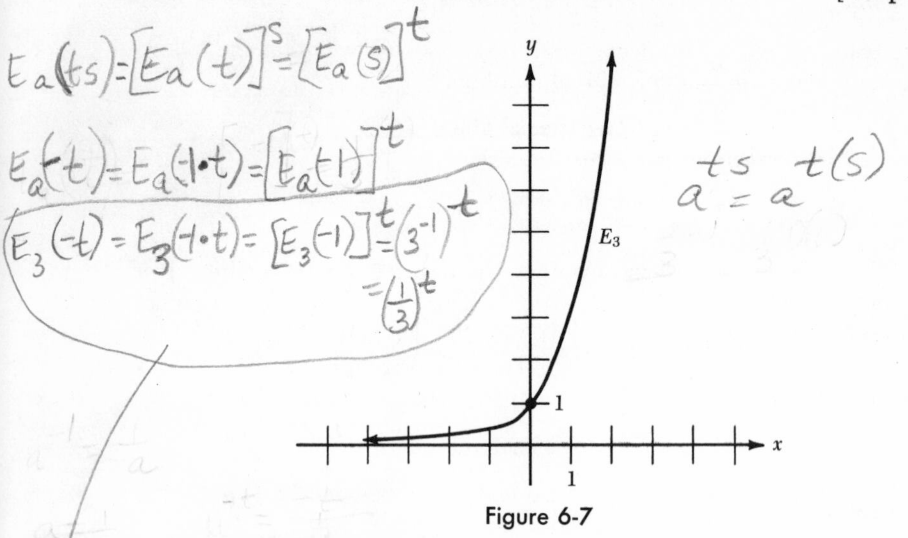

Figure 6-7

Now consider the graph of $E_{1/3}$. We have for any real number t

$$E_{1/3}(t) = (1/3)^t = 3^{-t} = E_3(-t).$$

Suppose now that (x, y) is a point on the graph of $E_{1/3}$, i.e., $(x, y) \in E_{1/3}$. Then $y = E_{1/3}(x) = E_3(-x)$ as above. But this says that $(-x, y) \in E_3$. And in like manner we can show that if $(z, w) \in E_3$, then $(-z, w) \in E_{1/3}$. Hence,

(*) $\qquad (x, y) \in E_{1/3}$ if and only if $(-x, y) \in E_3$.

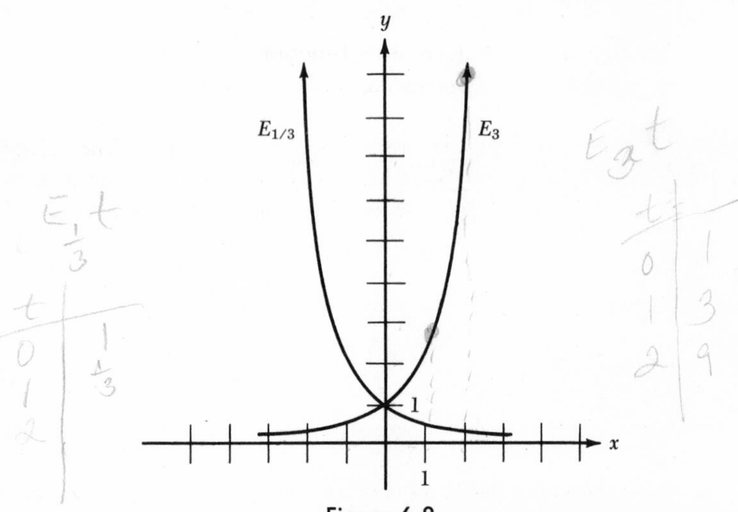

Figure 6-8

This is illustrated in Fig. 6-8 in which the graphs of both E_3 and $E_{1/3}$ have been given on the same coordinate-axis system.

There is, of course, nothing special about $a = 3$ in (*) and we may have for any real number a (>0)

$$(*') \qquad (x, y) \in E_{1/a} \text{ if and only if } (-x, y) \in E_a.$$

Notice that in Fig. 6-8 the graph of E_3 rises while the graph of $E_{1/3}$ drops (assuming that the curve is traversed in a direction of increasing first coordinates). This illustrates a general property of the exponential functions which we may state as follows:

5. if $0 < a < 1$ and $x < y$, then $E_a(y) < E_a(x)$.
6. if $1 < a$ and $x < y$, then $E_a(x) < E_a(y)$.

DEFINITION. Let f be a function.

(a) For every pair of numbers x, y in the domain of f such that $x < y$, if

$$f(x) < f(y),$$

then f is called a *strictly increasing* function.

(b) For every pair of numbers x, y in the domain of f such that $x < y$, if

$$f(x) > f(y),$$

then f is called a *strictly decreasing* function.

From these definitions, and 5 and 6 above, it is clear that

5′. E_a is a strictly decreasing function for $0 < a < 1$.
6′. E_a is a strictly increasing function for $a > 1$.

It will be obvious to the reader that *if a function is either strictly increasing or strictly decreasing, it is 1-1.* This implies, of course, that f^{-1}, for such a function f, is a function. Of immediate importance for us is the fact that for each $a > 0$ such that $a \neq 1$, ${E_a}^{-1}$ is a function. The function ${E_a}^{-1}$ is called the *logarithm function of base a.* ${E_a}^{-1}$ is usually denoted by "$\log_a$." Thus,

$$w = E_a(z) = a^z \quad \text{if and only if} \quad z = \log_a(w).$$

Therefore, for all z and w,

$$\log_a(a^z) = z \quad \text{and} \quad a^{\log_a(w)} = w.$$

The properties of the function E_a stated in 1′, 2′, and 3′ may be used to derive corresponding properties of $\log_a$. For example, 1′ may be used to prove the following:

$$7.\ \log_a(t \cdot s) = \log_a(t) + \log_a(s)$$

where t, s are positive numbers. To prove this, let $w = \log_a(t)$ and $z = \log_a(s)$. Then by definition $E_a(w) = t$ and $E_a(z) = s$.

Now according to 1′,

$$E_a(w + z) = E_a(w) \cdot E_a(z)$$

or substituting for $E_a(w)$ and $E_a(z)$,

$$E_a(w + z) = t \cdot s.$$

This gives

$$\log_a[E_a(w + z)] = \log\,(t \cdot s)$$

or

$$w + z = \log\,(t \cdot s)$$

which is the same as 7.

In a similar way, we may prove the following:

$$8.\ \log_a\left(\frac{s}{t}\right) = \log_a(s) - \log_a(t)$$

$$9.\ \log_a(s^t) = t \cdot \log_a(s)$$

where s, t are positive real numbers.

Since $a^t > 0$ for all real numbers t, the range of E_a is a subset of the positive real numbers. In fact, if $a \neq 1$,

$$\mathfrak{R}(E_a) = \{x \mid x > 0\}.$$

Because of the relationship between the domain and range of functions and their inverses,

$$\mathfrak{D}(\log_a) = \{x \mid x > 0\}$$

and

$$\mathfrak{R}(\log_a) = \{t \mid t \text{ is a real number}\}.$$

Example 6-10. Show that $\log_a$ is a 1-1 function.

Solution. Suppose that s, t are positive real numbers such that

$$\log_a(s) = \log_a(t).$$

Then

$$s = E_a[\log_a(s)] = E_a[\log_a(t)] = t.$$

Hence, by definition $\log_a$ is a 1-1 function.

Example 6-11. Compute the inverse f^{-1} of the function

$$f(x) = E_a(\sqrt{x}),\ x \geq 0,\ a \neq 1.$$

Solution. We know that $f(f^{-1}(x)) = x$. Thus

$$x = f(f^{-1}(x)) = E_a(\sqrt{f^{-1}(x)})$$

[How do we know here that $f^{-1}(x) \geq 0$?] Therefore,

$$\log_a(x) = \log_a[E_a(\sqrt{f^{-1}(x)})] = \sqrt{f^{-1}(x)}$$

and

$$f^{-1}(x) = [\log_a(x)]^2.$$

We may construct the graph of the functions $\log_a$ in the usual way by making use of the fact that $\log_a$ is the inverse of E_a. The graphs of $\log_3$ and $\log_{1/3}$ are given in Fig. 6-9.

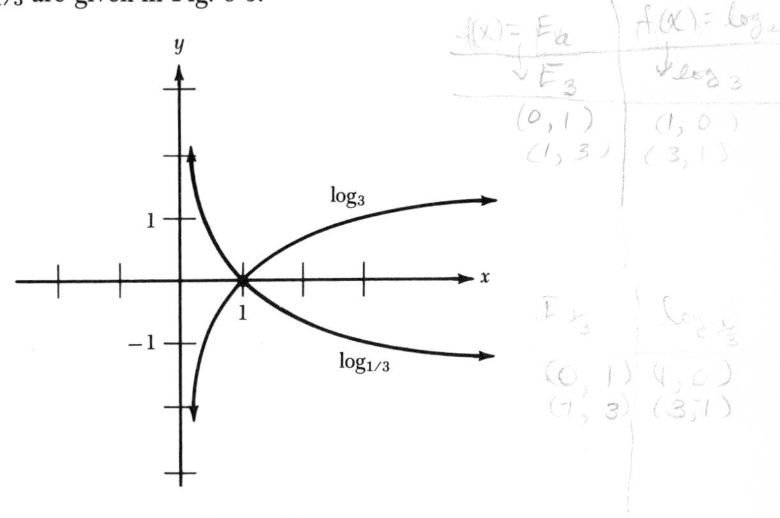

Figure 6-9

The graphs of $\log_{1/3}$ and $\log_3$ of Fig. 6-9 indicate that the functions $\log_{1/3}$ and $\log_3$ are strictly decreasing and strictly increasing respectively. These are properties which the functions $\log_a$ inherit from E_a.

10. if $0 < a < 1$, $\log_a$ is a strictly decreasing function.
11. if $a > 1$, $\log_a$ is a strictly increasing function.

To prove 10, suppose that $\log_a$ is *not* a strictly decreasing function for $0 < a < 1$. Then by definition, there are two numbers x, y in the domain of $\log_a$ such that $x < y$ and

$$\log_a(x) \not> \log_a(y).$$

From this, we may conclude that

$$\log_a(x) \leq \log_a(y).$$

If $\log_a(x) < \log_a(y)$, we know that $E_a[\log_a(x)] > E_a[\log_a(y)]$ since E_a is a strictly decreasing function. But this implies that $x > y$, contrary to the fact that $x < y$. Therefore, we cannot have $\log_a(x) < \log_a(y)$. On the other hand, if $\log_a(x) = \log_a(y)$, then $x = y$ (since $\log_a$ is 1-1) and this again contradicts the fact that $x < y$. This then proves 10. A similar proof for 11 may be given.

Exercises

5. Plot the graph of each of the following functions:

(a) E_2. (b) E_5. (c) E_{10}.

6. (a) Using only the graph of E_2, plot on the same axis the graph of $E_{1/2}$.
(b) Using only the graph of E_{10}, plot on the same axis the graph of $E_{1/10}$.

7. Prove the statements 1′, 2′, 3′.

8. Using the fact that E_a, $(a \neq 1)$, and $\log_a$ are 1-1 functions, solve the following equations.
(a) $2^x = 2^{2x-1}$.
(b) $a^{7x} = 1$. [*Hint:* $a^0 = 1$.]
(c) $3^{7x} = 2$. [*Hint:* $2 = 3^{\log_3 2}$.]
(d) $9(3^{x^2}) = 1$.
(e) $\log_a(x^2 - 1) = 0$.
(f) $\log_5(2x - 1) + \log_5(2x + 1) = 1$.
(g) $\log_{1/2}(x^2 - 7) - \log_{1/2}(2x^2 + 1) = 1$.

9. Use information about the functions E_a to prove the following properties of $\log_a$.
(a) If $a > 1$, $\log_a$ is strictly increasing.
(b) $\log_a\left(\frac{t}{s}\right) = \log_a(t) - \log_a(s)$ for positive numbers s, t.
(c) $\log_a(s^t) = t \log_a(s)$ for all numbers t and positive numbers s.
(d) $\log_a(t) = \dfrac{\log_b(t)}{\log_b(a)}$ for all positive numbers t, a, b such that $a \neq 1$, $b \neq 1$.
(e) If $\log_a(t) = \log_b(s) = w$, then $\log_{ab}(ts) = w$ for all positive numbers t, s, a, b such that $a \neq 1$, $b \neq 1$.

10. Compute the inverse of each of the following functions:
(a) $f(x) = 4^x$.
(b) $g(x) = 1/7(2^{x-1})$.
(c) $h(x) = E_a(1/x) + 1$.
(d) $f(x) = \log_2(x)$.
(e) $g(x) = \log_3(2x) + \log_3(x)$.
(f) $h(x) = \log_a(7x + 2)$.

11. Obtain the solution sets for each of the following inequalities:

(a) $2^x \leq 1$.
(b) $5^{x^2} < 5^x$.
(c) $3^{x-1} \leq 9^{1-2x}$.
(d) $(\frac{1}{2})^x \leq 2^{x^2}$.
(e) $E_{1/3}(\sin x) \leq E_{1/3}(\cos x)$, $x \in [0, 2\pi]$.
(f) $\log_2(1 - x) < \log_2(2x)$.
(g) $\log_{1/7}(x^3) < \log_{1/7}(2x)$.

6.3 The Inverse Trigonometric Functions

Consider a function f defined as follows:

$$f(x) = \sin(x), \quad x \in [a, b]$$

where a, b are real numbers and $a < b$. An examination of the graph of the sine function on the set of *all* real numbers reveals that whether or not f is 1-1 depends upon the interval $[a, b]$. In Fig. 6-10 (a), the interval chosen is $[-\pi, \pi/4]$ and in this case f is not 1-1. In Fig. 6-10 (b),

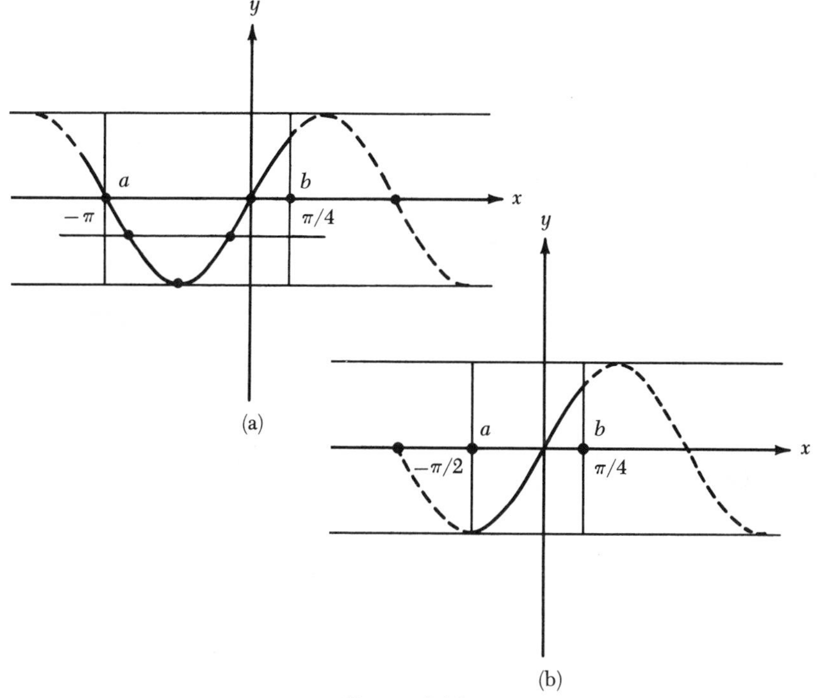

Figure 6-10

the interval chosen is $[-\pi/2, \pi/4]$ and here f is 1-1. This implies, of course, that in the first case f^{-1} is not a function, and in the second case f^{-1} is a function. Due to the fact that sine is periodic of period 2π, f^{-1} is not a function if $[a, b]$ is chosen to have a length greater than 2π.

We obviously may make an infinite number of choices for $[a, b]$ each of which will give us a 1-1 function f. All the functions listed below are 1-1, for example:

$$\begin{aligned}
f_1(x) &= \sin(x), & x &\in [-5\pi/2, -3\pi/2].\\
f_2(x) &= \sin(x), & x &\in [-3\pi/2, -\pi/2].\\
f_3(x) &= \sin(x), & x &\in [-\pi/2, \pi/2].\\
f_4(x) &= \sin(x), & x &\in [\pi/2, 3\pi/2].\\
f_5(x) &= \sin(x), & x &\in [3\pi/2, 5\pi/2].
\end{aligned}$$

Then each of the relations $f_1{}^{-1}, f_2{}^{-1}, f_3{}^{-1}, f_4{}^{-1}, f_5{}^{-1}$ is a function. The domain of each is $[-1, 1]$ since $\sin(x)$ takes as values all numbers of the set $[-1, 1]$ for $x \in [a, b]$, where $[a, b]$ is any one of the intervals above. It is customary to call $f_3{}^{-1}$ *the* inverse sine function and denote it by "Arc sin." Thus,

$$f_3{}^{-1}(x) = \text{Arc sin}(x) \qquad \text{for} \qquad x \in [-1, 1].$$

In a similar way we define Arc cos and Arc tan.

DEFINITION.

(a) If $f(x) = \sin(x)$, $x \in [-\pi/2, \pi/2]$, then

$$\text{Arc sin} = f^{-1}.$$

(b) If $g(x) = \cos(x)$, $x \in [0, \pi]$, then

$$\text{Arc cos} = g^{-1}.$$

(c) If $h(x) = \tan(x)$, $x \in (-\pi/2, \pi/2)$, then

$$\text{Arc tan} = h^{-1}.$$

From the definition, we have

$$\begin{aligned}
\mathfrak{D}(\text{Arc sin}) &= [-1, 1], & \mathfrak{R}(\text{Arc sin}) &= [-\pi/2, \pi/2].\\
\mathfrak{D}(\text{Arc cos}) &= [-1, 1], & \mathfrak{R}(\text{Arc cos}) &= [0, \pi].\\
\mathfrak{D}(\text{Arc tan}) &= R, & \mathfrak{R}(\text{Arc tan}) &= (-\pi/2, \pi/2).
\end{aligned}$$

The graphs of the functions Arc sin, Arc cos and Arc tan are given in Fig. 6-11.

Example 6-12. Show that $\cos(\text{Arc sin}\, x) = \sqrt{1 - x^2}$.

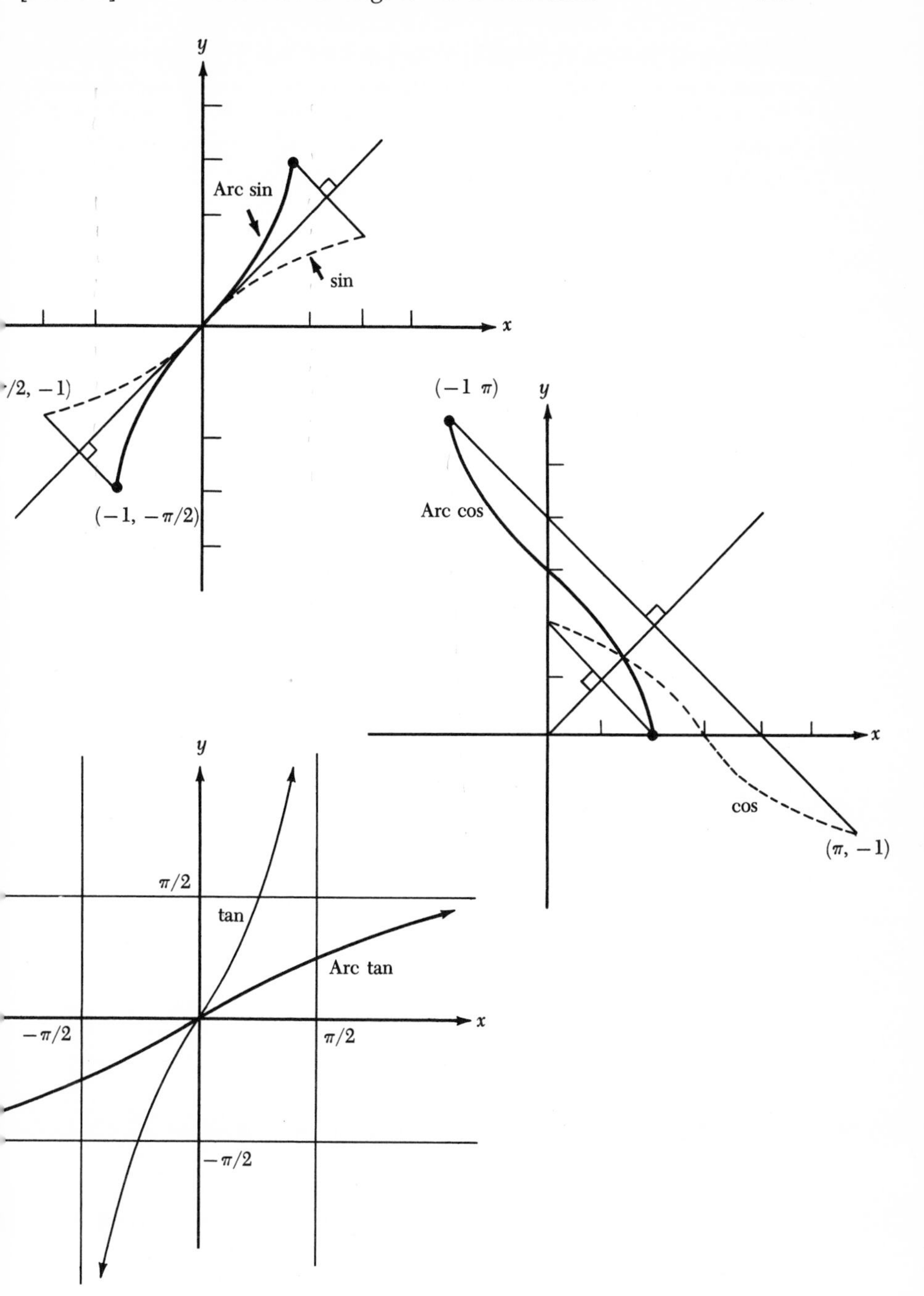
y
Arc sin
sin
x
/2, −1)
(−1, −π/2)
(−1 π)
y
Arc cos
cos
x
(π, −1)
y
π/2
tan
Arc tan
x
−π/2
π/2
−π/2

Figure 6-11

Solution. We use the identity

$$\cos^2 t + \sin^2 t = 1$$

and the fact that $\sin(\text{Arc}\sin x) = x$. Substitution of $t = \text{Arc}\sin x$ in the identity gives

$$\cos^2(\text{Arc}\sin x) + \sin^2(\text{Arc}\sin x) = 1$$

or

$$[\cos(\text{Arc}\sin x)]^2 + [\sin(\text{Arc}\sin x)]^2 = 1.$$

Then

$$[\cos(\text{Arc}\sin x)]^2 = 1 - x^2$$

and

$$\cos(\text{Arc}\sin x) = \pm\sqrt{1 - x^2}.$$

But since the range of $\text{Arc}\sin x$ is $[-\pi/2, \pi/2]$ and the cosine is not negative on this set, we must have

$$\cos(\text{Arc}\sin x) = \sqrt{1 - x^2}.$$

Example 6-13. Show that $\text{Arc}\sin(\cos x) = x + \pi/2$.

Solution. Using the identity $\sin(x + \pi/2) = \cos x$

$$\text{Arc}\sin(\cos x) = \text{Arc}\sin\big(\sin(x + \pi/2)\big) = x + \pi/2.$$

Example 6-14. Show that $\tan(\text{Arc}\sin x) = x/\sqrt{1 - x^2}$.

Solution. We have from Example 6-12 that $\cos(\text{Arc}\sin x) = \sqrt{1 - x^2}$. Hence,

$$\tan(\text{Arc}\sin x) = \frac{\sin(\text{Arc}\sin x)}{\cos(\text{Arc}\sin x)} = \frac{x}{\sqrt{1 - x^2}}.$$

Example 6-15. Compute $\text{Arc}\sin(\tfrac{1}{2}\sqrt{2})$, $\text{Arc}\cos(0)$, $\text{Arc}\tan(1)$.

Solution. By definition of Arc sin, we need to find a number $x \in [-\pi/2, \pi/2]$ such that

$$\sin(x) = \tfrac{1}{2}\sqrt{2}.$$

The number $x = \pi/4$ is the only one meeting these requirements. Hence,

$$\text{Arc}\sin(\tfrac{1}{2}\sqrt{2}) = \pi/4.$$

Similarly,

$$\text{Arc}\cos(0) = \pi/2$$

since

$$\cos(\pi/2) = 0 \qquad \text{and} \qquad \pi/2 \in [0, \pi].$$

Also,

$$\text{Arc tan } (1) = \pi/4$$

since

$$\tan(\pi/4) = 1 \qquad \text{and} \qquad \pi/4 \in (-\pi/2, \pi/2).$$

Exercises

12. Compute the following:

(a) Arc sin (0)
Arc cos (0)
Arc tan (0).

(b) Arc sin (1)
Arc cos (1)
Arc tan (1).

(c) Arc sin (-1)
Arc cos (-1)
Arc tan (-1).

(d) Arc sin $(\frac{1}{2}\sqrt{2})$
Arc cos $(-\frac{1}{2}\sqrt{2})$.

(e) Arc sin $(-\frac{1}{2})$
Arc cos $(\frac{1}{2})$.

(f) Arc sin $(\frac{1}{2}\sqrt{3})$
Arc cos $(-\frac{1}{2}\sqrt{3})$.

13. Prove each of the following:

(a) $\cos(2 \text{ Arc sin } x) = 1 - 2x^2$.

(b) $\sin(2 \text{ Arc cos } x) = 2x\sqrt{1 - x^2}$.

(c) $\sin(\text{Arc tan } x) = x/\sqrt{1 + x^2}$.

(d) $\sin(2 \text{ Arc sin } x) = 2x\sqrt{1 - x^2}$.

(e) $\cos(\text{Arc sin } t + \text{Arc cos } s) = s\sqrt{1 - t^2} - t\sqrt{1 - s^2}$.

(f) $\tan(x + \text{Arc tan } x) = \dfrac{x + \tan x}{1 - x \tan x}$.

14. Use the method of composites to compute f^{-1} for each of the functions below:

(a) $f(x) = \text{Arc cos } \sqrt{x^2 - 1}$, $x \in [1, 2]$. not defined for all $x \in [1, 2]$

(b) $f(x) = 1 + \sin(2x)$, $x \in [-\pi/4, \pi/4]$.

(c) $f(x) = \log_a(\sin x + 2)$, $x \in [-\pi/2, \pi/2]$.

(d) $f(x) = \text{Arc tan } 2^x$.

15. Prove the following:

(a) Arc sin is a strictly increasing function.

(b) Arc cos is a strictly decreasing function.

(c) Arc tan is a strictly increasing function.

7

The Binomial Theorem

Before discussing the binomial theorem, we take up two very useful notational devices. Both notations will be helpful in our discussion of the binomial theorem.

7.1 The Σ-notation

Let n be a natural number and suppose that $a_1, a_2, a_3, \ldots, a_n$ are numbers. Then, we mean by the symbol $\sum_{i=1}^{n} a_i$ the number

$$a_1 + a_2 + a_3 + \cdots + a_n.$$

The Greek letter "Σ" is supposed to suggest "sum" and we read $\sum_{i=1}^{n} a_i$ as "the sum of a_i from $i = 1$ to $i = n$."

Example 7-1. If for each natural number i, $a_i = i$ we have

$$\begin{aligned}\sum_{i=1}^{n} a_i &= a_1 + a_2 + a_3 + \cdots + a_n \\ &= 1 + 2 + 3 + \cdots + n \\ &= (½)(n)(n + 1).\end{aligned}$$

Example 7-2. Suppose that for each natural number i we have $a_i = 1$. Then

$$\begin{aligned}\sum_{i=1}^{n} a_i = \sum_{i=1}^{n} 1 &= a_1 + a_2 + \cdots + a_n \\ &= 1 + 1 + \cdots + 1 \\ &= n.\end{aligned}$$

Example 7-3. If $P(x) = c_0 + c_1x + c_2x^2 + \cdots + c_mx^m$, $c_m \neq 0$, is a polynomial function, we may express P by using the Σ-notation as follows. Let $a_i = c_ix^i$ for each i. Then

$$\sum_{i=0}^{m} a_i = \sum_{i=0}^{m} c_ix^i = c_0x^0 + c_1x + c_2x^2 + \cdots + c_mx^m$$

or

$$P(x) = \sum_{i=0}^{m} c_ix^i.$$

Example 7-4. Let $a_k = (1 + k)$ for each positive integer k. Then

$$\begin{aligned}\sum_{k=1}^{n} a_k &= \sum_{k=1}^{n} (1 + k) \\ &= a_1 + a_2 + a_3 + \cdots + a_n \\ &= (1 + 1) + (1 + 2) + (1 + 3) + \cdots + (1 + n) \\ &= (1 + 1 + 1 + \cdots + 1) + (1 + 2 + 3 + \cdots + n) \\ &= n + (½)(n)(n + 1) \\ &= \sum_{k=1}^{n} 1 + \sum_{k=1}^{n} k.\end{aligned}$$

In the following theorem we list some of the properties of the Σ-notation.

Theorem 25. If n, m are natural numbers with $m < n$, and c, a_i, b_i are any real numbers, then

(a) $\sum_{i=1}^{n} ca_i = c\sum_{i=1}^{n} a_i.$

(b) $\sum_{i=1}^{n} (a_i + b_i) = \sum_{i=1}^{n} a_i + \sum_{i=1}^{n} b_i.$

(c) $\sum_{i=1}^{n} (a_i - a_{i-1}) = a_n - a_0.$

(d) $\sum_{i=m}^{n} a_i = \sum_{i=m+k}^{n+k} a_{i-k}.$

Proof:

(a) This will be proved by applying the mathematical induction principle to the statement

$$P(n)\colon \sum_{i=1}^{n} ca_i = c\sum_{i=1}^{n} a_i.$$

By the definition of Σ we have:

$$\sum_{i=1}^{1} ca_i = ca_1 \qquad \text{and} \qquad \sum_{i=1}^{1} a_i = a_1,$$

and so

$$\sum_{i=1}^{1} ca_i = c\sum_{i=1}^{1} a_i$$

which shows that $P(1)$ is true. Next, the statements $P(k)$ and $P(k + 1)$ are

$$P(k)\colon \sum_{i=1}^{k} ca_i = c\sum_{i=1}^{k} a_i$$

and

$$P(k + 1)\colon \sum_{i=1}^{k+1} ca_i = c\sum_{i=1}^{k+1} a_i.$$

Now, if $P(k)$ is true, we have

$$\begin{aligned}\sum_{i=1}^{k+1} ca_i &= \sum_{i=1}^{k} ca_i + ca_{k+1}\\ &= c\sum_{i=1}^{k} a_i + ca_{k+1}\end{aligned}$$

$$= c\left(\sum_{i=1}^{k} a_i + a_{k+1}\right)$$

$$= c\sum_{i=1}^{k+1} a_i.$$

Hence, if $P(k)$ is true, then $P(k+1)$ is true. We conclude that $P(n)$ is true for all natural numbers n.

(d) By definition of Σ, we have

$$\sum_{i=m}^{n} a_i = a_m + a_{m+1} + a_{m+2} + \cdots + a_n$$

and,

$$\sum_{i=n+k}^{n+k} a_{i-k} = a_{(m+k)-k} + a_{(m+k+1)-k} + \cdots + a_{(n+k)-k}$$

$$= a_m + a_{m+1} + a_{m+2} + \cdots + a_n.$$

The proofs of (b) and (c) will be left to the reader. (See Exercise 2.)

The reader will have noticed that the subscript i in Σa_i is not important in the sense that any other letter would serve just as well. For example,

$$\sum_{i=1}^{n} a_i = \sum_{r=1}^{n} a_r = \sum_{j=1}^{n} a_j = \sum_{x=1}^{n} a_x, \text{ etc.}$$

Example 7-5. Show that $\sum_{k=1}^{n} a_k - \sum_{k=1}^{n} b_k = \sum_{k=1}^{n} (a_k - b_k)$.

Solution. From (a) of Theorem 23 with $c = -1$,

$$-\sum_{k=1}^{n} b_k = -1 \cdot \sum_{k=1}^{n} b_k = \sum_{k=1}^{n} -1 \cdot b_k = \sum_{k=1}^{n} (-b_k).$$

Then using (b),

$$\sum_{k=1}^{n} a_k - \sum_{k=1}^{n} b_k = \sum_{k=1}^{n} a_k + \left(-\sum_{k=1}^{n} b_k\right)$$

$$= \sum_{k=1}^{n} a_k + \sum_{k=1}^{n} (-b_k)$$

$$= \sum_{k=1}^{n} [a_k + (-b_k)] \qquad \text{by (b)}$$

$$= \sum_{k=1}^{n} (a_k - b_k).$$

Example 7-6. The results of Theorem 25 may be used to successively develop formulas for

$$\sum_{i=1}^{n} i, \sum_{i=1}^{n} i^2, \sum_{i=1}^{n} i^3, \text{ etc.}$$

We already know that $\sum_{i=1}^{n} i = (½)(n)(n + 1)$. Take $a_i = i^3$ in part (c) of Theorem 25. This results in

$$\sum_{i=1}^{n} (a_i - a_{i-1}) = a_n - a_o = n^3 - 0^3 = n^3.$$

Now, using the Theorem, we have

$$n^3 = \sum_{i=1}^{n} (a_i - a_{i-1})$$

$$= \sum_{i=1}^{n} [i^3 - (i - 1)^3]$$

$$= \sum_{i=1}^{n} i^3 - \sum_{i=1}^{n} (i - 1)^3 \quad \text{(by Example 7-5)}$$

$$= \sum_{i=1}^{n} i^3 - \sum_{i=1}^{n} (i^3 - 3i^2 + 3i - 1)$$

$$= \sum_{i=1}^{n} i^3 - \left(\sum_{i=1}^{n} i^3 - \sum_{i=1}^{n} 3i^2 + \sum_{i=1}^{n} 3i - \sum_{i=1}^{n} 1\right) \quad \text{(by parts (a) and (b) of Theorem 25)}$$

$$= \sum_{i=1}^{n} i^3 - \sum_{i=1}^{n} i^3 + 3\sum_{i=1}^{n} i^2 - 3\sum_{i=1}^{n} i + \sum_{i=1}^{n} 1 \quad \text{(by part (a) of Theorem 25)}$$

$$= 3\sum_{i=1}^{n} i^2 - 3(½)(n)(n + 1) + n$$

Therefore,

$$3\sum_{i=1}^{n} i^2 = n^3 + \tfrac{3}{2}(n)(n + 1) - n$$

$$= n(n^2 + \tfrac{3}{2}n + ½)$$

$$= \frac{n}{2}(2n^2 + 3n + 1)$$

and

$$\sum_{i=1}^{n} i^2 = \frac{n}{6}(2n^2 + 3n + 1).$$

Exercises

1. Use the definition of Σ-notation to write the following in unabbreviated form.

   (a) $\sum_{t=1}^{5} 7t.$ (c) $\sum_{s=1}^{8} a^s.$

   (b) $\sum_{j=5}^{10} (j - ½).$ (d) $\sum_{n=1}^{4} 7.$

2. Prove parts (b) and (c) of Theorem 23.

3. Prove each of the following by mathematical induction.

   (a) If, for each i, $a_i \neq 0$, then $\sum_{i=1}^{n} |a_i| > 0.$

   (b) $\sum_{t=1}^{n} t^3 = \left(\sum_{t=1}^{n} t\right)^2.$

   (c) $\sum_{t=1}^{m-1} t^3 < \frac{m^4}{4} < \sum_{t=1}^{m} t^3.$

   (d) $\sum_{i=1}^{n} (a + id) = an + (½)dn(n + 1).$

4. Use induction to prove that $\sum_{i=1}^{n} at^{i-1} = a(1 - t^n)/(1 - t)$, where a, t are numbers and $t \neq 1$. Use this result to compute the following:

   (a) $\sum_{i=1}^{6} 2^{i-1}.$ (d) $\sum_{t=0}^{3} \frac{1}{3^t}.$

   (b) $\sum_{i=1}^{5} (½)2^i.$ (e) $\sum_{k=1}^{n-1} \frac{4}{5_k}.$

   (c) $\sum_{t=1}^{3} 8^{(t-1)/3}.$ (f) $\sum_{k=1}^{n-1} (½)5^k.$

5. In a manner similar to Example 7-6, derive a formula for

$$\Sigma i^3.$$

6. Prove that if n is a natural number and $a_1, a_2, a_3, \ldots, a_n$ are real numbers, then

$$\left|\sum_{i=1}^{n} a_i\right| \leq \sum_{i=1}^{n} |a_i|.$$

*7.2 Binomial Coefficients

Suppose that a motorist wishes to travel from town A to town C by passing through town B, and that there are two roads connecting A to B and three roads connecting B to C. In how many different ways may

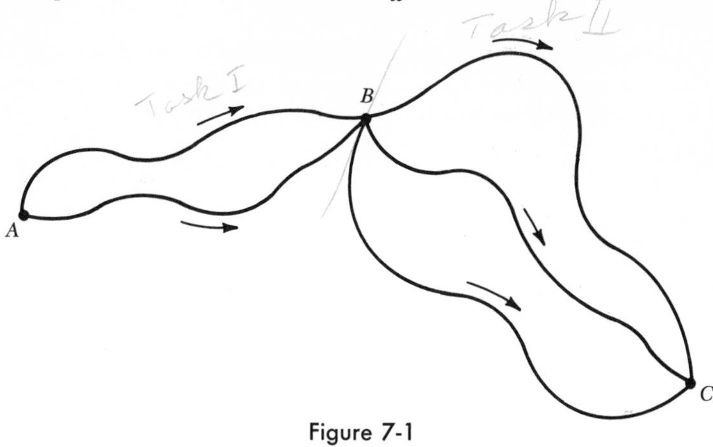

Figure 7-1

the motorist make the trip from A to C? (See Fig. 7-1.) If the motorist takes road 1 from A to B, then he may travel from B to C by any one of the three roads connecting these towns; i.e., he may make the trip from A to C in three ways by taking road 1. Similarly, he may make the trip in three ways if he takes road 2. We conclude that it is possible to make the trip in a total of six different ways.

This example illustrates the following general counting principle: *if a task T_1 can be performed in t_1 different ways and a task T_2 can be performed in t_2 ways, then the tasks T_1, T_2 can be performed successively in $t_1 \cdot t_2$ ways.*

The above counting principle is stated only for two tasks T_1, T_2. Suppose that we have n tasks $T_1, T_2, T_3, \ldots, T_n$ and T_1 can be performed in t_1 ways; T_2 can be performed in t_2 ways; etc. We claim that the sequence of tasks $T_1, T_2, T_3, \ldots, T_n$ can be performed in $t_1 \cdot t_2 \cdot t_3 \cdots t_n$ ways. To prove this we may apply mathematical induction to the statement:

$P(n)$: the sequence $T_1, T_2, T_3, \ldots, T_n$ can be performed in $t_1 \cdot t_2 \cdot t_3 \cdots t_n$ ways.

The statement $P(1)$ is simply "T_1 can be performed in t_1 ways." Since we are given this information, $P(1)$ is true. The sequence $T_1, T_2, T_3, \ldots, T_k, T_{k+1}$ of tasks may be performed by first performing $T_1, T_2, T_3, \ldots, T_k$ and then performing T_{k+1}. If $P(k)$ is true, the sequence $T_1, T_2, T_3, \ldots, T_k$ may be performed in $t_1 \cdot t_2 \cdot t_3 \cdots t_k$ ways; and by the counting principle, the sequence $T_1, T_2, T_3, \ldots, T_k, T_{k+1}$ may be performed in $(t_1 \cdot t_2 \cdot t_3 \cdots t_k) \cdot t_{k+1}$ many ways. But this says that $P(k + 1)$ is true if $P(k)$ is true. By mathematical induction we conclude that the following is true.

Theorem 26. Let n be a natural number and suppose that T_i is a task for each $i = 1, 2, 3, \ldots, n$ which can be performed in t_i ways. Then the sequence of tasks $T_1, T_2, T_3, \ldots, T_n$ can be performed in $t_1 \cdot t_2 \cdot t_3 \cdots t_n$ ways.

Example 7-7. How many 4-digit numbers are there which involve only the digits 1, 2, 3?

Solution. Any such number may be obtained by writing down four digits $a_1a_2a_3a_4$ where a_i is 1, 2 or 3 for each $i = 1, 2, 3, 4$. For example, 2132 is such a number. Each of the "tasks" of writing down a_i can be performed in three ways. Hence, there are $3 \cdot 3 \cdot 3 \cdot 3 = 81$ such numbers.

Example 7-8. If S is a set of n elements and T is a set of m elements, how many elements has the Cartesian product $S \times T$?

Solution. The set $S \times T$ consists of all ordered pairs (x, y) such that $x \in S$ and $y \in T$. Since the x may be chosen in n ways and the y in m ways, we may choose x, y in $n \cdot m$ ways. Hence, the set $S \times T$ contains nm elements.

Let S be a set having $n > 0$ number of elements, and suppose that $a_1, a_2, a_3, \ldots, a_n$ are the elements of S. If T is a subset of S, we may indicate that an element a_i is or is not a member of T by writing 1 or 0 respectively. For example, if $S = \{a_1, a_2, a_3, a_4\}$, then we could indicate that T is the set $\{a_2, a_4\}$ by writing

$$\begin{array}{cccc} a_1 & a_2 & a_3 & a_4 \\ | & | & | & | \\ 0 & 1 & 0 & 1 \end{array}$$

In this way, every subset of S corresponds uniquely to a sequence of n zeros and ones. In other words, every sequence of n zeros and ones represents a subset of S and conversely every subset of S has such a representation. The sequence $000 \cdots 0$ (all zeros) represents the null subset of S while $111 \cdots 1$ (all ones) represents S itself. The question of how many subsets of S there are may be answered by determining the number of sequences of n zeros and ones. Every such sequence may be obtained as

$$z_1z_2z_3 \cdots z_n$$

where each z_i is 0 or 1. Since there are 2 choices for each z_i, there are $2 \cdot 2 \cdots 2 = 2^n$ such sequences. Therefore, *a set S of n elements has 2^n subsets.*

If $S = \{a_1, a_2, a_3, \ldots, a_n\}$ is a set, and we impose an order on its elements—as we have done already for $n = 2$—we obtain an *ordered n-tuple* which is denoted by $(a_1, a_2, a_3, \ldots, a_n)$. If, for each i, j such that $i \neq j$, we have $a_i \neq a_j$, then the n-tuple $(a_1, a_2, a_3, \ldots, a_n)$ is called a *permutation* of n elements.

Example 7-9. How many ordered n-tuples can be formed from a set of m elements?

Solution. Since each a_i in an n-tuple $(a_1, a_2, a_3, \ldots, a_n)$ may be chosen in m different ways, there are $m \cdot m \cdot m \cdots m$ or m^n ordered n-tuples. From this it is evident that from a set of 10 elements we may construct 10^2 or 100 ordered pairs.

Example 7-10. How many permutations of n elements can be formed from a set of $m \geq n$ elements?

Solution. To construct a permutation $(a_1, a_2, a_3, \ldots, a_n)$, we must make certain that if $i \neq j$, then $a_i \neq a_j$. Since each a_i belongs to a set of m elements, we may reason as follows: a_1 may be chosen in m ways; a_2 may be chosen in $(m - 1)$ ways (since the choice for a_1 cannot be repeated); a_3 may be chosen in $(m - 2)$ ways (since the choice for a_1 and a_2 cannot be repeated); etc., finally, a_n may be chosen in $m - (n - 1)$ ways or in $m - n + 1$ ways. Therefore, there are $m \cdot (m - 1) \cdot (m - 2) \cdot (m - 3) \cdot \cdots \cdot (m - n + 1)$ permutations of n elements from a set of m elements. This number is sometimes denoted by $P(m, n)$; i.e., by definition,

$$P(m, n) = m(m - 1) \cdot (m - 2) \cdot (m - 3) \cdot \cdots \cdot (m - n + 1).$$

From Example 7-10, if $m = n$,

$$P(n, n) = n(n - 1)(n - 2)(n - 3) \cdots 2 \cdot 1.$$

The product $n(n - 1)(n - 2)(n - 3) \cdots 2 \cdot 1$ is usually denoted by $n!$ (Define $0! = 1$). Hence, $P(n, n) = n!$ and *the number of permutations of n elements is n!*

The symbol $\binom{n}{k}$, where n, k are non-negative integers and $k \leq n$, denotes the total number of subsets of k elements from a set of n elements. We just have seen that each set $\{b_1, b_2, b_3, \ldots, b_k\}$ of k elements gives rise to $k!$ permutations; and since each permutation of k elements from a set of n elements is obtained from a subset of k elements, we have

$$\binom{n}{k} \cdot k! = P(n, k) = n(n-1)(n-2)(n-3) \cdots (n-k+1)$$

or

$$\binom{n}{k} = \frac{n(n-1)(n-2)(n-3) \cdots (n-k+1)}{k!}.$$

Since

$$\begin{aligned} n! &= [n(n-1)(n-2) \cdots (n-k+1)][(n-k)(n-k-1) \cdots 2 \cdot 1] \\ &= [n(n-1)(n-2) \cdots (n-k+1)][(n-k)!], \end{aligned}$$

we may write

$$\binom{n}{k} = \frac{[n(n-1)(n-2) \cdots (n-k+1)][(n-k)!]}{k!(n-k)!} = \frac{n!}{k!(n-k)!}.$$

Example 7-11. A set of 10 elements contains $\binom{10}{5}$ 5-element subsets; i.e.,

$$\frac{10!}{5!\,5!} = \frac{6 \cdot 7 \cdot 8 \cdot 9 \cdot 10}{1 \cdot 2 \cdot 3 \cdot 4 \cdot 5} = 252.$$

Example 7-12. A set of 10 elements contains 10 one-element subsets. This agrees with the results just obtained since

$$\binom{10}{1} = \frac{10!}{1!\,(9!)} = 10.$$

Example 7-13. For a set of 4 elements there are $4! = 24$ permutations.

Example 7-14. From an ordinary pack of playing cards, how many bridge hands are possible?

Solution. An ordinary pack of playing cards contains 52 cards and a bridge hand consists of 13 cards. Therefore, the question is simply: "How many subsets are there of 13 elements from a set of 52?" Hence, the total number of bridge hands from a bridge deck of cards is

$$\binom{52}{13} = \frac{52!}{13!\,(52-13)!} = \frac{52!}{13!\,39!} = \frac{40 \cdot 41 \cdot 42 \cdots 52}{13!}.$$

This comes to 635,013,559,600.

Example 7-15. Suppose that license plates are to be made as follows:

$$A\text{-}B\text{-}CDEF$$

where A, C, D, E, F are digits $0, 1, 2, 3, 4, \cdots, 9$ except that $A \neq 0$, $C \neq 0$ and B can be any letter of the alphabet except "O". How many plates can be made subject to these restrictions?

Solution. A, C may each be chosen in nine ways; D, E, F each in 10 ways; and B in 25 ways. Thus, there are

$$9 \cdot 25 \cdot 9 \cdot 10 \cdot 10 \cdot 10 = 2{,}025{,}000$$

possible plates.

* Exercises

7. Compute each of the following:

(a) $P(3, 2)$. (d) $\binom{5}{4}$.

(b) $P(8, 5)$. (e) $P(m, n - 2)$.

(c) $\binom{5}{2}$. (f) $P(t - 1, t - 1)$.

8. How many 4-digit numbers are there which involve only 8, 5?

9. A student wishes to schedule his three classes at 8:30, 9:30 and 10:30. If there are three courses he can take at 8:30, two courses he can take at 9:30, and five courses he can take at 10:30, how many schedules are possible?

10. The student of Problem 9 discovers that the department of his major forbids taking Basketweaving 432 and Social Maladjustment 82.3, concurrently. One of these is taught at 8:30 and the other at 10:30. With this added restriction how many schedules are possible?

11. The chairman of a 10-man committee wishes to appoint a 4-man sub-committee. In how many ways can he do this?

12. The chairman of a 10-man committee wishes to appoint two 4-man sub-committees with himself as chairman of each. In how many ways can he appoint these two sub-committees if he is to be the only common member?

13. In a poker game, Sucker Charlie was dealt 2, 3 of hearts, jack of diamonds, 10 of spades and 6 of clubs. He discards the jack and 10 and asks for two cards in an attempt to fill the inside straight 2, 3, 6. In how many ways is it possible for him to do this? In how many ways if he saw his neighbor discard a 5?

14. Let $S = \{a, b, c, d\}$ be a 4-element set.

(a) Using the technique described above of associating a sequence of 0,s and 1's with subsets, write the appropriate sequence for each of the following subsets of S:

(i) $\{a\}$.	(ix) $\{b, d\}$.
(ii) $\{b\}$.	(x) $\{c, d\}$.
(iii) $\{c\}$.	(xi) $\{a, b, c\}$.
(iv) $\{d\}$.	(xii) $\{a, b, d\}$.
(v) $\{a, b\}$.	(xiii) $\{b, c, d\}$.
(vi) $\{a, c\}$.	(xiv) $\{a, c, d\}$.
(vii) $\{a, d\}$.	(xv) $\{a, b, c, d\}$.
(viii) $\{b, c\}$.	(xvi) $\varnothing$.

(b) Give the appropriate subset of S that goes with the following sequences:

(i) 0101.	(ix) 0100.
(ii) 0111.	(x) 0010.
(iii) 1010.	(xi) 1100.
(iv) 1110.	(xii) 0110.
(v) 0001.	(xiii) 0011.
(vi) 1001.	(xiv) 0000.
(vii) 1011.	(xv) 1111.
(viii) 1000.	(xvi) 1101.

15. List all the permutations of the set $\{a, b, c\}$.

16. In how many ways can 5 persons be seated about a round table? In how many ways could King Arthur seat himself and his knights, assuming that there were 12 knights.

7.3 The Binomial Theorem

If n, k are non-negative integers and $n \geq k$, the symbol $\binom{n}{k}$ denotes the number

$$\frac{n!}{k!\,(n-k)!}.$$

By definition $n! = n(n-1)(n-2)(n-3)\cdots 2\cdot 1$ if $n \geq 1$ and $0! = 1$. The numbers $\binom{n}{k}$ are called the *binomial coefficients.*

Example 7-16. $$\binom{6}{3} = \frac{6!}{3!\,(6-3)!} = \frac{6!}{3!\,3!} = \frac{1\cdot 2\cdot 3\cdot 4\cdot 5\cdot 6}{(1\cdot 2\cdot 3)(1\cdot 2\cdot 3)} = 20.$$

Example 7-17. If n is any non-negative integer, then

$$\binom{n}{0} = \frac{n!}{0!\,(n-0)!} = \frac{n!}{1 \cdot (n)!} = 1.$$

Also

$$\binom{n}{n} = \frac{n!}{n!\,(n-n)!} = 1.$$

Example 7-18. Prove that if m, k are integers such that $m \geq 1, k \geq 1$ and $m > k$, then

$$\binom{m+1}{k} = \binom{m}{k} + \binom{m}{k-1}.$$

Solution. Using the definition,

$$\begin{aligned}\binom{m}{k} + \binom{m}{k-1} &= \frac{m!}{k!\,(m-k)!} + \frac{m!}{(k-1)!\,(m-k+1)!} \\ &= \frac{(m!)(m-k+1)}{k!\,(m-k)!\,(m-k+1)} + \frac{k(m!)}{k(k-1)!\,(m-k+1)!} \\ &= \frac{(m!)(m-k+1)}{k!\,(m-k+1)!} + \frac{k(m!)}{k!\,(m-k+1)!} \\ &= \frac{(m!)(m-k+1) + k(m!)}{k!\,(m-k+1)!} \\ &= \frac{(m+1)!}{k!\,[(m+1)-k]!} = \binom{m+1}{k}.\end{aligned}$$

This result will be used below in the proof of the binomial theorem.

Theorem 27 (The Binomial Theorem). If a, b are numbers and n is an integer such that $n \geq 1$, then

$$(a+b)^n = \sum_{i=0}^{n} \binom{n}{i} a^{n-i} b^i.$$

Before proving the binomial theorem, a few illustrations will be given.

Example 7-19. $(a+b)^2 = a^2 + 2ab + b^2$ by the distributive axiom. Using the binomial theorem,

$$\begin{aligned}(a+b)^2 &= \sum_{i=0}^{2}\binom{2}{i}a^{2-i}b^i \\ &= \binom{2}{0}a^{2-0}b^0 + \binom{2}{1}a^{2-1}b^1 + \binom{2}{2}a^{2-2}b^2 \\ &= a^2 + 2ab + b^2.\end{aligned}$$

Example 7-20. Using the binomial theorem to compute $(x-y)^5$, we have

$$\begin{aligned}(x-y)^5 &= [x+(-y)]^5 \\ &= \sum_{i=0}^{5}\binom{5}{i}x^{5-i}(-y)^i \\ &= \binom{5}{0}x^5(-y)^0 + \binom{5}{1}x^4(-y)^1 + \binom{5}{2}x^3(-y)^2 + \binom{5}{3}x^2(-y)^3 \\ &\qquad + \binom{5}{4}x^1(-y)^4 + \binom{5}{5}x^0(-y)^5 \\ &= x^5 - 5x^4y + 10x^3y^2 + 5xy^4 - y^5.\end{aligned}$$

Proof (of Theorem 27): The proof is by induction. Apply the induction principle to the statement

$$P(n)\text{: } (a+b)^n = \sum_{i=0}^{n}\binom{n}{i}a^{n-i}b^i.$$

The statement $P(1)$ is

$$(a+b)^1 = \sum_{i=0}^{1}\binom{1}{i}a^{1-i}b^i$$

and this is true since $(a+b)^1 = a+b$ and

$$\begin{aligned}\sum_{i=0}^{1}\binom{1}{i}a^{1-i}b^i &= \binom{1}{0}a^{1-0}b^0 + \binom{1}{1}a^{1-1}b^1 \\ &= a+b.\end{aligned}$$

Now suppose that $P(k)$ is true; i.e., that

$$(a+b)^k = \sum_{i=0}^{k}\binom{k}{i}a^{k-i}b^i.$$

Then

$$\begin{aligned}(a+b)^{k+1} &= (a+b)(a+b)^k \\ &= (a+b)\sum_{i=0}^{k}\binom{k}{i}a^{k-i}b^i \text{ (if } P(k) \text{ is true)}\end{aligned}$$

$$= a\sum_{i=0}^{k}\binom{k}{i}a^{k-i}b^{i} + b\sum_{i=0}^{k}\binom{k}{i}a^{k-i}b^{i}$$

$$= \sum_{i=0}^{k}\binom{k}{i}a^{k-i+1}b^{i} + \sum_{i=0}^{k}\binom{k}{i}a^{k-i}b^{i+1}$$

$$= \sum_{i=0}^{k}\binom{k}{i}a^{k-i+1}b^{i} + \sum_{i=1}^{k+1}\binom{k}{i-1}a^{k-i+1}b^{i}$$

$$= \binom{k}{0}a^{k+1}b^{0} + \sum_{i=1}^{k}\binom{k}{i}a^{k-i+1}b^{i} + \sum_{i=1}^{k}\binom{k}{i-1}a^{k-i+1}b^{i} + \binom{k}{k}a^{0}b^{k+1}$$

$$= \binom{k+1}{0}a^{k+1}b^{0} + \sum_{i=1}^{k}\left[\binom{k}{i} + \binom{k}{i-1}\right]a^{k-i+1}b^{i} + \binom{k+1}{k+1}a^{0}b^{k+1}$$

$$= \binom{k+1}{0}a^{k+1}b^{0} + \sum_{i=1}^{k}\binom{k+1}{i}a^{(k+1)-i}b^{i} + \binom{k+1}{k+1}a^{0}b^{k+1}$$

$$= \sum_{i=0}^{k+1}\binom{k+1}{i}a^{(k+1)-i}b^{i}.$$

This completes the proof since

$$(a + \mathrm{b})^{k+1} = \sum_{i=0}^{k+1}\binom{k+1}{i}a^{k+1-i}b^{i}$$

is the statement $P(k + 1)$, and we have shown that this is true if $P(k)$ is true.

Example 7-21. In the binomial expansion of $(2x - 1)^{10}$, what is the fifth term?

Solution. By the theorem,

$$(2x - 1)^{10} = \sum_{i=0}^{10}\binom{10}{i}(2x)^{10-i}(-1)^{i}.$$

Notice that the number of a term $\binom{10}{i}\cdot(2x)^{10-i}(-1)^{i}$ can be determined by the i. Since i starts at 0, the term $\binom{10}{i} \cdot (2x)^{10-i}(-1)^i$ is the $(i+1)$ – st. Hence, the fifth term is

$$\binom{10}{4} \cdot (2x)^{10-4}(-1)^4 = 210(2x)^6 = 13{,}440x^6.$$

For an excellent discussion of the binomial theorem and related matters the reader may consult I. Niven, *Mathematics of Choice,* Random House.

Exercises

17. Use the binomial theorem to expand each of the following:

(a) $(a - b)^3$.
(b) $(-3x + 1)^4$.
(c) $(x - 1)^6$.
(d) $(x^{1/3} + y^{1/3})^6$.
(e) $(2/x + x/2)^5$.
(f) $(a^2 - bx + x^2)^3$.

18. Compute $(a + \sqrt{3})^4 + (a - \sqrt{3})^4$.

19. Compute $(\sqrt{2} + 1)^6 - (\sqrt{2} - 1)^6$.

20. Prove the following:

(a) $\binom{n}{k} = \binom{n}{n-k}$.

(b) $\binom{n}{k+1} = \frac{n-k}{k+1} \cdot \binom{n}{k}$.

(c) $\sum_{i=0}^{n} \binom{n}{i} = 2^n$.

(d) $\sum_{i=0}^{n} (-1)^i \binom{n}{i} = 0$.

21. (a) In the expansion of $(x - 1)^{15}$ give the 8th term.

(b) In the expansion of $\left(\frac{2}{c} + \frac{d}{2}\right)^{10}$ give the 5th term.

(c) Compute the coefficient of x^{18} in the expansion of $(x^2 + 5/x)^{15}$.

8

Analytic Geometry

In Chapter 3, the concepts of coordinate systems, the graphs of relations, etc., were discussed to some extent. These concepts are basic to a study of analytic geometry. The guiding principle behind analytic geometry is that of making questions of a geometric nature depend upon the real number system. This dependence is initiated in the case of *plane* analytic geometry with the correspondence between ordered pairs of real numbers and points of the plane. The reason that such a dependency is desirable is that it helps our understanding of geometry and aids in the solving of geometric problems.

8.1 Lines

We have seen (see Chapter 3) that the graph of a linear relation $\{(x, y) | Ax + By = C\}$ is a line and that every line is the graph of some linear relation. If $B \neq 0$, we may write

$$\{(x, y) | Ax + By = C\} = \{(x, y) | y = [(-A)/B]x + C/B\}.$$

Now let $m = (-A)/B$ and $b = C/B$. The number m is called the *slope* of the line L which is the graph of

$$\{(x, y) | y = mx + b\}.$$

If $B = 0$, the graph of $\{(x, y) | Ax = C\} = \{(x, y) | x = C/A\}$ is a vertical line; and, in this case, we say that *the line has no slope.* The significance of the slope m is that it measures the "steepness" of the line L with respect to the x-axis. (See Fig. 8-1.) In Fig. 8-1, φ is an angle that line L

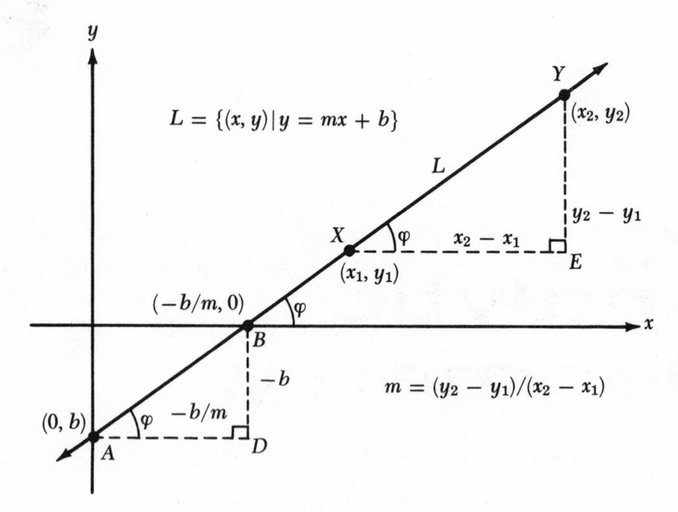

Figure 8-1

makes with the x-axis and $\tan \varphi$ can be computed by using triangle ABD. We have

$$\tan \varphi = (-b)/(-b/m) = m.$$

From this we may conclude:

$$0 \leq \varphi < \pi/2 \text{ if and only if } m > 0 \text{ (see Fig. 8-2(a))} \quad (1)$$
$$\pi/2 < \varphi < \pi \text{ if and only if } m < 0 \text{ (see Fig. 8-2(b)).} \quad (2)$$

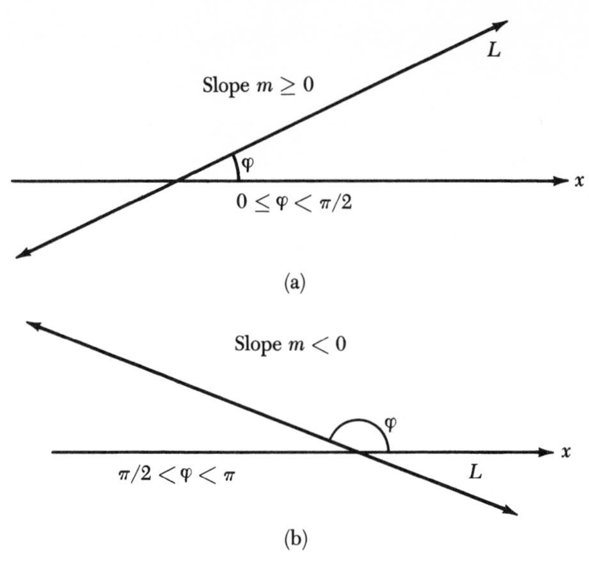

Figure 8-2

It should be noted that the line L of Fig. 8-1 used to obtain $\tan \varphi = m$ is a special case in that it does not pass through the origin. The result still holds for lines which pass through the origin (see Exercise 4 in this section).

As indicated in Fig. 8-1, the slope m of L may be computed by using *any* pair of points on L. For if $X(x_1, y_1)$ and $Y(x_2, y_2)$ are two points of L, then, triangle XYE is similar to triangle ABD so that

$$\frac{x_2 - y_1}{x_2 - x_1} = (-b)/((-b)/m) = m.$$

The reader should check to see that this result still holds for points X, Y of L other than those in quadrant I.

The reader will recall that there is one and only one line on two points P, Q. Given the points P, $Q (P \neq Q)$, is it possible to determine a linear relation whose graph is the line on P, Q? To answer this, suppose that (a, b), (c, d) are the coordinates of P, Q respectively. The distances that P, Q are respectively from the y-axis is given by $|a|$, $|c|$. Hence, if $a = c$, P, Q are each $|a|$ units from the y-axis; so that the line on P, Q is parallel to the y-axis. Therefore, a linear relation having this line as its graph is

$$\{(x, y) \mid x = a\} = \{(a, y) \mid y \text{ is a real number}\}.$$

If $a \neq c$, we may use the coordinates of P, Q as above to compute the slope of the line on P, Q:

$$\frac{d - b}{c - a} = m.$$

Now if the relation $L = \{(x, y) \mid y = mx + p\}$ is to have the line on P, Q as its graph, we must have

$$(a, b) \in L \qquad \text{and} \qquad (c, d) \in L.$$

Hence,

$$b = ma + p \qquad \text{and} \qquad d = mc + p.$$

Thus, $p = b - ma = d - mc$. This shows that we may use the two points to compute the slope m (if the line is not vertical) and either of the two points to compute p. We then know that the relation

$$L = \{(x, y) \mid y = mx + p\},$$

where m, p are given as above, has a graph which is the line on P, Q; for the graph of *every* linear relation is a line and in particular the graph of L is a line—the unique line on P, Q.

Example 8-1. What is a linear relation whose graph is the line on the points $(1, 0)$, $(½, 3)$?

Solution. The slope is

$$\frac{3 - 0}{½ - 1} = \frac{3}{-½} = -6.$$

The relation is then $\{(x, y) \mid y = -6x + p\}$ where p is to be determined. Since $(1, 0) \in \{(x, y) \mid y = -6x + p\}$, we have

$$0 = -6 \cdot 1 + p$$

or $p = 6$. The desired relation is thus

$$\{(x, y) \mid y = -6x + 6\}.$$

Example 8-2. What is the slope and y-intercept of the graph of the relation

$$\{(x, y) \mid 3x - 7y = 2\}?$$

Solution. To determine the slope and y-intercept, we express the "connection" between x and y in the form $y = mx + p$:

$$\{(x, y) \mid 3x - 7y = 2\} = \{(x, y) \mid y = (3/7)x - 2/7\}.$$

Therefore, the slope is $3/7$ and the y-intercept is $(0, -2/7)$.

If two lines k_1 and k_2 are parallel, then they make equal angles with the x-axis. If each of k_1, k_2 is perpendicular to the x-axis, then they are each graphs of linear relations of the form

$$\{(x, y) \mid x = a\}.$$

If k_1, k_2 are not vertical lines, they have equal slopes. Thus k_1, k_2 are graphs of linear relations as follows:

$$k_1: \{(x, y) \mid y = mx + p_1\}$$
$$k_2: \{(x, y) \mid y = mx + p_2\}.$$

(See Fig. 8-3.)

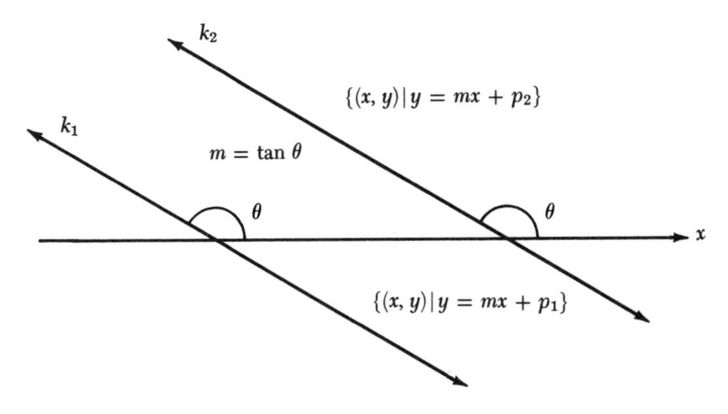

Figure 8-3

Conversely, two relations

$$\{(x, y) \mid y = mx + p_1\} \quad \text{and} \quad \{(x, y) \mid y = mx + p_2\}$$

have graphs which are parallel lines.

From this point we shall not always clearly distinguish between a relation and its graph.

Let k_1, k_2 be two lines which are perpendicular to each other and neither is parallel to the x-axis. (See Fig. 8-4.) If m_1 is the slope of k_1 and m_2 is the slope of k_2, we have $\tan \varphi_1 = m_1$ and $\tan \varphi_2 = m_2$ where φ_1, φ_2 are the angles as shown in Fig. 8-4. Since φ_1 is an exterior angle of the triangle in Fig. 8-4, it is the sum of the opposite interior angles: $\varphi_1 = \pi/2 + \varphi_2$ or $\varphi_1 - \varphi_2 = \pi/2$. Then

$$\begin{aligned} 0 = \cos(\pi/2) &= \cos(\varphi_1 - \varphi_2) \\ &= \cos \varphi_1 \cos \varphi_2 + \sin \varphi_1 \sin \varphi_2. \end{aligned}$$

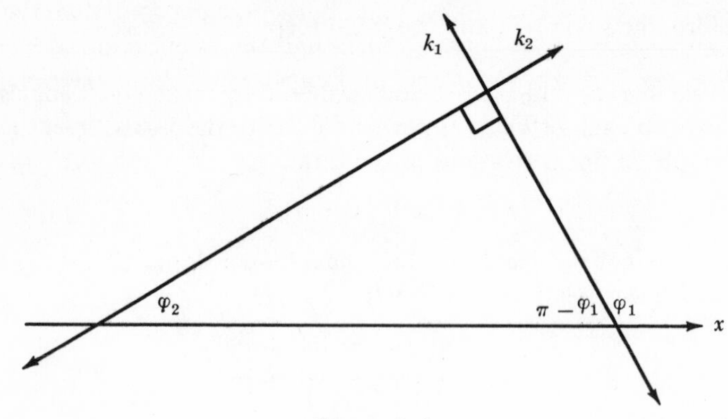

Figure 8-4

Hence,

$$\sin \varphi_1 \sin \varphi_2 = -\cos \varphi_1 \cos \varphi_2 \tag{3}$$

and since $\cos \varphi_1 \cos \varphi_2 \neq 0$ (why?), we may divide in Eq. (3) and obtain

$$\frac{\sin \varphi_1 \sin \varphi_2}{\cos \varphi_1 \cos \varphi_2} = -1.$$

But from this last equation,

$$\tan \varphi_1 \cdot \tan \varphi_2 = -1 \qquad \text{or} \qquad m_1 m_2 = -1.$$

Conversely, if k_1, k_2 are not perpendicular, then $m_1 m_2 \neq -1$.

If one of the two lines k_1, k_2 is parallel to the x-axis, it makes an angle 0 with the x-axis so that its slope, tan 0, is 0. Then if the other line is perpendicular to the first, it is vertical and has no slope. To summarize: Two lines k_1, k_2 are perpendicular if and only if

(a) one line has 0 slope and the other no slope, or
(b) the product of their slopes is -1.

Example 8-3. The lines $\{(x, y) \mid 2x + y = \frac{1}{2}\}$, $\{(x, y) \mid 2x + y = 10\}$ are parallel since each has slope -2. The lines $\{(x, y) \mid y = 8x\}$, $\{(x, y) \mid y = -\frac{1}{8}x - 7\}$ are perpendicular since the slope of the first is 8 and that of the second is $-\frac{1}{8}$: $8(-\frac{1}{8}) = -1$.

Example 8-4. Let (a, b) be a point not on the line

$$k = \{(x, y) \mid y = mx + q\}.$$

Develop a formula for the perpendicular distance from (a, b) to k, if $m \neq 0$.

Solution. If j is the line on (a, b) and perpendicular to k, then the distance in question is that between (a, b) and the intersection of k and j. (See Fig. 8-5.) Then the slope of j must be $-1/m$. Hence, $j =$

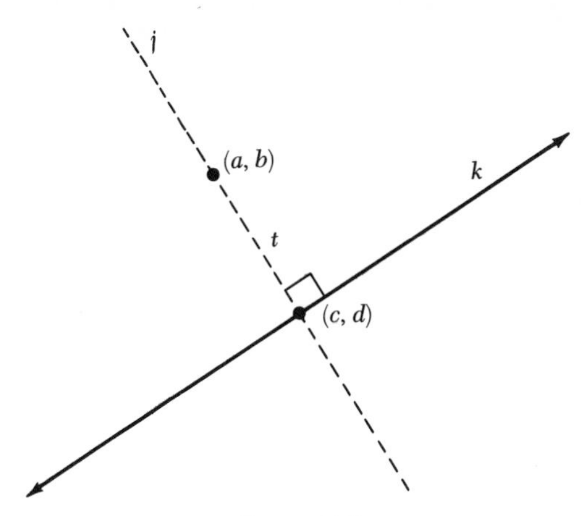

Figure 8-5

$\{(x, y) | y = (-1/m)x + p\}$ for some number p. If (c, d) is the intersection point of j, k, we have

$$(c, d) \in j \qquad \text{and} \qquad (c, d) \in k.$$

Hence,

$$d = mc + q \qquad \text{and} \qquad d = (-1/m)c + p.$$

Also, we must have $b = (-1/m)a + p$ since $(a, b) \in j$. Then $p = b + a/m$ and substituting this for p in the equation $d = (-1/m)c + p$:

$$\begin{aligned} d &= (-1/m)c + p \\ &= (-1/m)c + b + a/m = (1/m)(a - c) + b. \end{aligned} \tag{4}$$

Then from $d = mc + q$ and Eq. (4)

$$mc + q = (1/m)(a - c) + b$$

and multiplying by m gives

$$m^2c + mq = a - c + bm.$$

From this equation we may solve for c:

$$c = \frac{a + m(b - q)}{m^2 + 1}. \tag{5}$$

If t is the distance between (a, b) and (c, d), the distance formula may be applied:

$$t^2 = (a - c)^2 + (b - d)^2$$

$$t^2 = (a - c)^2 + [1/m(a - c)]^2 \qquad \text{from Eq. (4)}$$

$$= (a - c)^2[1 + (1/m)^2]$$

$$= \left(\frac{m(b - q) - am^2}{m^2 + 1}\right)^2 \cdot \frac{m^2 + 1}{m^2} \qquad \text{from Eq. (5)}$$

$$= \frac{(b - q - am)^2}{m^2 + 1} = \frac{(am + q - b)^2}{m^2 + 1}.$$

Therefore,

$$t = \frac{|am + q - b|}{\sqrt{m^2 + 1}}.$$

This formula gives the distance between the point (a, b) and the line $\{(x, y)\,|\,y = mx + q\}$ in terms of the numbers a, b, m, q.

Example 8-5. What is the distance between the point (1, 1) and the line

$$\{(x, y)\,|\,y = 7x - 1\}?$$

Solution. From Example 8-4 the distance t is

$$t = \frac{|1 \cdot 7 + (-1) - 1|}{\sqrt{7^2 + 1}} = \frac{|7 - 2|}{\sqrt{50}} = \frac{5}{5\sqrt{2}} = \frac{1}{\sqrt{2}}.$$

Exercises

1. In each of the following, write a linear relation whose graph is the line indicated:

(a) the line on the points $(0, 0)$ and $(4, -5)$.
(b) the line on the points $(0, -5)$ and $(98, -5)$.
(c) the line on the points $(\frac{1}{2}, 4)$ and $(\frac{1}{2}, \pi)$.
(d) the line on the points $(1, \sqrt{2})$ and $(\frac{2}{5}, -1)$.
(e) the line with slope 1 and on the point $(0, 10)$.
(f) the line with slope $\frac{1}{2}$ and on the point $(1, 0)$.
(g) the line with slope -1 and on the point $(0, 0)$.
(h) the line with slope -2 and on the point $(-6, -1)$.
(i) the line with slope 0 and on the point $(-5, \pi)$.
(j) the line with no slope and on the point $(4, 1)$.

2. Graph each of the lines of Exercise 1.

3. In each of the following, write a linear relation whose graph is tangent to the given circle at the point indicated:
(a) $\{(x, y) | x^2 + y^2 = 1\}$; $(-1, 0)$.
(b) $\{(x, y) | x^2 + y^2 = 1\}$; $(0, 1)$.
(c) $\{(x, y) | x^2 + y^2 = 1\}$; $(\frac{1}{2}\sqrt{2}, \frac{1}{2}\sqrt{2})$.
(d) $\{(x, y) | (x - 1)^2 + (y + 1)^2 = 1\}$; $(2, -1)$.
(e) $\{(x, y) | (x - 1)^2 + (y + 1)^2 = 1\}$; $(1, 0)$.
(f) $\{(x, y) | (x - 1)^2 + (y + 1)^2 = 1\}$; $\left(\frac{1}{2}, \frac{\sqrt{3}}{\cdot 2} - 1\right)$.

4. In Section 8-1 the formula

$$(y_2 - y_1)/(x_2 - x_1) = m$$

was derived. This gives the slope m of a line in terms of two points $X(x_1, y_1)$, $Y(x_2, y_2)$ on the line. The formula was shown to hold only in one case. List the other possibilities and show that the formula holds in each case.

5. If $A(a, b)$ and $B(c, d)$ are points such that $a \neq c$, show that the line on A, B is the graph of $\{(x, y) | y - b = m(x - a)\}$ where $m = (d - b)/(c - a)$. This is called the *point-slope* form of the line.

6. Let $A(a, b)$, $B(c, d)$ be two distinct points. Show that the relation $\{(x, y) |$ the distance from (x, y) to A is the same as the distance from (x, y) to $B\}$ is a linear relation. [*Hint:* use the distance formula.]

7. Show that the point $M\left(\frac{a + b}{2}, \frac{c + d}{2}\right)$ is the midpoint of the line segment connecting the points $A(a, c)$, $B(b, d)$.

8. Show that the diagonals of a parallelogram bisect each other.

9. In each of the following, write a linear relation having a graph parallel to the given line and passing through the given point.
(a) $\{(x, y) | 2x - (\frac{1}{2})y = 1\}$; $(1, 1)$.
(b) $\{(x, y) | 7 - 5y + x = 0\}$; $(6, 2)$.

10. In each of the following, write a linear relation having a graph perpendicular to the given line and passing through the given point.
(a) $\{(x, y) | x - y = 0\}$; $(-1, -1)$.
(b) $\{(x, y) | y + 1 = (\frac{1}{3})x\}$; $(2, \frac{5}{4})$.

11. Show that the graphs of the linear relations

$$\{(x, y) | Ax + By = C\} \qquad \text{and} \qquad \{(x, y) | Dx + Ey = F\}$$

intersect in exactly one point if and only if $AE - BD \neq 0$.

12. In each of the following, compute the distance between the given line and point:
(a) $\{(x, y) \mid x + y - 1 = 0\}$; $(2, 5)$.
(b) $\{(x, y) \mid 2x - 8 = y\}$; $(0, 0)$.

13. Show that a line k which intersects the x-axis at a distance $|a|$ from the origin and intersects the y-axis at a distance $|b|$ from origin is the graph of the relation $\{(x, y) \mid (x/a) + (y/b) = 1\}$.

8.2 The Parabola

It is convenient to denote the distance between two points X, Y by $d(X, Y)$; also denote by $d(X, k)$ the distance (perpendicular) between the point X and the line k.

DEFINITION. Let F be a point and let k be a line such that F is not on k. Then a relation

$$\{(x, y) \mid d((x, y), F) = d((x, y), k)\}$$

is called a *parabola*. The point F is called the *focus* of the parabola and k is called the *directrix*.

In Fig. 8-6 the definition is illustrated.

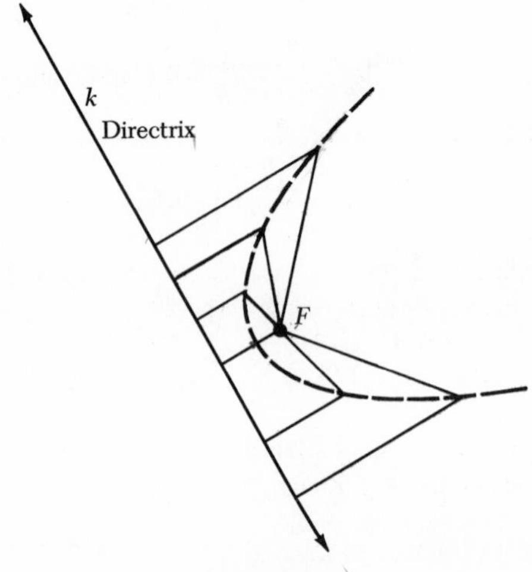

Figure 8-6

For the present, let us consider the two following cases: (1) the focus F is on the x-axis and the directrix k is perpendicular to the x-axis; and (2) the focus F is on the y-axis and the directrix k is perpendicular to the y-axis.

Consider case (1) with $(c, 0)$ the coordinates of F and $k = \{(x, y) \mid x = -c\}$. (See Fig. 8-7.) The expressions in the definition are

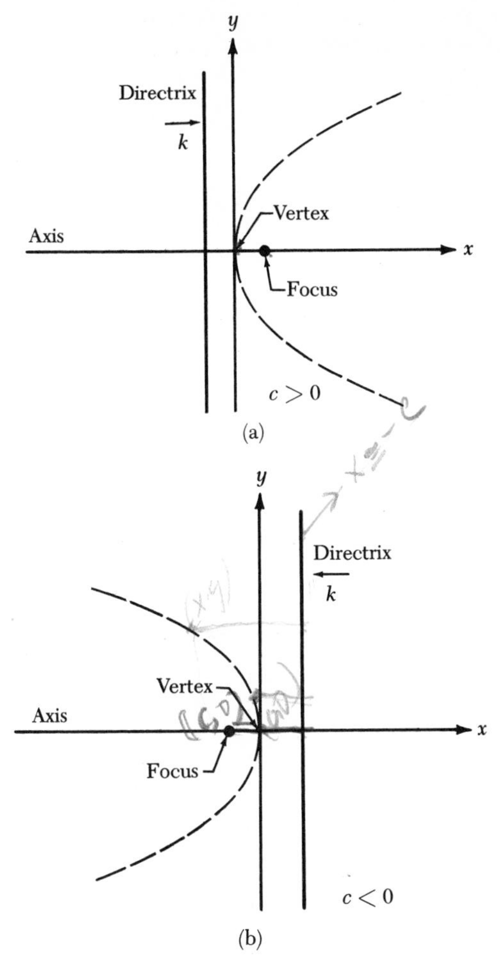

Figure 8-7

$$d((x, y), (c, 0)) = \sqrt{(x - c)^2 + y^2} \qquad \text{and} \qquad d((x, y), k) = |x + c|.$$

These are equal if and only if

$$(x - c)^2 + y^2 = (x + c)^2,$$

and hence if and only if

$$y^2 = 4cx.$$

The parabola in this case is

$$\{(x, y) \mid y^2 = 4cx\}.$$

The graphs of these parabolas are indicated in Fig. 8-7. Note that the graph is nowhere to the left of the y-axis if $c > 0$ and nowhere to the right of the y-axis if $c < 0$.

If F is taken to be $(0, c)$ and k is $\{(x, y) \mid y = -c\}$, the parabola is

$$\{(x, y) \mid x^2 = 4cy\}.$$

These are illustrated in Fig. 8-8.

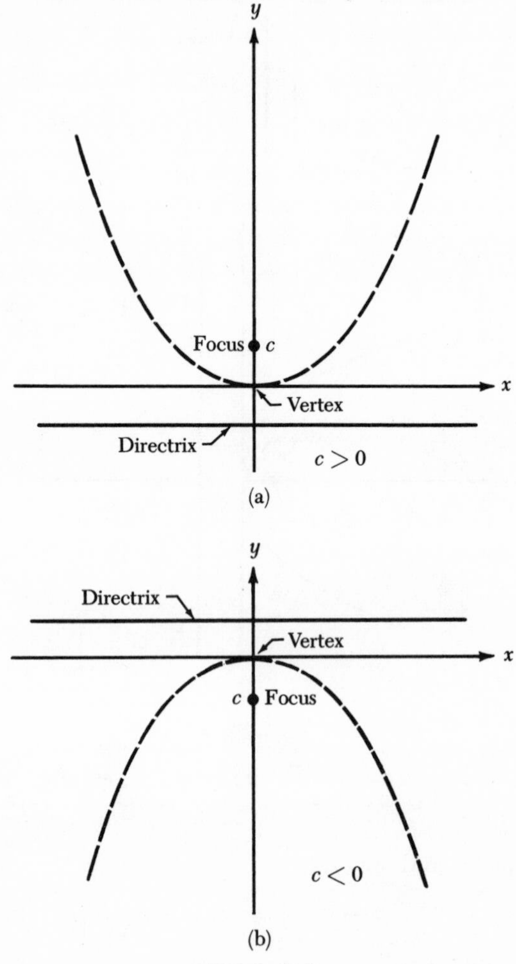

Figure 8-8

Example 8-6. The parabola with focus $(1, 0)$ and directrix $\{(-1, y)\}$ is $\{(x, y) \mid y^2 = 4x\}$. Here $c = 1$.

Example 8-7. The parabola with focus $(0, \frac{1}{4})$ and directrix $\{(x, -\frac{1}{4})\}$ is $\{(x, y) \mid y = x^2\}$. This, of course, is the function $f(x) = x^2$.

The line on the focus of a parabola which is perpendicular to the directrix is called the *axis* of the parabola; the point on the axis and midway between the focus and directrix is called the *vertex* of the parabola. Note that the vertex is a point of the parabola. (See Fig. 8-7 and 8-8.)

Example 8-8. Describe the parabola $\{(x, y) \mid y = 2x^2\}$.

Solution. We may write the equation $y = 2x^2$ as $x^2 = 4(\frac{1}{8})y$. Then,

$$\{(x, y) \mid y = 2x^2\} = \{(x, y) \mid x^2 = 4(\tfrac{1}{8})y\}.$$

Now this is seen to be the parabola with focus $(0, \frac{1}{8})$, directrix $\{(x, -\frac{1}{8})\}$; the axis of the parabola is the y-axis and vertex is the origin.

Consider now a parabola with focus F at the point $(a + c, b)$ and directrix k: $\{(a - c, y)\}$. We will show that such a parabola is a relation as follows:

$$\{(x, y) \mid (y - b)^2 = 4c(x - a)\}.$$

We have

$$d((x, y), (a + c, b)) = \sqrt{[x - (a + c)]^2 + (y - b)^2}$$

and

$$d((x, y), k) = |x - (a - c)|.$$

These numbers are equal if and only if

$$[x - (a + c)]^2 + (y - b)^2 = [x - (a - c)]^2$$

or if and only if

$$(y - b)^2 = 4c(x - a).$$

By definition the axis of the parabola in this case is the line $\{(x, b)\}$ and the vertex is the midpoint of the segment connecting $(a - c, b)$ and $(a + c, b)$; i.e., (a, b) is the vertex. (See Fig. 8-9.)

In a similar fashion if we consider a parabola with focus at $(a, b + c)$ and directrix $\{(x, b - c)\}$ we obtain the description

$$\{(x, y) \mid (x - a)^2 = 4c(y - b)\}.$$

In this case the parabola has (a, b) as vertex; the axis is $\{(a, y)\}$.

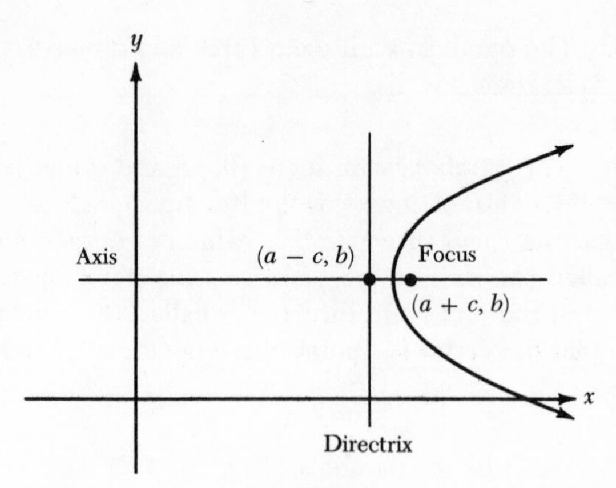

Figure 8-9

Example 8-9. Describe the relation $\{(x, y) | 4y - x^2 - 4x = 0\}$.

Solution. We write the equation $4y - x^2 - 4x = 0$ as

$$\begin{aligned} 4y &= x^2 + 4x \\ &= (x^2 + 4x + 4) - 4 \\ &= (x + 2)^2 - 4. \end{aligned}$$

Then,

$$\{(x, y) | 4y - x^2 - 4x = 0\} = \{(x, y) | (x + 2)^2 = 4(y + 1)\}.$$

The relation is now easy to recognize as a parabola with vertex at $(-2, -1)$; focus at $(-2, -1 + 1) = (-2, 0)$ (since $c = 1$); directrix: $\{(x, -2)\}$. (See Fig. 8-10 for the graph of this relation.)

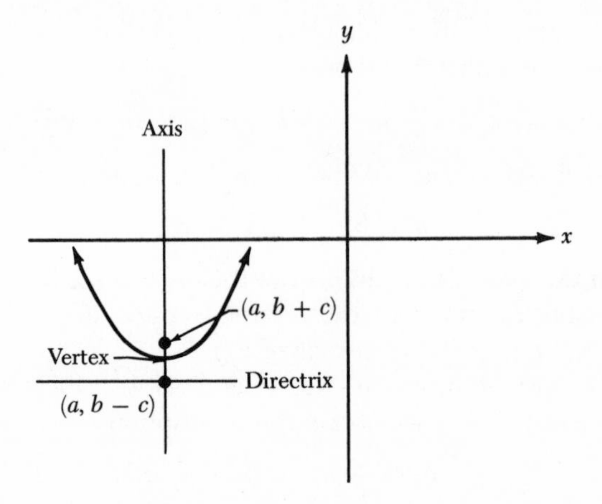

Figure 8-10

Exercises

Each of the following relations is a parabola. In each case give the vertex, directrix, axis, focus and sketch its graph.

14. $\{(x, y) \mid y^2 = 2x\}$.

15. $\{(x, y) \mid x^2 = 16y\}$.

16. $\{(x, y) \mid x^2 = 4(y - 1)\}$.

17. $\{(x, y) \mid (x - 1)^2 - 8(y + 2) = 0\}$.

18. $\{(x, y) \mid y = 7x^2 + 2\}$.

19. $\{(x, y) \mid x + 8 - y^2 + 2y = 0\}$.

In each of the Exercises 20–23, write a description of the parabola and sketch its graph.

20. Focus: $(0, 1)$; directrix: $\{x, -1\}$.

21. Focus: $(-2, 0)$; directrix: $\{(2, y)\}$.

22. Focus: $(2, 0)$; directrix $\{(0, y)\}$.

23. Focus: $(-1, 8)$; directrix: $\{(x, 2)\}$.

24. Use the definition of parabola to write an analytic description of a parabola whose focus is $(0, 0)$ and directrix is $\{(x, y) \mid y = x + 1\}$.

8.3 The Ellipse

The next relation that will be studied in some detail is called the ellipse.

DEFINITION. Let F_1, F_2 be points and let a be a positive number. Then the relation

$$E = \{(x, y) \mid d((x, y), F_1) + d((x, y), F_2) = 2a\}$$

is called an *ellipse*. The points F_1, F_2 are called the *foci* of the ellipse.

It should be noted that in the definition the important aspect is that the sum $d((x, y), F_1) + d((x, y), F_2)$ is constant; it is only for convenience that we take this constant to be $2a$.

If we take $F_1 = (c, 0)$ and $F_2 = (-c, 0)$ for some number c such that $0 \leq c < a$, then the equation

$$d((x, y), F_1) + d((x, y), F_2) = 2a$$

takes the form

$$\sqrt{(x - c)^2 + y^2} + \sqrt{(x + c)^2 + y^2} = 2a.$$

From this last equation we obtain the following sequence of equations:

$$\begin{aligned}
\sqrt{(x - c)^2 + y^2} &= 2a - \sqrt{(x + c)^2 + y^2} \\
(x - c)^2 + y^2 &= 4a^2 - 4a\sqrt{(x + c)^2 + y^2} + (x + c)^2 + y^2 \\
a\sqrt{(x + c)^2 + y^2} &= cx + a^2 \\
a^2(x + c)^2 + a^2y^2 &= c^2x^2 + 2cxa^2 + a^4 \\
a^2x^2 + a^2c^2 + a^2y^2 &= c^2x^2 + a^4 \\
(a^2 - c^2)x^2 + a^2y^2 &= a^4 - a^2c^2 = a^2(a^2 - c^2) \\
\frac{x^2}{a^2} + \frac{y^2}{a^2 - c^2} &= 1.
\end{aligned}$$

This shows that in this case

$$E \subseteq \{(x, y) \,|\, x^2/a^2 + y^2/(a^2 - c^2) = 1\} = S.$$

Conversely, if $(x, y) \in S$, then

$$\frac{x^2}{a^2} + \frac{y^2}{a^2 - c^2} = 1$$

and the steps to obtain the above equations may be reversed to show that $(x, y) \in E$, and hence that $S \subseteq E$. In this case, then, the ellipse is the set

$$\{(x, y) \,|\, x^2/a^2 + y^2/(a^2 - c^2) = 1\}.$$

See Fig. 8-11 for the graph of this ellipse. It will be clear from Fig. 8-11 why the restriction $0 \leq c < a$ is made; for if $a \leq c$ we have

$$d((x, y), F_1) + d((x, y), F_2) = 2a \leq 2c$$

which indicates that the sum of the lengths of two sides of the triangle F_1F_2X is at most equal to the length of the third. Therefore, without the restriction $c < a$ we would have at most one point on the ellipse.

Since $0 \leq c < a$, it follows that $c^2 < a^2$ and $0 < a^2 - c^2$. Now let $b = \sqrt{a^2 - c^2}$. The ellipse above may be expressed as

$$\{(x, y) \,|\, x^2/a^2 + y^2/b^2 = 1\}.$$

This is said to be the *standard form* of the ellipse.

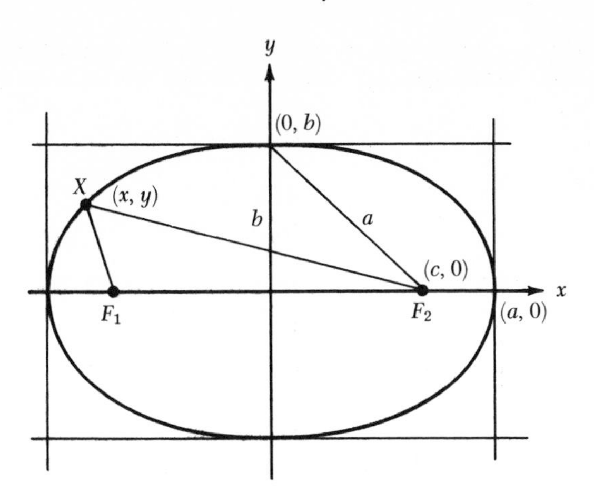

Figure 8-11

The points $(a, 0)$, $(-a, 0)$, $(0, b)$, $(0, -b)$ are on the ellipse; the line containing the two foci F_1, F_2 is called the *major axis* and its midpoint is called the *center* of the ellipse. The line perpendicular to the major axis at the center of the ellipse is the *minor axis.*

For the case just discussed with $F_1 = (c, 0)$, $F_2 = (-c, 0)$, the points of the ellipse $(a, 0)$, $(-a, 0)$ are on the major axis; the points of the ellipse $(0, b)$, $(0, -b)$ are on the minor axis. If the foci are taken to be $F_1 = (0, c)$, $F_2 = (0, -c)$, then the role's of the x-axis and y-axis are reversed: the points $(0, a)$, $(0, -a)$ are on the major axis and the points $(b, 0)$, $(-b, 0)$ are on the minor axis. In this case the ellipse is described by

$$\{(x, y) \mid x^2/b^2 + y^2/a^2 = 1\}.$$

Notice that in these two cases the major axis of the ellipse coincides with either the x-axis or the y-axis and that this is determined by whether x^2 or y^2 has the larger coefficient.

If a point (x, y) is on the ellipse $\{(x, y) \mid x^2/a^2 + y^2/b^2 = 1\}$, we have that

$$\frac{x^2}{a^2} + \frac{y^2}{b^2} = 1$$

and hence,

$$x^2/a^2 \leq 1 \quad \text{and} \quad y^2/b^2 \leq 1.$$

Therefore,

$$x^2 \leq a^2 \quad \text{and} \quad y^2 \leq b^2.$$

Thus,

$$-a \leq x \leq a \quad \text{and} \quad -b \leq y \leq b.$$

All the points (x, y) satisfying these two conditions must lie within the rectangle of Fig. 8-12. The graph of the ellipse will be contained within this rectangle.

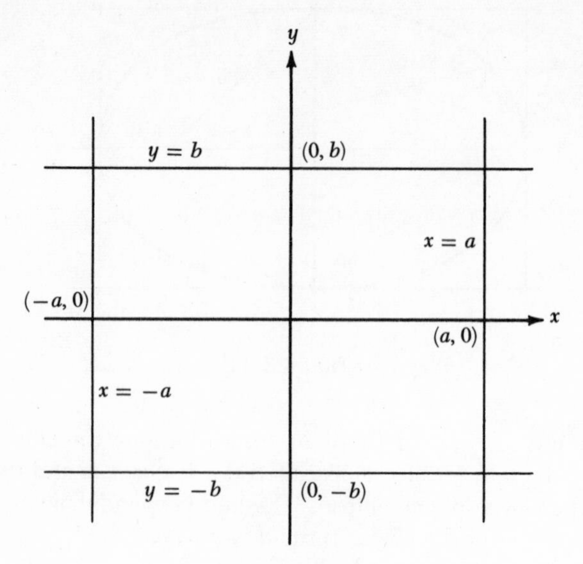

Figure 8-12

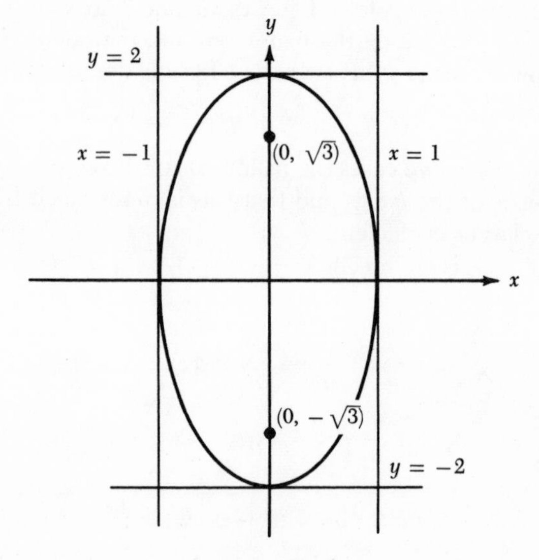

Figure 8-13

Example 8-10. Graph the ellipse $\{(x, y) | x^2 + y^2/4 = 1\}$.

Solution. In this case $b^2 = 1$, $a^2 = 4$; the minor axis is on the x-axis and the major axis is on the y-axis. The graph lies within the rectangle defined by $-1 \leq x \leq 1$, $-2 \leq y \leq 2$. The foci may be determined by solving the equation $b^2 = a^2 - c^2$ or $1 = 4 - c^2$. Then $c = \sqrt{3}$. (See Fig. 8-13.)

Example 8-11. Graph the ellipse $\{(x, y) | 2x^2 + 8y^2 - 16 = 0\}$.

Solution. First, express the ellipse in standard form:

$$\{(x, y) | 2x^2 + 8y^2 - 16 = 0\} = \{(x, y) | x^2/8 + y^2/2 = 1\}.$$

Then $a^2 = 8$, $b^2 = 2$. The major axis is the x-axis, the minor axis is the y-axis. Since $b^2 = a^2 - b^2$, $c = \sqrt{a^2 - b^2} = \sqrt{6}$ and the foci are $(\sqrt{6}, 0)$, $(-\sqrt{6}, 0)$. The graph lies within the rectangle defined by $-2\sqrt{2} \leq x \leq 2\sqrt{2}$, $-\sqrt{2} \leq y \leq \sqrt{2}$. (See Fig. 8-14.)

The ellipse $\{(x, y) | x^2/a^2 + y^2/b^2 = 1\}$ is a circle if $a = b$ with center at (0, 0) and radius a. Since the ellipse lies within the rectangle $-a \leq x \leq a$, $-b \leq y \leq b$, it is evident that the smaller b is, when

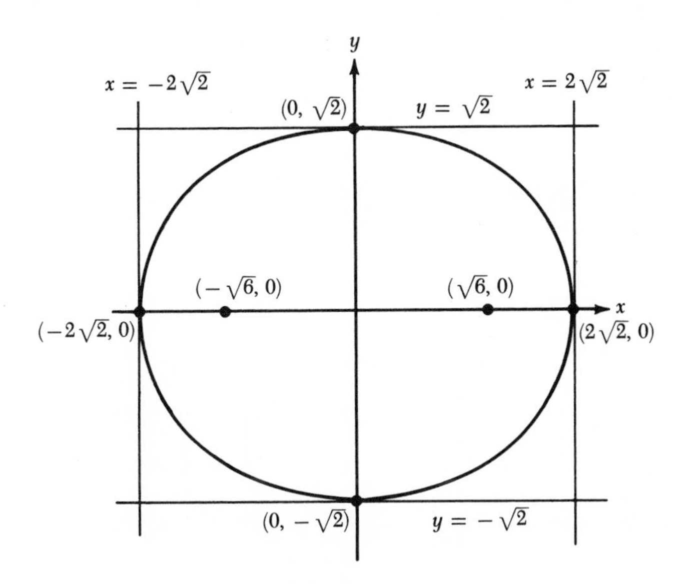

Figure 8-14

compared with a, the more the ellipse deviates from a circle. (See Fig. 8-15.) A very convenient way of measuring an ellipse's deviation from a circle is with the number $\sqrt{1 - (b/a)^2}$, which is called the *eccentricity*

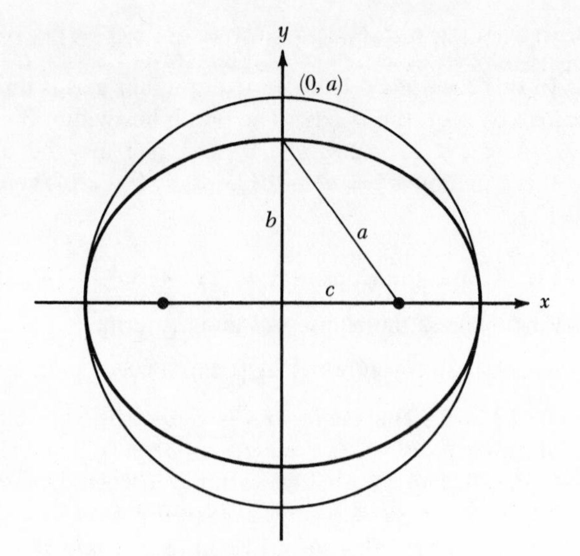

Figure 8-15

of the ellipse. Since $b^2 = a^2 - c^2$—by definition—and since $c < a$, we have $0 < b^2 \leq a^2$ and $(b/a)^2 \leq 1$. Therefore,

$$0 \leq 1 - (b/a)^2 < 1$$
$$0 \leq \sqrt{1 - (b/a)^2} < 1.$$

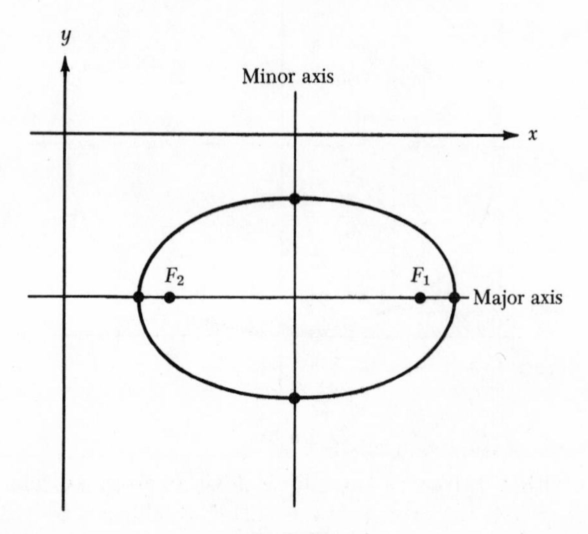

Figure 8-16

Thus, the eccentricity of an ellipse is a number between 0 and 1. We see from this that *an ellipse has eccentricity* 0 *if and only if it is a circle;* the closer the eccentricity is to 1, the "flatter" is the ellipse. The eccentricity is also the number c/a since

$$\sqrt{1-(b/a)^2} = \sqrt{\frac{a^2-b^2}{a^2}} = \sqrt{\frac{c^2}{a^2}} = \frac{c}{a}.$$

If the foci F_1, F_2 are taken to be $(d + c, e)$, $(d - c, e)$ respectively instead of $(c, 0)$, $(-c, 0)$ as above, then the ellipse—by using arguments similar to those above—may be shown to be

$$\{(x, y) \mid (x-d)^2/a^2 + (y-e)^2/b^2 = 1\}.$$

The center is then (d, e), the major axis is the line $\{(x, e)\}$, and the minor axis is the line $\{(d, y)\}$. (See Fig. 8-16.)

As before, the roles of the x-axis and y-axis may be interchanged by taking the foci as $(d, e + c)$, $(d, e - c)$. The ellipse is

$$\{(x, y) \mid (x-d)^2/b^2 + (y-e)^2/a^2 = 1\}.$$

(See Fig. 8-17.)

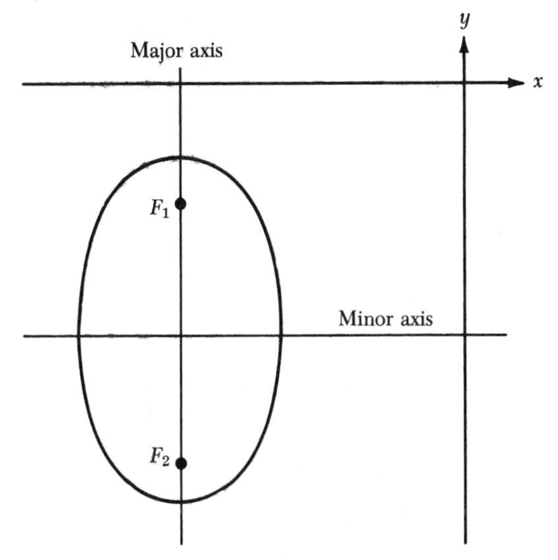

Figure 8-17

Example 8-12. Graph the relation

$$\{(x, y) \mid 9x^2 - 18x + 4y^2 + 8y - 23 = 0\}.$$

Solution. We first write the equation $9x^2 - 18x + 4y^2 + 8y - 23 = 0$

in a more convenient form by completing the squares in x and y:

$$9(x^2 - 2x) + 4(y^2 + 2y) = 23$$
$$9(x^2 - 2x + 1) + 4(y^2 + 2y + 1) = 23 + 9 + 4$$
$$9(x - 1)^2 + 4(y + 1)^2 = 36$$
$$\frac{(x-1)^2}{4} + \frac{(y+1)^2}{9} = 1.$$

This is now recognized as an ellipse with center $(1, -1)$. Also $b = 2$, $a = 3$ so that the major axis is parallel to the y-axis and $c = \sqrt{a^2 - b^2} = \sqrt{9 - 4} = \sqrt{5}$. Hence, the foci are $(1, -1 + \sqrt{5})$, $(1, -1 - \sqrt{5})$. In this case

$$\frac{(x-1)^2}{4} \leq 1 \qquad \text{and} \qquad \frac{(y+1)^2}{9} \leq 1$$

or,

$$(x - 1)^2 \leq 4 \qquad \text{and} \qquad (y + 1)^2 \leq 9.$$

Therefore,

$$-2 \leq x - 1 \leq 2 \qquad \text{and} \qquad -3 \leq y + 1 \leq 3.$$

This shows that the graph lies within the rectangle defined by

$$-1 \leq x \leq 3 \qquad \text{and} \qquad -4 \leq y \leq 2.$$

See Fig. 8-18 for the graph.

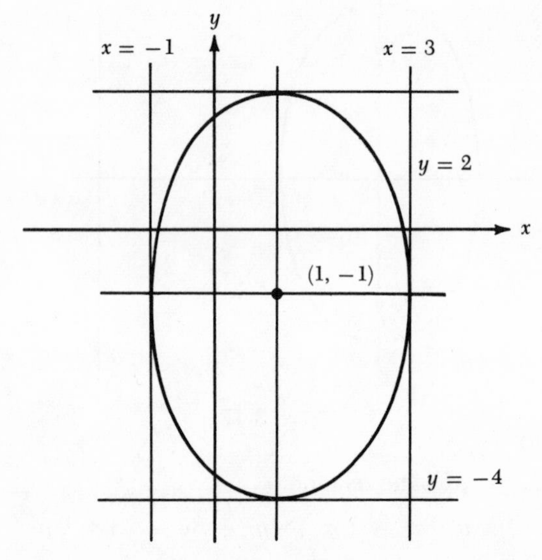

Figure 8-18

Exercises

25. Graph each of the following relations.

(a) $\{(x, y) | x^2/4 + y^2 = 1\}$.
(b) $\{(x, y) | x^2 + 8y^2 = 8\}$.
(c) $\{(x, y) | 4x^2 + 9y^2 = 36\}$.
(d) $\{(x, y) | x^2 + (y - 1)^2 = 1\}$.
(e) $\{(x, y) | 6x^2 + (y + 2)^2 = 4\}$.
(f) $\{(x, y) | 2x^2 - 2y^2 = 0\}$.
(g) $\{(x, y) \Big| \frac{(2x - 1)^2}{4} + \frac{(y + 2)^2}{16} = 1\}$.
(h) $\{(x, y) | x^2 + 16x + 4y^2 - 16y + 76 = 0\}$.
(i) $\{(x, y) | 4x^2 - 4x + 8y^2 + 8y - 1 = 0\}$.

26. For each of the relations in Exercise 25 that are ellipses give the eccentricity.

27. Graph each of the following:

(a) $\{(x, y) | x^2 + 8(y^2 - 1) \leq 0\}$.
(b) $\{(x, y) | x^2 + 8(y^2 - 1) \leq 0 \text{ and } x \leq y\}$.
(c) $\{(x, y) | 4(4x^2 - 1) + (y + 2)^2 \leq 0\}$.
(d) $\{(x, y) | x^2 - y^2 = 0 \text{ and } x^2 + y^2 \leq 1\}$.
(e) $\{(x, y) | x^2 + y^2 \leq 4 \text{ and } \frac{x^2}{4} + y^2 \geq 1\}$.

8.4 The Hyperbola

The definition of a hyperbola is very close to that of an ellipse; instead of sums of distances—as with the ellipse—the hyperbola is defined by differences of certain distances.

DEFINITION. Let a be a positive number and let F_1, F_2 be points. Then the relation

$$\{(x, y) | \, |d((x, y), F_1) - d((x, y), F_2)| = 2a\}$$

is called a *hyperbola*. The points F_1, F_2 are called the *foci* of the hyperbola.

As with the ellipse, we may show that for foci $F_1 = (c, 0)$ and $F_2 = (-c, 0)$ the hyperbola is

$$\{(x, y) | x^2/a^2 - y^2/(c^2 - a^2) = 1\}.$$

Notice that this description of the hyperbola differs in two ways from the corresponding description of the ellipse: the left-hand side of the equation is a difference instead of a sum and $c^2 - a^2$ occurs rather than $a^2 - c^2$. For the ellipse, c was a number such that $0 \leq c < a$; for the hyperbola c must satisfy the condition $a < c$. This condition $a < c$ is illustrated in Fig. 8-19 where $d_1 < d_2 + 2c$. Hence, $2a = d_1 - d_2 < 2c$

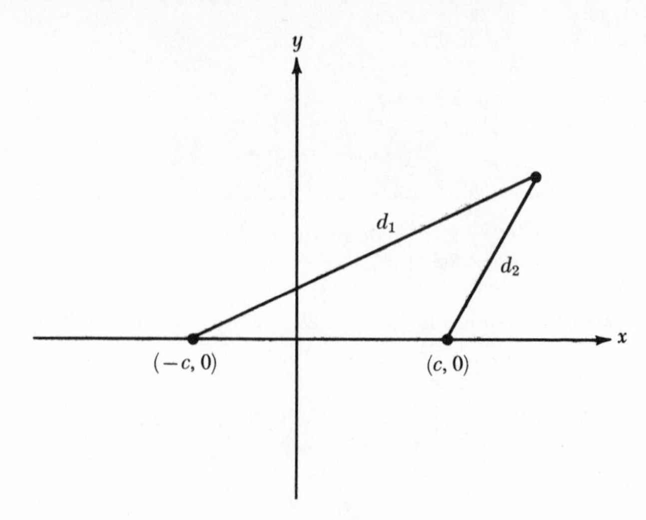

Figure 8-19

or $a < c$. Therefore, the number $c^2 - a^2$ is positive so that we may define $b = \sqrt{c^2 - a^2}$. The hyperbola may be expressed more simply therefore as

$$\{(x, y) \,|\, x^2/a^2 - y^2/b^2 = 1\}.$$

Example 8-13. Graph the relation $\{(x, y) \,|\, x^2 - y^2 = 1\}$.

Solution. This is a hyperbola in which $a = 1$, $b = 1$ and thus $1 = \sqrt{c^2 - a^2}$, $c = \sqrt{2}$. The foci are $(\sqrt{2}, 0)$, $(-\sqrt{2}, 0)$. If (x, y) is any point on the graph of this relation, $x^2 - y^2 = 1$ and so

$$y^2 = x^2 - 1$$
$$y = \pm\sqrt{x^2 - 1}.$$

Consider $y = \sqrt{x^2 - 1}$ for $x \geq 1$. Then $y = \sqrt{x^2 - 1} < \sqrt{x^2} = |x| = x$ (since $x > 0$). This implies that the second coordinate on the graph of $y = \sqrt{x^2 - 1}$ is less than the corresponding second coordinate on the graph of $y = x$. It also appears that the larger is x, the closer $\sqrt{x^2 - 1}$ is to $\sqrt{x^2} = x (x > 0)$. See Fig. 8-20 for the graph of $y = \sqrt{x^2 - 1}$,

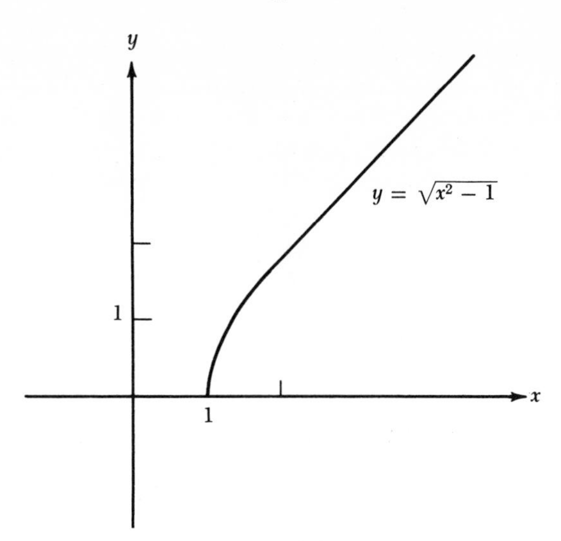

Figure 8-20

$x \geq 1$. The graph of $\{(x, y) \mid x^2 - y^2 = 1\}$ may now be completed by graphing $y = -\sqrt{x^2 - 1}$ for $x \geq 1$, $y = \sqrt{x^2 - 1}$ for $x \leq -1$, $y = -\sqrt{x^2 - 1}$ for $x \leq -1$. (See Fig. 8-21.)

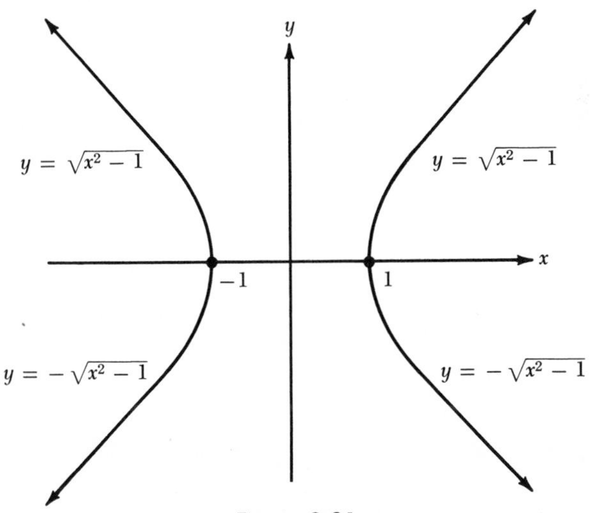

Figure 8-21

The numbers a, b associated with the hyperbola $\{(x, y) \mid x^2/a^2 - y^2/b^2 = 1\}$ define a rectangle as is the case with an ellipse; the hyperbola is, however, outside the rectangle rather than contained in it. This may be seen by considering a point (x, y) on the hyperbola:

$$\{(x, y) \mid x^2/a^2 - y^2/b^2 = 1\}.$$

Then,

$$y^2/b^2 = x^2/a^2 - 1$$

and hence,

$$y^2 = b^2\left(\frac{x^2 - a^2}{a^2}\right)$$

$$y = \pm(b/a)\sqrt{x^2 - a^2}.$$

This shows at once that we must have $x^2 - a^2 \geq 0$ and

$$a^2 \leq x^2.$$

This implies that $x \geq a$ or $x \leq -a$. Also for $x \geq a$, $\sqrt{x^2 - a^2} < \sqrt{x^2} = |x| = x$. Thus,

$$(b/a)\sqrt{x^2 - a^2} < (b/a)x.$$

Therefore, a point (x, y) on the hyperbola with $x \geq a$ and $y = (b/a)\sqrt{x^2 - a^2}$ lies below the corresponding point on the line $y = (b/a)x$. (See Fig. 8-22.) Similar considerations with $y = -(b/a)\sqrt{x^2 - a^2}$ show that the graph of the hyperbola $\{(x, y) \mid x^2/a^2 - y^2/b^2 = 1\}$ lies between the lines $\{(x, (b/a)x)\}$ and $\{(x, -(b/a)x)\}$ as shown in Fig. 8-22.

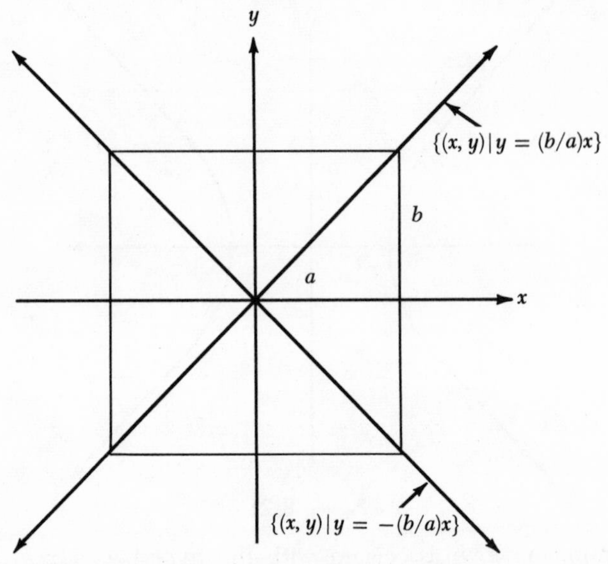

Figure 8-22

The *major axis* and *minor axis* of a hyperbola are defined in the same way that they are defined for an ellipse.

A more general situation is obtained if we take foci $(d + c, e)$, $(d - c, e)$. Then, the hyperbola is

$$\{(x, y) \mid (x - d)^2/a^2 - (y - e)^2/b^2 = 1\}.$$

Here the major axis is the line $\{(x, e)\}$, the minor axis is $\{(d, y)\}$ and the center is (d, e). The graph lies between the lines $y - e = (b/a)(x - d)$ and $y - e = -(b/a)(x - d)$ as shown in Fig. 8-23. These lines are called the *asymptotes* of the hyperbola.

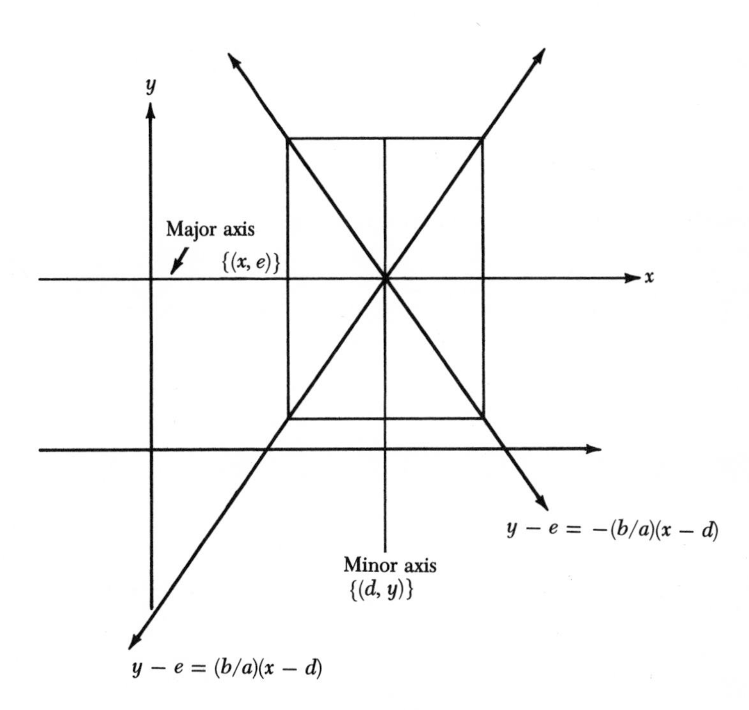

Figure 8-23

The roles of the x- and y-axes are reversed by taking the foci to be $(d, e + c)$ and $(d, e - c)$. Then, the hyperbola is

$$\{(x, y) \mid (y - e)^2/b^2 - (x - d)^2/a^2 = 1\}.$$

In this situation the major axis is parallel to the y-axis as shown in Fig. 8-24.

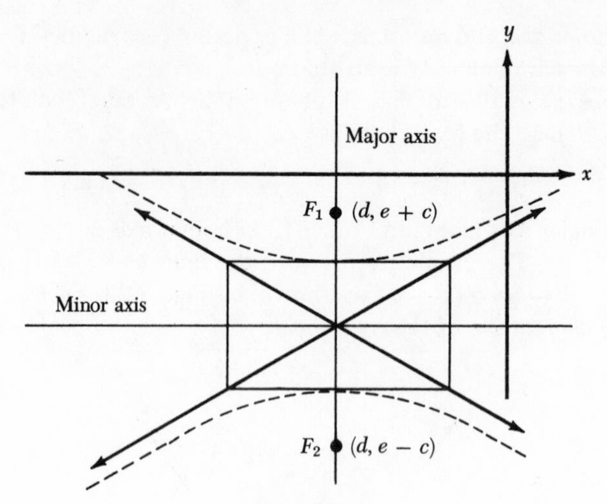

Figure 8-24

Example 8-14. Graph the relation $\{(x, y) \mid 4x^2 - 8x - y^2 - 2y - 1 = 0\}$.

Solution. Completing the squares in x and y in the equation $4x^2 - 8x - y^2 - 2y - 1 = 0$:

$$4(x^2 - 2x) - (y^2 + 2y + 1) = 0$$
$$4(x^2 - 2x + 1) - (y^2 + 2y + 1) = 4$$
$$4(x - 1)^2 - (y + 1)^2 = 4$$
$$(x - 1)^2 - \frac{(y + 1)^2}{4} = 1.$$

Hence, the graph is a hyperbola with center at $(1, -1)$ and major axis parallel to the x-axis. The graph is contained between the lines

$$y + 1 = (1/4)(x - 1) \qquad \text{and} \qquad y + 1 = -(1/4)(x - 1)$$

as shown in Fig. 8-25. Since $a = 1$ and $b = 2$, we have

$$c = \sqrt{a^2 + b^2} = \sqrt{1 + 4} = \sqrt{5}.$$

The foci are hence $(1 + \sqrt{5}, -1)$ and $(1 - \sqrt{5}, -1)$.

Exercises

28. Graph each of the following.
(a) $\{(x, y) \mid x^2/4 - y^2/16 = 1\}$.
(b) $\{(x, y) \mid y^2/16 - x^2/4 = 1\}$
(c) $\{(x, y) \mid (x + 2)^2/4 - y^2/16 = 1\}$

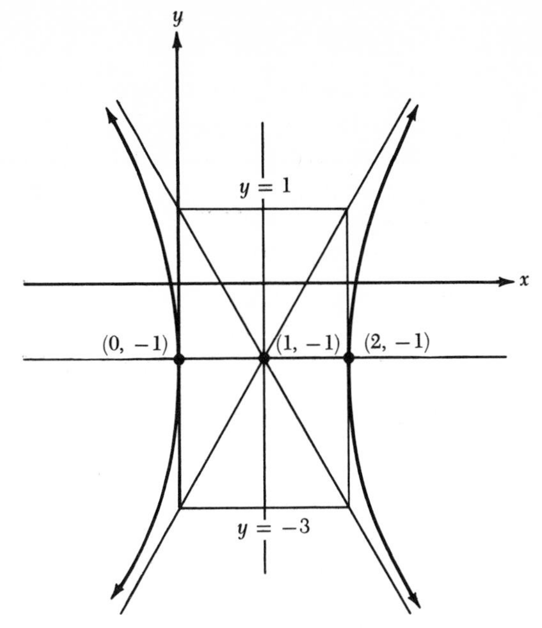

Figure 8-25

(d) $\{(x, y) \mid y^2/16 - (x + 2)^2/4 = 1\}$.
(e) $\{(x, y) \mid (y - 1)^2/9 - (x - 1)^2/2 = 1\}$.
(f) $\{(x, y) \mid (x - 1)^2/2 - (y - 1)^2/9 = 1\}$.
(g) $\{(x, y) \mid (2y + 1)^2 - (2x - 1)^2 = 4\}$.
(h) $\{(x, y) \mid (2y + 1)^2 - (2x - 1)^2 = 1\}$.
(i) $\{(x, y) \mid 12x^2 - 12x - 8y^2 - 21 = 0\}$.
(j) $\{(x, y) \mid 12y^2 - 12y - 8x^2 - 21 = 0\}$.

29. In each of the following, determine a hyperbola satisfying the given conditions.
(a) Foci: $(1, 0)$, $(-1, 0)$; asymptotes: $y = \pm(1/7)x$.
(b) Asymptotes: $y + 1 = \pm(x - 1)$; the point $(4, 1)$ is on the hyperbola.

8.5 Translations and Rotations

We consider now two different coordinate systems in the plane. An example of what is meant by this is given in Fig. 8-26 where corresponding axes are taken parallel to each other. In coordinate system II, the axis of first coordinates is called the $\bar{x}$-axis; the axis of second coordinates is the $\bar{y}$-axis. Each of these coordinate systems is said to be a *translation* of the other.

Each point P in the plane now has an ordered pair $(\bar{x}, \bar{y})$ associated

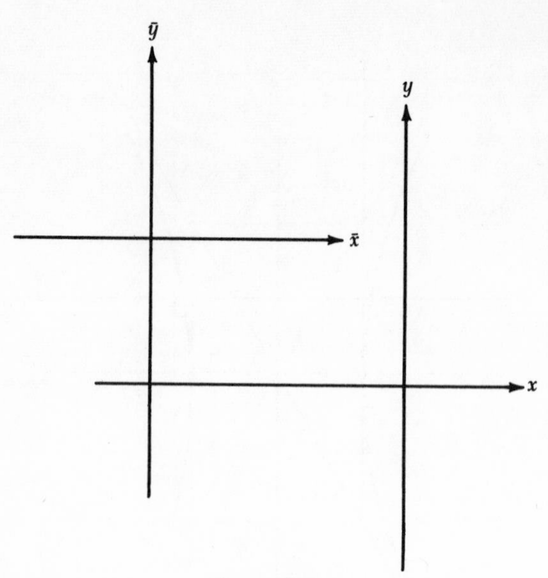

Figure 8-26

with it by system I and also an ordered pair $(\bar{x}, \bar{y})$ associated with it by system II. An obvious question here is whether there is a routine method of obtaining one of these ordered pairs if given the other one. The answer to this is as follows: *if the origin of coordinate system II, has coordinates (h, k) when referred to system I, then the coordinates (x, y) and $(\bar{x}, \bar{y})$ of a point P are related by the equations*

$$\bar{x} = x - h$$
$$\bar{y} = y - k.$$

This is illustrated in Fig. 8-27. With two coordinate systems I and II as described above, we say that the origin of the first system has been translated to the point (h, k)—where h, k refer to the first system.

Example 8-15. If a coordinate system is translated to the point $(1, -\sqrt{2})$, then a point P which has coordinates (x, y) in the first system has coordinates $(x - 1, y + \sqrt{2})$ in the second system. Points on the y-axis of the first system have coordinates $(0, c)$; these points in the second system have coordinates $(-1, c + \sqrt{2})$.

Example 8-16. If a coordinate system is translated to the point $(1, -\sqrt{2})$, how is the description of the unit circle with center at the origin affected?

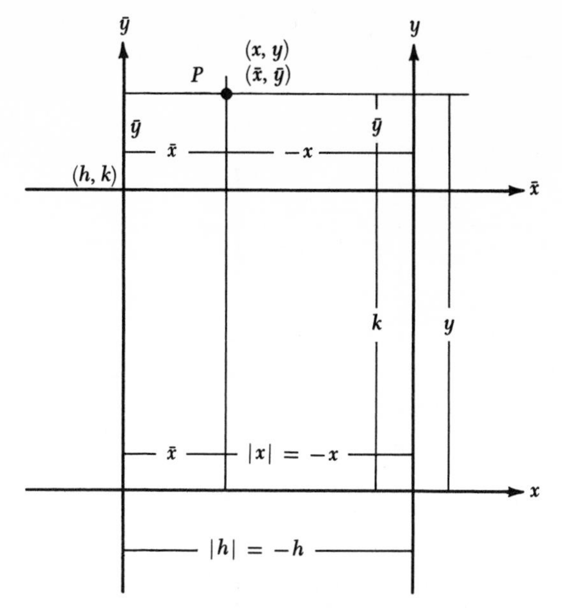

Figure 8-27

Solution. This relation $\{(x, y) | x^2 + y^2 = 1\}$ describes the unit circle with center at the origin. Let P be a point on this circle and have coordinates (a, b) in System I. Then after translating to $(1, -\sqrt{2})$, P has new coordinates $(\bar{a}, \bar{b})$ in System II such that $\bar{a} = a - 1$, $\bar{b} = b + \sqrt{2}$. Hence, $a = \bar{a} + 1$ and $b = \bar{b} - \sqrt{2}$. Since P is on the circle, $a^2 + b^2 = 1$ and substitution gives

$$(\bar{a} + 1)^2 + (\bar{b} - \sqrt{2})^2 = 1.$$

This unit circle therefore is described in System II as

$$\{(\bar{x}, \bar{y}) | (\bar{x} + 1)^2 + (\bar{y} - \sqrt{2})^2 = 1\}.$$

(See Fig. 8-28.)

If a geometric figure has a certain description relative to a given coordinate system, it may be that the description can be replaced by one much simpler by making a translation. For instance, the hyperbola H may be under consideration and it may be described as

$$H = \{(x, y) | (x - e)^2/a^2 - (y - d)/b^2 = 1\}$$

in the given coordinate system. Translation to the point (e, d) produces the simpler description:

$$\{(\bar{x}, \bar{y}) | \bar{x}^2/a^2 - \bar{y}^2/b^2 = 1\}.$$

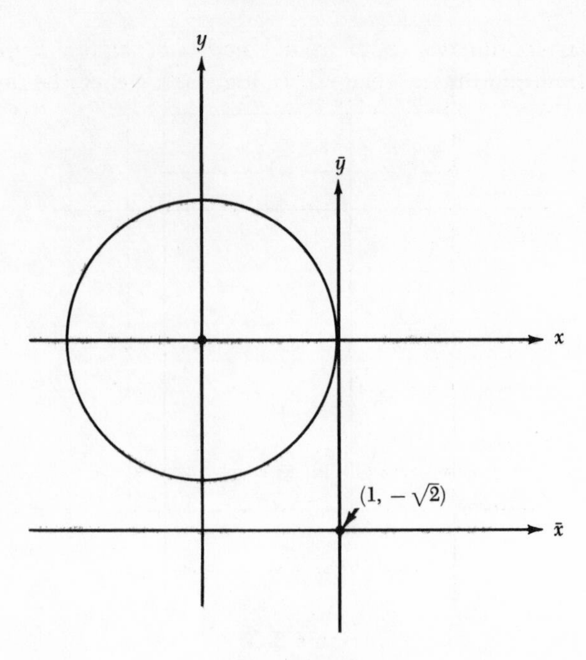

Figure 8-28

Consider now two coordinate systems—I and II—both having the same origin but such that the x-axis and $\bar{x}$-axis make an angle φ as in Fig. 8-29. System II is said to be a *rotation* of System I. As before, a

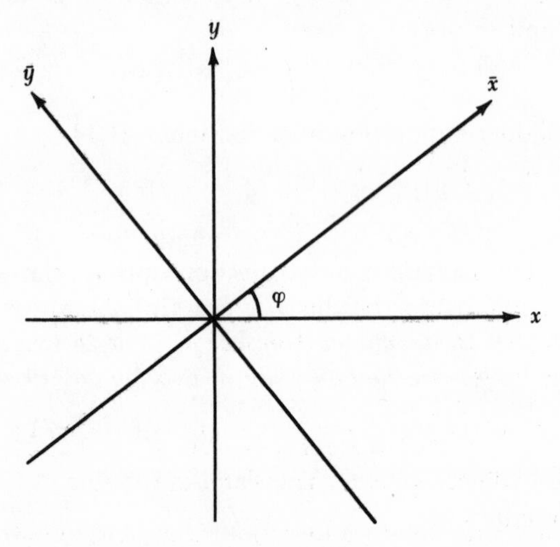

Figure 8-29

point P has coordinates (x, y) from I and coordinates $(\bar{x}, \bar{y})$ from II. How are these coordinates related? In Fig. 8-30, we let r be the distance

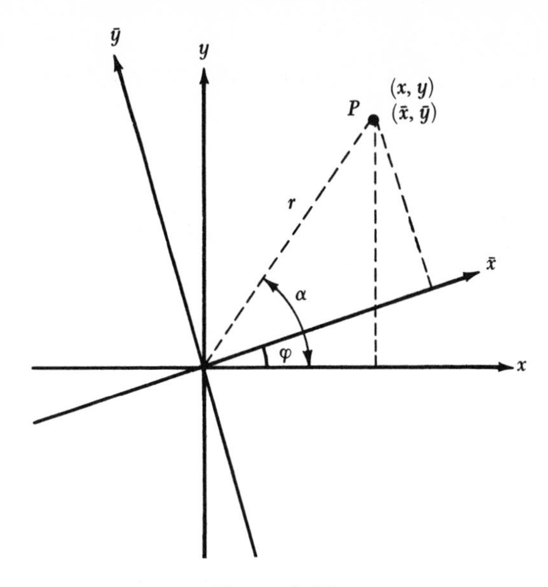

Figure 8-30

that P is from the origin of the two systems and α is the angle as shown. Then $x = r \cos \alpha$, $y = r \sin \alpha$, $\bar{x} = r \cos (\alpha - \varphi)$, $\bar{y} = r \sin (\alpha - \varphi)$. Hence,

$$\begin{aligned} \bar{x} &= r[\cos (\alpha - \varphi)] \\ &= r[\cos \alpha \cos \varphi + \sin \alpha \sin \varphi] \\ &= (r \cos \alpha) \cos \varphi + (r \sin \alpha) \sin \varphi \\ &= x \cos \varphi + y \sin \varphi \end{aligned}$$

and

$$\begin{aligned} \bar{y} &= r \sin (\alpha - \varphi) \\ &= r[\sin \alpha \cos \varphi - \cos \alpha \sin \varphi] \\ &= (r \sin \alpha) \cos \varphi - (r \cos \alpha) \sin \varphi \\ &= y \cos \varphi - x \sin \varphi. \end{aligned}$$

This gives the equations:

$$\begin{aligned} \bar{x} &= x \cos \varphi + y \sin \varphi \\ \bar{y} &= y \cos \varphi - x \sin \varphi. \end{aligned} \tag{1}$$

These equations may be used to compute the coordinates $(\bar{x}, \bar{y})$ if we are given the coordinates (x, y). From Fig. 8-31 we have—by computing $r \cos(\alpha + \varphi)$ and $r \sin(\alpha + \varphi)$—the equations

$$x = \bar{x} \cos \varphi - \bar{y} \sin \varphi \qquad (2)$$
$$y = \bar{y} \cos \varphi + \bar{x} \sin \varphi.$$

The Eq. (2) may be used to compute the coordinates (x, y) if we are given $(\bar{x}, \bar{y})$.

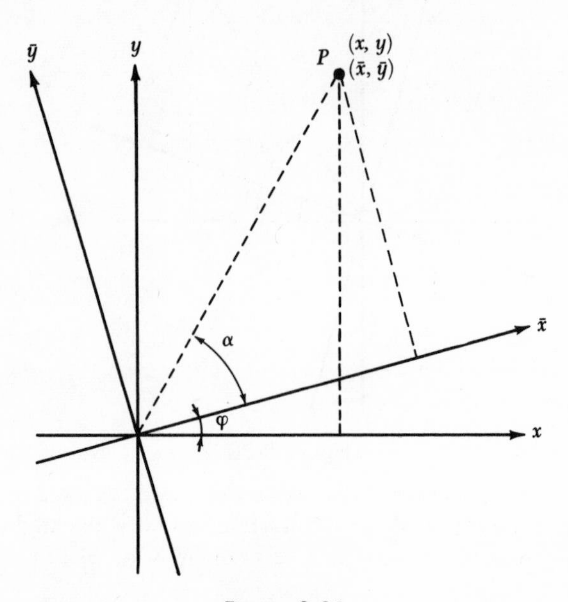

Figure 8-31

Example 8-17. Suppose that a coordinate system is given and the line bisecting the first and third quadrant is under consideration. When referred to the given coordinate system, the line is described by $\{(x, y) \mid x = y\} = \{(x, x)\}$. Suppose now that the given system is rotated by $\pi/4$ radians. What is the description of the line when referred to the new system?

Solution. The old and new coordinates of every point are related by Eq. (2) where in this case $\varphi = \pi/4$:

$$x = \bar{x} \cos(\pi/4) - \bar{y} \sin(\pi/4)$$
$$y = \bar{y} \cos(\pi/4) + \bar{x} \sin(\pi/4)$$

or

$$x = \tfrac{1}{2}\sqrt{2}\bar{x} - \tfrac{1}{2}\sqrt{2}\bar{y}$$
$$y = \tfrac{1}{2}\sqrt{2}\bar{y} + \tfrac{1}{2}\sqrt{2}\bar{x}.$$

For a point on the line in question, $x = y$ and therefore,

$$\tfrac{1}{2}\sqrt{2}\bar{x} - \tfrac{1}{2}\sqrt{2}\bar{y} = \tfrac{1}{2}\sqrt{2}\bar{y} + \tfrac{1}{2}\sqrt{2}\bar{x}.$$

This simplifies to

$$\bar{y} = 0.$$

This implies that when referred to the new coordinate system every point $(\bar{x}, \bar{y})$ of the given line is such that $\bar{y} = 0$; i.e., the given line is now described as the $\bar{x}$-axis or

$$\{(\bar{x}, \bar{y}) \mid \bar{y} = 0\} = \{(\bar{x}, 0)\}.$$

(See Fig. 8-32.)

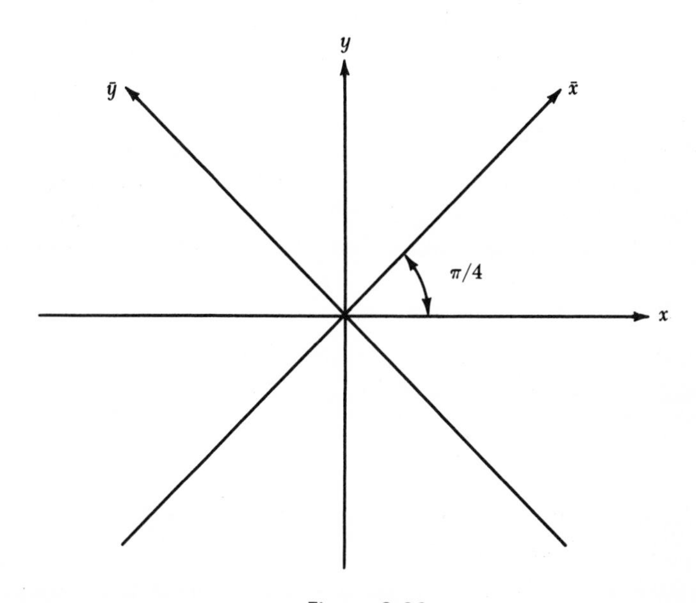

Figure 8-32

Example 8-18. Let us consider the graph of the relation $\{(x, y) \mid xy = 1\}$. If a rotation of the coordinate system is made, the graph of $\{(x, y) \mid xy = 1\}$ will not change; this description of the graph will change, however. If the rotation is through $\pi/4$ radians as above, we have

$$x = (\tfrac{1}{2})\sqrt{2}\bar{x} - (\tfrac{1}{2})\sqrt{2}\bar{y}$$
$$y = (\tfrac{1}{2})\sqrt{2}\bar{y} + (\tfrac{1}{2})\sqrt{2}\bar{x}.$$

Then,

$$xy = \tfrac{1}{2}(\bar{x})^2 - \tfrac{1}{2}(\bar{y})^2$$

and if $xy = 1$,

$$(\bar{x})^2 - (\bar{y})^2 = 2.$$

The original graph is described in the new system as

$$\{(\bar{x}, \bar{y}) \mid (\bar{x})^2 - (\bar{y})^2 = 2\}.$$

We recognize this as the hyperbola

$$\{(\bar{x}, \bar{y}) \mid \bar{x}^2/(\sqrt{2})^2 - \bar{y}^2/(\sqrt{2})^2 = 1\}$$

in standard form with $a = b = \sqrt{2}$.

A relation of the form

$$\{(x, y) \mid Ax^2 + By^2 + Cxy + Dx + Ey + F = 0\}$$

is called a *quadratic* relation where A, B, C, D, E, F are numbers and not all of A, B, C are zero. The circle, parabola, ellipse and hyperbola are all graphs of quadratic relations. If the quadratic relation is such that $C = 0$, then we may determine its graph by completing the square in x and y as was done in example 8-14. If $C \neq 0$, a rotation of axes may be made in such a way that the new quadratic relation has no xy-term. Then the graph may be determined by completing the squares.

Example 8-19. Graph the relation $\{(x, y) \mid x^2 + 3xy + y^2 = 1\}$.

Solution. If a rotation of axes is made through φ radians, then the old and new coordinates are related by

$$x = \bar{x} \cos \varphi - \bar{y} \sin \varphi$$
$$y = \bar{y} \cos \varphi + \bar{x} \sin \varphi.$$

If the coordinates (x, y) of a point satisfy the condition $x^2 + 3xy + y^2 = 1$, then substitution from above gives

$$(\bar{x} \cos \varphi - \bar{y} \sin \varphi)^2 + 3(\bar{x} \cos \varphi - \bar{y} \sin \varphi)(\bar{y} \cos \varphi + \bar{x} \sin \varphi)$$
$$+ (\bar{y} \cos \varphi + \bar{x} \sin \varphi)^2 = 1.$$

This last equation may be written as follows:

$$(\bar{x})^2 \cos^2\varphi - 2\bar{x}\bar{y} \cos \varphi \sin \varphi + (\bar{y})^2 \sin^2\varphi$$
$$+ 3(\bar{x}\bar{y} \cos^2\varphi - \bar{x}\bar{y} \sin^2\varphi + (\bar{x})^2 \sin \varphi \cos \varphi - (\bar{y})^2 \sin \varphi \cos \varphi)$$
$$+ (\bar{y})^2 \cos^2\varphi + 2\bar{x}\bar{y} \sin \varphi \cos \varphi + (\bar{x})^2 \sin^2\varphi = 1$$

or

$$(1 + 3 \sin \varphi \cos \varphi)(\bar{x})^2 + (1 - 3 \sin \varphi \cos \varphi)(\bar{y})^2$$
$$+ 2(\cos^2\varphi - \sin^2\varphi)\bar{x}\bar{y} = 1$$

or

$$(1 + \tfrac{3}{2} \sin 2\varphi)(\bar{x})^2 + (1 - \tfrac{3}{2} \sin 2\varphi)(\bar{y})^2 + (2 \cos 2\varphi)\bar{x}\bar{y} = 1.$$

From this it is easy to see that a very convenient choice for φ is $\pi/4$; for then $(2 \cos 2\varphi)\bar{x}\bar{y} = (2 \cos \pi/2)\bar{x}\bar{y} = 0$. Making this choice for φ, the above equation is

$$(\tfrac{5}{2})(\bar{x})^2 - (\tfrac{1}{2})(\bar{y})^2 = 1.$$

We conclude that the graph of the original relation is the graph of

$$\{(\bar{x}, \bar{y}) \mid (\bar{x})^2/(\tfrac{2}{5}) - (\bar{y})^2/2 = 1\}.$$

This graph is easily seen to be a hyperbola with $a = \sqrt{2/5}$, $b = \sqrt{2}$ and $c = \sqrt{2/5 + 2} = 2\sqrt{3/5}$. When referred to the $\bar{x}$, $\bar{y}$ system the center of this hyperbola is at $(0, 0)$, the foci are $(2\sqrt{3/5}, 0)$, $(-2\sqrt{3/5}, 0)$. The asymptotes are the lines

$$\{(\bar{x}, \bar{y}) \mid \bar{y} = \pm(\sqrt{5})\bar{x}\}.$$

If we wish a description of these points and lines in terms of the original x, y-coordinate system, we must use the equations relating the x, y-system to the $\bar{x}$, $\bar{y}$-system. We use the equations

$$x = \bar{x} \cos \pi/4 - \bar{y} \sin \pi/4$$
$$y = \bar{y} \cos \pi/4 + \bar{x} \sin \pi/4$$

or

$$x = \tfrac{1}{2}\sqrt{2}\bar{x} - \tfrac{1}{2}\sqrt{2}\bar{y}$$
$$y = \tfrac{1}{2}\sqrt{2}\bar{y} + \tfrac{1}{2}\sqrt{2}\bar{x}.$$

Thus, in the x, y-system, the point $(0, 0)$ has coordinates

$$x = \tfrac{1}{2}\, 2 \cdot 0 - \tfrac{1}{2}\, 2 \cdot 0 = 0$$
$$y = \tfrac{1}{2}\, 2 \cdot 0 + \tfrac{1}{2}\, 2 \cdot 0 = 0.$$

The foci $(2\sqrt{3/5}, 0)$, $(-2\sqrt{3/5}, 0)$ in the x, y-system have coordinates

$$x = (\tfrac{1}{2}\sqrt{2})(2\sqrt{3/5}) - \tfrac{1}{2}\sqrt{2} \cdot 0 = \sqrt{6/5}$$
$$y = \tfrac{1}{2}\sqrt{2} \cdot 0 + \tfrac{1}{2}\sqrt{2}(2\sqrt{3/5}) = \sqrt{6/5}$$

and

$$x = (\tfrac{1}{2}\sqrt{2})(-2\sqrt{3/5}) - \tfrac{1}{2}\sqrt{2} \cdot 0 = -\sqrt{6/5}$$
$$y = (\tfrac{1}{2}\sqrt{2}) \cdot 0 + \tfrac{1}{2}\sqrt{2}(-2\sqrt{3/5}) = -\sqrt{6/5}.$$

We use the equations

$$\bar{x} = (\tfrac{1}{2})\sqrt{2}x + (\tfrac{1}{2})\sqrt{2}y$$
$$\bar{y} = (\tfrac{1}{2})\sqrt{2}y - (\tfrac{1}{2})\sqrt{2}x$$

to obtain a description of the asymptotes in the x, y-system. Since the asymptotes are described by

$$\{(\bar{x}, \bar{y}) \mid \bar{y} = (\pm\sqrt{5})\bar{x}\}$$

in the $\bar{x}$, $\bar{y}$-system, substitution into the equation $\bar{y} = (\pm\sqrt{5})\bar{x}$ gives

$$\tfrac{1}{2}\sqrt{2}y - \tfrac{1}{2}\sqrt{x} = (\pm\sqrt{5})[\tfrac{1}{2}\sqrt{2}x + \tfrac{1}{2}\sqrt{2}y]$$

which simplifies to

$$y = \left(\frac{1 + \sqrt{5}}{1 - \sqrt{5}}\right)x \qquad (\text{for } +\sqrt{5})$$

and

$$y = \left(\frac{1 - \sqrt{5}}{1 + \sqrt{5}}\right)x \qquad (\text{for } -\sqrt{5}).$$

Hence, the asymptotes in the x, y-system are

$$\{(x, y) \mid y = ax \quad \text{or} \quad y = a^{-1}x\}$$

where $a = (1 + \sqrt{5})/(1 - \sqrt{5})$. (See Fig. 8-33.)

Exercises

30. A coordinate system is translated to the point $(\tfrac{1}{2}, -\tfrac{3}{5})$. Each of the following gives the coordinates of points referred to the original system; compute the coordinates of these points in the new system.

(a) $(0, 0)$. (c) $(0, 5)$. (e) $(\sqrt{2}, \tfrac{1}{2})$.
(b) $(1, 0)$. (d) $(1, 1)$. (f) $(x + \tfrac{1}{2}, -\tfrac{3}{5})$.

31. Give a description of the graph of each of the following after a translation to the point $(\tfrac{1}{2}, -\tfrac{3}{5})$ has been made.

(a) $\{(x, y) \mid x = y\}$.
(b) $\{(x, y) \mid x + \tfrac{1}{2} = y - \tfrac{3}{5}\}$.
(c) $\{(x, y) \mid x - \tfrac{1}{2} = y + \tfrac{3}{5}\}$.
(d) $\{(x, y) \mid (y + \tfrac{3}{5})^2 = 4(x - \tfrac{1}{2})\}$.
(e) $\{(x, y) \mid (y - \tfrac{3}{5})^2 = 4(x + \tfrac{1}{2})\}$.
(f) $\{(x, y) \mid x^2 + 2x + 3y = 1\}$.

32. Describe the graph of each of the following after a rotation of $\pi/6$ radians has been made.

(a) $\{(x, y) \mid y = (1/\sqrt{3})x\}$.
(b) $\{(x, y) \mid x(x - y) = 1\}$.
(c) $\{(x, y) \mid y^2 - 2xy + x = 7\}$.
(d) $\{(x, y) \mid x^2 + y^2 = 1\}$.

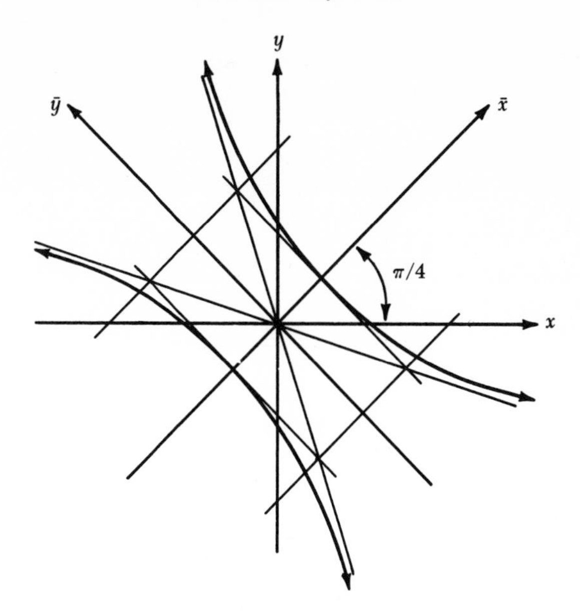

Figure 8-33

33. Graph each of the following (if possible):
    (a) $\{(x, y) \mid x^2 + y^2 = 0\}$.
    (b) $\{(x, y) \mid 2x^2 + y^2 + 1 = 0\}$.
    (c) $\{(x, y) \mid x^2 + 2xy + y^2 = 1\}$.
    (d) $\{(x, y) \mid x^2 - y^2 = 0\}$.
    (e) $\{(x, y) \mid 2x^2 - 2xy + 2y^2 = 1\}$.
    (f) $\{(x, y) \mid x^2 + \sqrt{3}xy = 1\}$.
    (g) $\{(x, y) \mid 2x^2 - 3xy + y^2 - 2x - 3y = 0\}$.

34. If the graphs of any of the relations in 32 above are parabolas, ellipses or hyperbolas, find the foci, center and asymptotes (for hyperbolas).

8.6 Parametric Equations

For any real number t consider the point $(\cos t, \sin t)$ in the plane. Since $\cos^2 t + \sin^2 t = 1$, this point lies on the unit circle $\{(x, y) \mid x^2 + y^2 = 1\}$. We have already seen that if $P(x, y)$ is any point (not the origin) in the plane and r is the distance between the origin and P, then

$$x = r \cos t$$
$$y = r \sin t$$

where t is a measure of an angle made by the x-axis and the line on P and the origin. (See Fig. 8-34.) If (x, y) is a point of the unit circle with

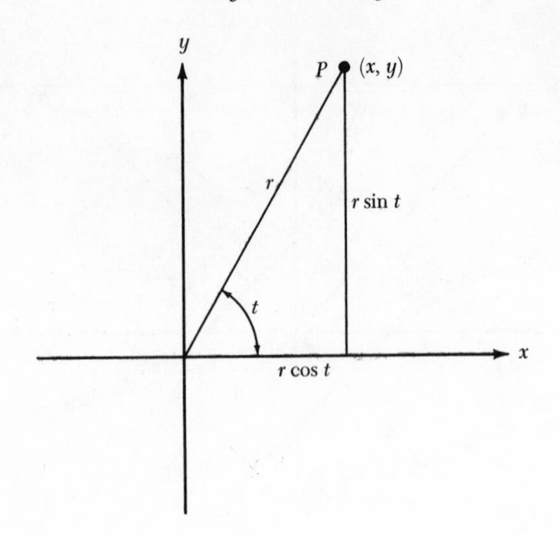

Figure 8-34

center at the origin, then $r = 1$ and

$$x = \cos t$$
$$y = \sin t.$$

This shows that

$$\{(x, y) \mid x^2 + y^2 = 1\} = \{(\cos t, \sin t) \mid t \text{ is a real number}\}.$$

It is common practice to express this fact by saying that the equations

$$x = \cos t$$
$$y = \sin t$$

are *parametric* equations, or a *parametric representation,* for the unit circle, center at the origin, and that t is a *parameter.*

If u, s are functions, the set

$$\{(u(t), s(t)) \mid t \in \mathfrak{D}(u) \cap \mathfrak{D}(s)\}$$

determines a graph in the plane. We say that the graph is given *parametrically* by

$$x = u(t)$$
$$y = s(t)$$

with parameter t. It is often convenient to think of t as representing time and to imagine the pairs $(u(t), s(t))$ traversing the points of the curve as t takes on values in $\mathfrak{D}(u) \cap \mathfrak{D}(s)$. (See Fig. 8-35.)

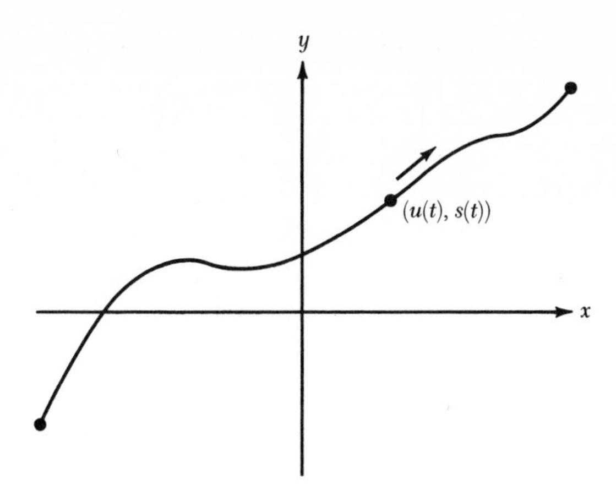

Figure 8-35

Example 8-20. Graph the curve given by the parametric equations

$$x = \cos t$$
$$y = \sin t \qquad \text{for} \qquad t \in [0, \pi].$$

Solution. All the points $(\cos t, \sin t)$ are on the unit circle with center at the origin. However, not all the points of the unit circle are given by $(\cos t, \sin t)$ for some $t \in [0, \pi]$. In fact,

$$\mathcal{R}(\cos t) = [-1, 1] \qquad \text{and} \qquad \mathcal{R}(\sin t) = [0, 1]$$

for $t \in [0, \pi]$. Hence, the second coordinate of the pairs $(\cos t, \sin t)$ is never negative and the graph is the top half of the unit circle. (See Fig. 8-36.)

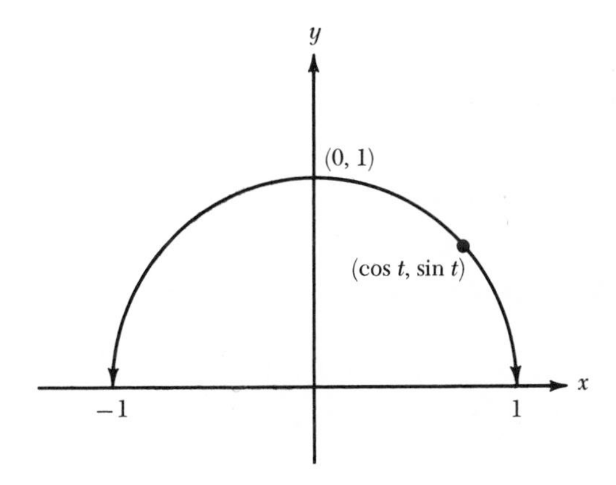

Figure 8-36

Example 8-21. Graph the curve given by the parametric equations

$$x = t^2$$
$$y = t^4$$

where t is any real number.

Solution. It is clear that $x \geq 0$, $y \geq 0$ and that $y = x^2$. Hence, the graph is given by

$$\{(x, y) \mid y = x^2 \text{ and } x \geq 0\}.$$

This has a graph that is part of a parabola as shown in Fig. 8-37.

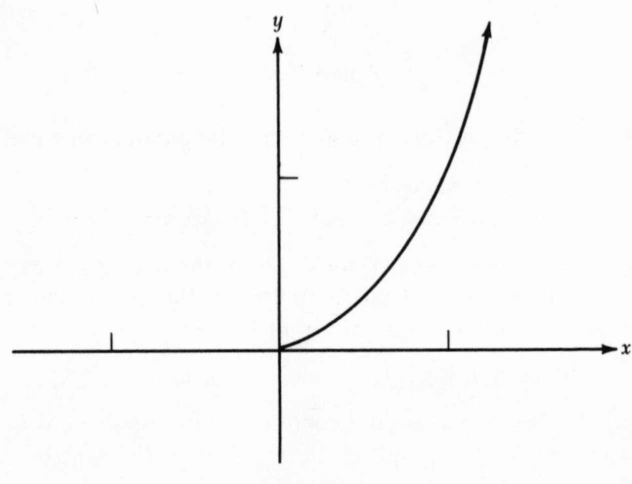

Figure 8-37

Consider two points in the plane (a, b) and (c, d) that are not on a line parallel to the y-axis. Then $a \neq c$ and the slope of the line on these points is

$$m = (d - b)/(c - a).$$

The line on these two points is then the graph of

$$\{(x, y) \mid y - b = m(x - a)\}.$$

(See Exercise 5.)

Parametric equations for this line are

$$x = a + t(c - a)$$
$$y = b + t(d - b) \qquad \text{for} \qquad t \in \mathbf{R}.$$

Notice that for $t = 0$ the equations give (a, b) and for $t = 1$, (c, d). For $t \in (0, 1)$, the parametric equations represent points between (a, b) and (c, d). To see this, suppose that $c - a$ and $d - b$ are positive. Then if $0 < t < 1$ we have

$$a < a + t(c - a) < c$$

and

$$b < b + t(d - b) < d.$$

(See Fig. 8-38.)

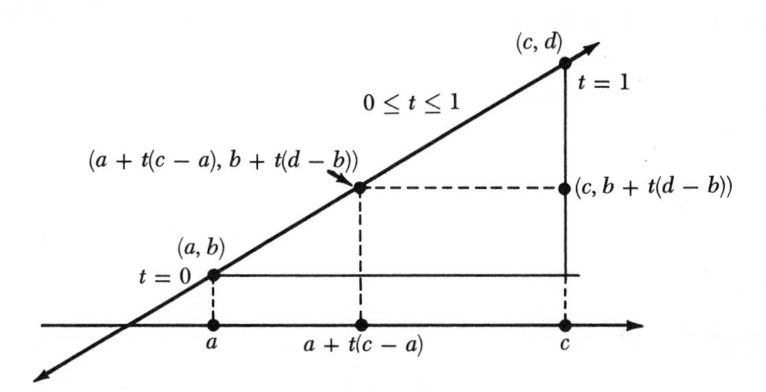

Figure 8-38

Exercises

35. Graph the following parametric equations.

(a) $x = 2 \cos t$
$y = 2 \sin t,\ t \in [0, \pi]$.

(b) $x = 1 + \cos t$
$y = 1 - \sin t,\ t \in [0, \pi]$.

(c) $x = \sin t$
$y = \cos 2t,\ t \in (0, \pi/2)$.

(d) $x = \tan t$
$y = \sec t,\ t \in (-\pi/2, \pi/2)$.

(e) $x = 1 - t$
$y = t + 1,\ t \in \mathbf{R}$.

(f) $x = 2 \cos t$
$y = 3 \sin t,\ t \in [0, \pi]$.

(g) $x = a \cos t$
$y = b \sin t,\ a, b > 0,\ t \in [0, \pi]$.

(h) $x = 2^t$
$y = 2^t(2^t + 1),\ t \geq 0$.

(i) $x = 3^t$
$y = 3^{-t}, t \geq 0.$

(j) $x = \frac{1}{2}t$
$y = \sqrt{1 - t^2}, t \in [-1, 1].$

36. (a) Show that the graph of the parametric equations

$$x = a + t(c - a)$$
$$y = b + t(d - b),\ t \in R$$

is the line on the points (a, b) and (c, d) if $(a, b) \neq (c, d)$.

(b) It was shown above that the equations in (a) represent points of the line segment between (a, b), (c, d) for $0 < t < 1$ in case $c - a > 0$ and $d - b > 0$. Enumerate the other cases and show that this result holds in each.

(c) Show that every line is the graph of some parametric equations

$$x = a + t \cos \varphi$$
$$y = b + t \sin \varphi,\ t \in \mathbf{R}$$

for some number φ.

37. Show that the graph of the following parametric equations is an ellipse

$$x = c + a \cos t$$
$$y = d + b \sin t,\ t \in [0, 2\pi]$$

where a, b, c, d are real numbers and $a > 0$, $b > 0$.

*9

Complex Numbers

This chapter is devoted to a brief introduction to the study of the complex number system. The complex numbers are, in a certain sense, an enlargement of the real number system. An expansion of the set of real numbers is desirable for several reasons; one of the most important reasons is that in the system of complex numbers we can solve equations of the type $x^2 + 1 = 0$ which have no real number solution.

9.1 Definitions

By the *complex number system* $\mathbf{C}$ we mean the set $\mathbf{R} \times \mathbf{R}$ (the set of all ordered pairs of real numbers) with an addition and multiplication defined as follows:

Addition of Complex Numbers.

$$(a, b) + (c, d) = (a + c, b + d)$$

for all ordered pairs (a, b), (c, d).

Multiplication of Complex Numbers.

$$(a, b) \cdot (c, d) = (ac - bd, ad + bc)$$

for all ordered pairs (a, b), (c, d).

It should be noted that in the equation

$$(a, b) + (c, d) = (a + c, b + d),$$

defining addition of complex numbers, the "+" on the left is being *defined* and the "+" on the right denotes ordinary real number addition. Thus the symbol "+" is being used in two different ways here. Similar remarks are in order for the multiplication definition. It also should be observed that since complex numbers are ordered pairs of real numbers, we have the usual condition governing equality of ordered pairs:

$$(a, b) = (c, d) \text{ if, and only if, } a = c \text{ and } b = d.$$

The complex numbers satisfy many of the axioms for real numbers. For example, the definitions of addition and multiplication show that the sum and product of complex numbers are each unique complex numbers.

Theorem 28. The complex numbers **C** have the following properties:

1. The sum, $\alpha + \beta$, and product, $\alpha\beta$, of any complex numbers α, β is a unique complex number.
2. For any two complex numbers α, β

$$\alpha + \beta = \beta + \alpha \quad \text{and} \quad \alpha\beta = \beta\alpha.$$

3. If α, β, γ are complex numbers, then

$$\alpha + (\beta + \gamma) = (\alpha + \beta) + \gamma \quad \text{and} \quad \alpha(\beta\gamma) = (\alpha\beta)\gamma.$$

4. If α, β, γ are complex numbers, then

$$\alpha(\beta + \gamma) = \alpha\beta + \alpha\gamma.$$

5. If α is any complex number, then
   (a) $\alpha + (0, 0) = \alpha$
   (b) $\alpha \cdot (1, 0) = \alpha$.

6. (a) For each complex number α, there is a complex number $-\alpha$ such that

$$\alpha + (-\alpha) = (0, 0).$$

(b) For each complex number $\alpha \neq (0, 0)$, there is a complex number α^{-1} such that

$$\alpha \cdot \alpha^{-1} = (1, 0).$$

Proof: We have already noted that the sum and product of complex numbers is each a unique complex number. The proof of 4 and 6 will be given and the others will be left to the student.

To prove 3, let $\alpha = (a, b)$, $\beta = (c, d)$ and $\gamma = (e, f)$ for real numbers a, b, c, d, e, f. Then, using the definitions of addition and multiplication,

$$\begin{aligned}
\alpha(\beta + \gamma) &= (a, b) \cdot ((c, d) + (e, f)) \\
&= (a, b)(c + e, d + f) \\
&= (a(c + e) - b(d + f), a(d + f) + b(c + e)) \\
\alpha\beta &= (a, b)(c, d) = (ac - bd, ad + bc) \\
\alpha\gamma &= (a, b)(e, f) = (ae - bf, af + be) \\
\alpha\beta + \alpha\gamma &= (ac - bd, ad + bc) + (ae - bf, af + be) \\
&= (ac - bd + ae - bf, ad + bc + af + be).
\end{aligned}$$

Now, by the condition for equality of complex numbers, $\alpha(\beta + \gamma) = \alpha\beta + \alpha\gamma$ if and only if

$$a(c + e) - b(d + f) = ac - bd + ae - bf$$

and

$$a(d + f) + b(c + e) = ad + bc + af + be.$$

Since these last two equations are seen to be true by the distributive, commutative and associative axioms for real numbers, we may conclude that

$$\alpha(\beta + \gamma) = \alpha\beta + \alpha\gamma.$$

If $\alpha = (a, b)$, then by definition of addition

$$\begin{aligned}
\alpha + (-a, -b) &= (a, b) + (-a, -b) \\
&= (a - a, b - b).
\end{aligned}$$

Then, since $a - a = 0$ and $b - b = 0$, we have $\alpha + (-a, -b) = (0, 0)$ by complex number equality. Therefore, we take $-\alpha$ to *mean* the complex number $(-a, -b)$. This proves 6 (a). For 6 (b), the condition that $\alpha \neq (0, 0)$ implies that if $\alpha = (a, b)$, $a \neq 0$ or $b \neq 0$.

Then $a^2 + b^2 \neq 0$. Define α^{-1} to be the complex number

$$(a/(a^2 + b^2), -b/(a^2 + b^2)).$$

By definition of multiplication,

$$\begin{aligned}
\alpha \cdot \alpha^{-1} &= (a, b)\left(\frac{a}{a^2 + b^2}, \frac{-b}{a^2 + b^2}\right) \\
&= \left(\frac{a^2}{a^2 + b^2} + \frac{b^2}{a^2 + b^2}, \frac{-ab}{a^2 + b^2} + \frac{ab}{a^2 + b^2}\right) \\
&= \left(\frac{a^2 + b^2}{a^2 + b^2}, 0\right) \\
&= (1, 0).
\end{aligned}$$

The last two lines above follow from the previous lines because of the condition for equality. This completes the proof of 6(b).

Consider the set of all complex numbers $(a, 0)$. These numbers add and multiply as follows:

$$\begin{aligned}
(a, 0) + (b, 0) &= (a + b, 0 + 0) \\
&= (a + b, 0) \\
(a, 0) \cdot (b, 0) &= (ab - 0 \cdot 0, a \cdot 0 + 0 \cdot b) \\
&= (ab, 0).
\end{aligned}$$

This shows that the additive and multiplicative properties of these numbers depend only on the real numbers a, b and for this reason the complex numbers $(a, 0)$ are identified with the corresponding real numbers a. It is in this sense that the complex numbers are an expansion of the real number system.

Theorem 29. The equation

$$x^2 + 1 = 0$$

has a solution in the complex number system.

Proof: By the principle, stated above, for identifying real numbers a with their corresponding complex numbers $(a, 0)$, the equation in question is

$$x^2 + (1, 0) = (0, 0).$$

The complex number $(0, 1)$ is a solution:

$$\begin{aligned}
(0, 1)^2 + (1, 0) &= (0, 1) \cdot (0, 1) + (1, 0) \\
&= (0 \cdot 0 - 1 \cdot 1, 0 \cdot 1 + 1 \cdot 0) + (1, 0) \\
&= (0 - 1, 0 + 0) + (1, 0) \\
&= (-1, 0) + (1, 0) \\
&= (0, 0).
\end{aligned}$$

The complex number $(0, 1)$, shown above to be a solution of the equation

$$x^2 + 1 = 0,$$

is usually denoted by i. Using this notation, every complex number (a, b) may be expressed

$$a + bi$$

as the following computation shows:

$$\begin{aligned}(a, b) &= (a + 0, 0 + b)\\ &= (a, 0) + (0, b)\\ &= (a, 0) + (b \cdot 0 - 0 \cdot 1, b \cdot 1 + 0 \cdot 0)\\ &= (a, 0) + (b, 0) \cdot (0, 1)\\ &= a + bi.\end{aligned}$$

Example 9-1. Solve the equation

$$(1, 3)\alpha = (7, 1).$$

Solution. Since $(1, 3) \neq (0, 0)$, compute

$$(1, 3)^{-1} = \big(1/(1^2 + 3^2), -3/(1^2 + 3^2)\big) = (1/10, -3/10).$$

Then,

$$(1/10, -3/10)(1, 3)\alpha = (1/10, -3/10)(7, 1)$$

or

$$\begin{aligned}\alpha &= (7/10 + 3/10, 1/10 - 21/10)\\ \alpha &= (1, -2).\end{aligned}$$

To check this solution,

$$\begin{aligned}(1, 3)(1, -2) &= (1 + 6, -2 + 3)\\ &= (7, 1).\end{aligned}$$

Example 9-2. Solve the equation $x^2 + 8 = 0$.

Solution. We seek a complex number x such that $x^2 = -8$. Since

$$\begin{aligned}i^2 &= (0, 1)(0, 1)\\ &= (-1, 0) = -1\end{aligned}$$

and $(2\sqrt{2})^2 = 8$, it seems reasonable that $2i\sqrt{2}$ might be a solution:

$$\begin{aligned}(2i\sqrt{2})^2 + 8 &= (2i\sqrt{2})(2i\sqrt{2}) + 8\\ &= i^2(2\sqrt{2})^2 + 8\\ &= -1 \cdot 8 + 8\\ &= 0.\end{aligned}$$

Hence, $2i\sqrt{2}$ is a solution and $-2i\sqrt{2}$ also may be shown to be a solution.

Example 9-3. Express the complex number $\dfrac{2 + 3i}{1 + i}$ in the form $a + bi$.

Solution. The number $\dfrac{2 + 3i}{1 + i}$ means $(2 + 3i) \cdot (1 + i)^{-1}$. Hence,

$$
\begin{aligned}
\frac{2 + 3i}{1 + i} &= (2 + 3i) \cdot (1 + i)^{-1} \\
&= (2, 3) \cdot (1, 1)^{-1} \\
&= (2, 3) \cdot (1/2, -1/2) \\
&= (1 + 3/2, -1 + 3/2) \\
&= (5/2, 1/2) \\
&= (5/2) + (1/2)i.
\end{aligned}
$$

Exercises

1. Compute the following sums and products.

(a) $(1, 5) + (1/2, 4)$.
(b) $(7/8, -9) + (-1/2, 2)$.
(c) $(1, 2) \cdot (3, 2)$.
(d) $(0, 5) \cdot (\sqrt{2}, 1/8)$.
(e) $(1 + i) + (-3 - 5i)$.
(f) $(2 + 6i) + 1/2$.
(g) $3(2 + 7i) - 2(1 - i)$.
(h) $(1/8 - i) \cdot (-1 + i)$.
(i) $(\sqrt{2} + i) \cdot (\sqrt{2} - i)$.

2. Compute the multiplicative inverse of each of the following; i.e., compute α^{-1}.

(a) $\alpha = (1, 0)$.
(b) $\alpha = (0, 1)$.
(c) $\alpha = 1 - i$.
(d) $\alpha = 1/2 + (3/4)i$.
(e) $\alpha = 2i$.
(f) $\alpha = 4$.

3. Express each of the following in the form $a + bi$.

(a) $(1, 0)$.
(b) $(7, 2)$.
(c) $4 \cdot (1/2, 1)$.
(d) $\dfrac{1 - i}{1 + i}$.
(e) $\dfrac{1/2 + i}{i}$.
(f) $\dfrac{-9 + 3i}{7(2 - 9i)}$

4. Solve each of the following equations:

(a) $(2 + i)x + 5 = i$.
(b) $ix - 7i = 1$.
(c) $x^2 + 2 = 0$.
(d) $x^2 + i = 0$.

5. Prove parts 2, 3, 5 of Theorem 28.

6. Prove each of the following by mathematical induction.
(a) $i^{4n} = 1$, for all positive integers n.
(b) $i^{4n+1} = i$, for all positive integers n.
(c) $i^{4n+2} = -1$, for all positive integers n.

7. Prove: $a(c, d) = (ac, ad)$ or $a(c + di) = ac + (ad)i$ and that $[a(c, d)][b(e, f)] = ab(c, d)(e, f)$ [*Hint:* $a = (a, 0)$].

9.2 Polar Representation

Complex numbers are ordered pairs of real numbers and may therefore be represented as points in the plane. If the point $P(a, b)$ is a distance r from the origin, we have the equations

$$a = r \cos \varphi$$
$$b = r \sin \varphi$$

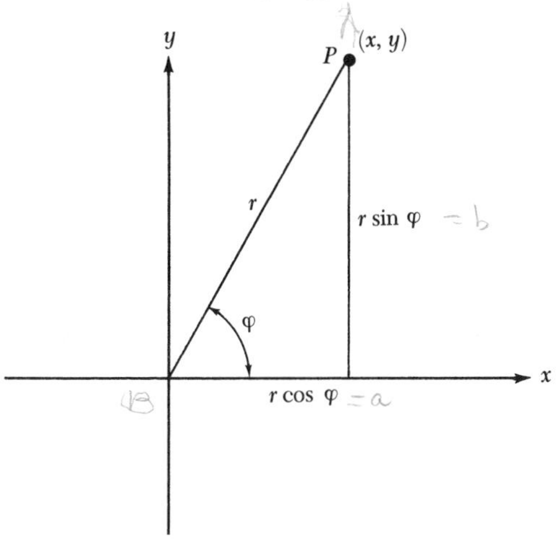

Figure 9-1

where φ measures the angle shown in Fig. 9-1. Then

$$\begin{aligned} a + bi &= (a, b) \\ &= (r \cos \varphi, r \sin \varphi) \\ &= r(\cos \varphi, \sin \varphi) \qquad \text{(See Exercise 7.)} \\ &= r(\cos \varphi + i \sin \varphi). \end{aligned}$$

Hence, every complex number $a + bi$ may be expressed as

$$r(\cos \varphi + i \sin \varphi)$$

where $r = \sqrt{a^2 + b^2}$ and φ is a suitably chosen number. This is known as the *polar form* of the complex number.

Example 9-4. Represent the complex number $1 + i$ in polar form.

Solution. The point $P(1, 1)$ in the plane is on the line bisecting the first and third quadrants. Thus, we may take $\pi/4$ for the angle measure. Also $P(1, 1)$ is $\sqrt{1^2 + 1^2} = \sqrt{2}$ distance from the origin. Then,

$$1 + i = \sqrt{2}(\cos \pi/4 + i \sin \pi/4)$$

so that $\sqrt{2}(\cos \pi/4 + i \sin \pi/4)$ is the polar form of $1 + i$. (See Fig. 9-2.)

Example 9-5. Show that every complex number of the form $\cos \varphi + i \sin \varphi$ represents a point on the unit circle, center at the origin.

Solution. The complex number $\cos \varphi + i \sin \varphi$ is the ordered pair $(\cos \varphi, \sin \varphi)$; and since $\cos^2\varphi + \sin^2\varphi = 1$, it is a point of the unit circle, center at the origin: $\{(x, y) \mid x^2 + y^2 = 1\}$.

The polar form of a complex number is convenient especially for multiplying. Suppose that the polar form of two complex numbers α, β is $r_1(\cos \varphi_1 + i \sin \varphi_1)$ and $r_2(\cos \varphi_2 + i \sin \varphi_2)$, respectively. Then,

$$\begin{aligned}
\alpha\beta &= [r_1(\cos \varphi_1 + i \sin \varphi_1)][r_2(\cos \varphi_2 + i \sin \varphi_2)] \\
&= r_1r_2(\cos \varphi_1, \sin \varphi_1) \cdot (\cos \varphi_2, \sin \varphi_2) \\
&= r_1r_2(\cos \varphi_1 \cos \varphi_2 - \sin \varphi_1 \sin \varphi_2, \cos \varphi_1 \sin \varphi_2 + \sin \varphi_1, \cos \varphi_2) \\
&= r_1r_2[\cos (\varphi_1 + \varphi_2), \sin (\varphi_1 + \varphi_2)] \\
&= r_1r_2[\cos (\varphi_1 + \varphi_2) + i \sin (\varphi_1 + \varphi_2)].
\end{aligned}$$

This shows—roughly speaking—that complex numbers in polar form may be multiplied by multiplying their distances from the origin and adding their angles.

Example 9-6. Multiply the complex numbers

$$\sqrt{2}(\cos \pi/4 + i \sin \pi/4) \qquad \text{and} \qquad 2(\cos \pi/3 + i \sin \pi/3).$$

Solution.

$$\begin{aligned}
&[\sqrt{2}(\cos \pi/4 + i \sin \pi/4)] \cdot [2(\cos \pi/3 + i \sin \pi/3)] \\
&= 2\sqrt{2}[\cos (\pi/4 + \pi/3) + i \sin (\pi/4 + \pi/3)] \\
&= 2\sqrt{2}(\cos 7\pi/12 + i \sin 7\pi/12).
\end{aligned}$$

Example 9-7.

$$\begin{aligned}
&[\sqrt{2}(\cos \pi/4 + i \sin \pi/4)]^2 \\
&\qquad = \sqrt{2} \cdot \sqrt{2}(\cos (\pi/4 + \pi/4) + i \sin (\pi/4 + \pi/4)) \\
&\qquad = 2(\cos (\pi/2) + i \sin (\pi/2)).
\end{aligned}$$

Hence, since $1 + i = \sqrt{2}(\cos \pi/4 + i \sin \pi/4)$,

$$(1 + i)^2 = 2i.$$

Theorem 30 (De Moivre's Theorem). If n is a natural number, then

$$[r(\cos \varphi + i \sin \varphi)]^n = r^n(\cos n\varphi + i \sin n\varphi).$$

Proof: Apply the induction principle to the statement $P(n)$. $P(1)$ is

$$[r(\cos \varphi + i \sin \varphi)]^1 = r^1(\cos 1 \cdot \varphi + i \sin 1 \cdot \varphi)$$

which is seen to be true. $P(k)$ and $P(k + 1)$ are respectively

$$[r(\cos \varphi + i \sin \varphi)]^k = r^k(\cos k\varphi + i \sin k\varphi)$$

and

$$[r(\cos \varphi + i \sin \varphi)]^{k+1} = r^{k+1}[\cos (k + 1)\varphi + i \sin (k + 1)\varphi].$$

If $P(k)$ is true, we have

$$\begin{aligned}[r(\cos \varphi + i \sin \varphi)]^{k+1} &= [r(\cos \varphi + i \sin \varphi)]^k \cdot [r(\cos \varphi + i \sin \varphi)] \\ &= [r^k(\cos k\varphi + i \sin k\varphi)] \cdot [r(\cos \varphi + i \sin \varphi)] \\ &= r^{k+1}[\cos (k\varphi + \varphi) + i \sin (k\varphi + \varphi)] \\ &= r^{k+1}[\cos (k + 1)\varphi + i \sin (k + 1)\varphi].\end{aligned}$$

This shows that if $P(k)$ is true, then so is $P(k + 1)$ and proves the theorem.

Example 9-8. Compute $(1 + i)^{64}$.

Solution. $1 + i = \sqrt{2}(\cos \pi/4 + i \sin \pi/4)$ and therefore,

$$\begin{aligned}(1 + i)^{64} &= [\sqrt{2}(\cos \pi/4 + i \sin \pi/4)]^{64} \\ &= (\sqrt{2})^{64}(\cos 64 \cdot \pi/4 + i \sin 64 \cdot \pi/4) \\ &= 2^{32}(\cos 16\pi + i \sin 16\pi) \\ &= 2^{32}(1 + i \cdot 0) = 2^{32}.\end{aligned}$$

Example 9-9. Find a complex number $a + bi$ such that $(a + bi)^3 = 1 + i$.

Solution. Suppose that $a + bi = r(\cos \varphi + i \sin \varphi)$ and that $(a + bi)^3 = 1 + i$. Then,

$$[r(\cos \varphi + i \sin \varphi)]^3 = 1 + i = \sqrt{2}(\cos \pi/4 + i \sin \pi/4)$$

or

$$r^3(\cos 3\varphi + i \sin 3\varphi) = \sqrt{2}(\cos \pi/4 + i \sin \pi/4)$$

or

$$(r^3 \cos 3\varphi, r^3 \sin 3\varphi) = (\sqrt{2} \cos \pi/4, \sqrt{2} \sin \pi/4).$$

Hence,

$$r^3 \cos 3\varphi = \sqrt{2} \cos \pi/4 = \sqrt{2}(\tfrac{1}{2}\sqrt{2}) = 1$$

and

$$r^3 \sin 3\varphi = \sqrt{2} \sin \pi/4 = \sqrt{2}(\tfrac{1}{2}\sqrt{2}) = 1.$$

Therefore, $r^3(\cos 3\varphi - \sin 3\varphi) = 0$; and since r^3 cannot be zero, we must have

$$\cos 3\varphi = \sin 3\varphi.$$

Then

$$\sin^2 3\varphi + \cos^2 3\varphi = 1$$

and

$$2 \sin^2 3\varphi = 1$$
$$\sin^2 3\varphi = \tfrac{1}{2}.$$

Thus, $\sin 3\varphi = \pm\tfrac{1}{2}\sqrt{2}$, but $\sin 3\varphi$ cannot be negative ($r^3 \sin 3\varphi = 1$ and $r^3 > 0$) so

$$\sin 3\varphi = \tfrac{1}{2}\sqrt{2} \qquad \text{and} \qquad \cos 3\varphi = \tfrac{1}{2}\sqrt{2}.$$

One solution of these equations is obtained if $3\varphi = \pi/4$ or $\varphi = \pi/12$. If we take this number for φ and substitute into

$$r^3 \sin 3\varphi = 1,$$

we obtain

$$r^3 = \sqrt{2}$$

and

$$r = (2^{1/2})^{1/3} = 2^{1/6}.$$

We conclude from this that the complex number

$$2^{1/6}\left(\cos \frac{\pi}{12} + i \sin \frac{\pi}{12}\right)$$

may be a solution to the problem. That it is indeed a solution follows from the computations below:

$$\begin{aligned}\left[2^{1/6}\left(\cos \frac{\pi}{12} + i \sin \frac{\pi}{12}\right)\right]^3 &= (2^{1/6})^3\left(\cos 3 \cdot \frac{\pi}{12} + i \sin 3 \cdot \frac{\pi}{12}\right)\\ &= 2^{1/2}\left(\cos \frac{\pi}{4} + i \sin \frac{\pi}{4}\right)\\ &= \sqrt{2}(\tfrac{1}{2}\sqrt{2} + i(\tfrac{1}{2}\sqrt{2}))\\ &= 1 + i.\end{aligned}$$

Theorem 31. Let α be a non-zero complex number and let n be a natural number. Then there are exactly n complex numbers β_0, $\beta_1, \beta_2, \beta_3, \ldots, \beta_{n-1}$ such that for each $k = 0, 1, 2, 3, \ldots, n-1$,

$$(\beta_k)^n = \alpha.$$

Proof: (The word "exactly" is used here to mean that there are n of these numbers and only n.) Suppose that in polar form $\alpha = r(\cos\varphi + i \sin\varphi)$; and suppose that $\gamma = s(\cos\theta + i\sin\theta)$ is a complex number such that $\gamma^n = \alpha$. Thus, by De Moivre's Theorem, we have

$$s^n(\cos n\theta + i \sin n\theta) = r(\cos\varphi + i\sin\varphi)$$

or

$$s^n \cos n\theta + is^n \sin n\theta = r\cos\varphi + ir\sin\varphi.$$

It follows from this that

$$s^n \cos n\theta = r\cos\varphi \qquad \text{and} \qquad s^n \sin n\theta = r\sin\varphi \tag{1}$$

and hence,

$$\begin{aligned} r^2 &= r^2(\sin^2\varphi + \cos^2\varphi) \\ &= r^2\sin^2\varphi + r^2\cos^2\varphi \\ &= s^{2n}\sin^2 n\theta + s^{2n}\cos^2 n\theta \\ &= s^{2n}(\sin^2 n\theta + \cos^2 n\theta) \\ &= s^{2n}. \end{aligned}$$

Since both r and s must be positive, we conclude that $r = s^n$ or $s = r^{1/n}$. Using this result in Eq. (1) leads to

$$\cos n\theta = \cos\varphi \qquad \text{and} \qquad \sin n\theta = \sin\varphi. \tag{2}$$

From Section 5-4, $\cos n\theta = \cos\varphi$ if, and only if, $n\theta = \varphi + 2k\pi$ or $n\theta = -\varphi + 2k\pi$ for some integer k. Also, $\sin n\theta = \sin\varphi$ if and only if $n\theta = \varphi + 2m\pi$ or $n\theta = -\varphi + (2m+1)\pi$ for some integer m. Therefore, since both equations in (2) must hold, there is some integer k such that $n\theta = \varphi + 2k\pi$ or $\theta = \dfrac{1}{n}(\varphi + 2k\pi)$. We thus have shown that if $\gamma = s(\cos\theta + i\sin\theta)$ is a complex number such that $\gamma^n = \alpha$, then there is some integer k such that

$$s = r^{1/n} \qquad \text{and} \qquad \theta = (1/n)(\varphi + 2k\pi).$$

Now define, for each integer k,

$$\beta_k = r^{1/n}\left[\cos\left(\frac{\varphi + 2k\pi}{n}\right) + i\sin\left(\frac{\varphi + 2k\pi}{n}\right)\right].$$

By De Moivre's Theorem,

$$\begin{aligned}(\beta_k)^n &= r[\cos(\varphi + 2k\pi) + i \sin(\varphi + 2k\pi)]\\ &= r[\cos\varphi + i\sin\varphi]\\ &= \alpha.\end{aligned}$$

This shows that all the numbers β_k have the required property; i.e., that $(\beta_k)^n = \alpha$. These numbers are, however, not all distinct. In fact, for *every* integer k, β_k is one of the numbers $\beta_0, \beta_1, \beta_2, \ldots, \beta_{n-1}$. For if k is any integer, we may divide k by n and obtain a quotient and remainder with the remained less than n. That is, we may find integers q and j such that

$$k = nq + j \qquad \text{and} \qquad 0 \le j < n.$$

Then,

$$\begin{aligned}\cos\left(\frac{\varphi + 2k\pi}{n}\right) &= \cos\left(\frac{\varphi + 2(nq + j)\pi}{n}\right)\\ &= \cos\left(\frac{\varphi + 2j\pi}{n} + 2q\pi\right)\\ &= \cos\left(\frac{(\varphi + 2j\pi)}{n}\right);\end{aligned}$$

and similarly,

$$\sin\left(\frac{\varphi + 2k\pi}{n}\right) = \sin\left(\frac{\varphi + 2j\pi}{n}\right).$$

From this,

$$\begin{aligned}\beta_k &= r^{1/n}\left[\cos\left(\frac{\varphi + 2k\pi}{n}\right) + i\sin\left(\frac{\varphi + 2k\pi}{n}\right)\right]\\ &= r^{1/n}\left[\cos\left(\frac{\varphi + 2j\pi}{n}\right) + i\sin\left(\frac{\varphi + 2j\pi}{n}\right)\right]\\ &= \beta_j\end{aligned}$$

and j is one of the integers $0, 1, 2, 3, \ldots, n - 1$. Now suppose that $\beta_h = \beta_j$ for $0 \le h < j \le n - 1$. Then by definition of β_h and β_j,

$$\cos\left(\frac{\varphi + 2h\pi}{n}\right) = \cos\left(\frac{\varphi + 2j\pi}{n}\right)$$

$$\sin\left(\frac{\varphi + 2h\pi}{n}\right) = \sin\left(\frac{\varphi + 2j\pi}{n}\right).$$

As in the earlier part of the proof, we conclude that

$$\frac{\varphi + 2h\pi}{n} = \frac{\varphi + 2j\pi}{n} + 2m\pi$$

for some integer m. Then,

$$\frac{2h\pi}{n} = \frac{2j\pi}{n} + 2m\pi$$

or

$$h = j + 2mn;$$

and consequently, $j - h = -2mn$. This implies that $j - h$, which is a positive number, is a multiple of n. But since

$$0 < j - h \leq n - 1,$$

we must have $m = 0$ and $j = h$. However, this is a contradiction since we assumed that $h < j$. Thus the numbers

$$\beta_0, \beta_1, \beta_2, \beta_3, \ldots, \beta_{n-1}$$

are exactly n in number and this completes the proof.

The numbers $\beta_0, \beta_1, \beta_2, \ldots, \beta_{n-1}$ are called the *nth roots* of the complex number α.

Example 9-10. Find the 4th roots of $1 + i$.

Solution. In polar form $1 + i$ is $\sqrt{2}(\cos \pi/4 + i \sin \pi/4)$. The 4th roots are, according to Theorem 31, $\beta_0, \beta_1, \beta_2, \beta_3$ where

$$\begin{aligned}\beta_k &= (\sqrt{2})^{1/4}\left[\cos\left(\frac{\pi/4 + 2k\pi}{4}\right) + i \sin\left(\frac{\pi/4 + 2k\pi}{4}\right)\right]\\ &= 2^{1/8}[\cos(\pi/16 + \tfrac{1}{2}k\pi) + i \sin(\pi/16 + \tfrac{1}{2}k\pi)].\end{aligned}$$

Therefore,

$$\begin{aligned}\beta_0 &= 2^{1/8}(\cos \pi/16 + i \sin \pi/16)\\ \beta_1 &= 2^{1/8}[\cos(\pi/16 + \pi/2) + i \sin(\pi/16 + \pi/2)]\\ \beta_2 &= 2^{1/8}[\cos(\pi/16 + \pi) + i \sin(\pi/16 + \pi)]\\ \beta_3 &= 2^{1/8}[\cos(\pi/16 + 3\pi/2) + i \sin(\pi/16 + 3\pi/2)].\end{aligned}$$

Example 9-11. Find the 5th roots of 1.

Solution. In polar form $1 = 1 \cdot (\cos 0 + i \sin 0)$ and so

$$\beta_k = 1^{1/5}\left[\cos\left(\frac{0 + 2k\pi}{5}\right) + i \sin\left(\frac{0 + 2k\pi}{5}\right)\right]$$

for $k = 0, 1, 2, 3, 4$:

$$\begin{aligned}
\beta_0 &= \cos 0 + i \sin 0 = 1 \\
\beta_1 &= \cos (2\pi/5) + i \sin (2\pi/5) \\
\beta_2 &= \cos (4\pi/5) + i \sin (4\pi/5) \\
\beta_3 &= \cos (6\pi/5) + i \sin (6\pi/5) \\
\beta_4 &= \cos (8\pi/5) + i \sin (8\pi/5).
\end{aligned}$$

Exercises

8. Express each of the following complex numbers in polar form.
(a) $(\frac{1}{2}) + (\frac{1}{2})i$.
(b) $(\frac{1}{2}) - (\frac{1}{2})i$.
(c) $-7 + 7i$.
(d) 2.
(e) $2i$.
(f) 0.
(g) $-2 - 2\sqrt{3}i$.
(h) $1 + \sqrt{3}i$.
(i) $\sqrt{3} - i$.

9. Use De Moivre's Theorem to compute the following:
(a) i^{14}.
(b) $[(\frac{1}{2}) - (\frac{1}{2})i]^6$.
(c) $(-2 - 2\sqrt{3}i)^5$.
(d) $(1 + \sqrt{3}i)^8$.
(e) $(\sqrt{3} - i)^6$.

10. Find the square root of each of the following:
(a) -1.
(b) $-\sqrt{2}$.
(c) -7.
(d) -4.
(e) d, where d is a real number such that $d < 0$.

11. Let $Q(x) = ax^2 + bx + c$ be a quadratic function and suppose that a, b, c are real numbers such that $b^2 - 4ac < 0$. It has been shown in Chapter 4 that Q has no zeros which are real numbers. Show that Q does have zeros which are complex numbers.

12. Solve the following equations:
(a) $x^2 + x + 1 = 0$.
(b) $x^3 - 1 = 0$.
(c) $x^2 + 2x + 2 = 0$.
(d) $x^2 - x + 1 = 0$.
(e) $2x^2 - x + 1 = 0$.
(f) $x^4 + 1 = 0$.
(g) $y^6 + 2y^3 + 2 = 0$.
(h) $z^6 - 1 = 0$.

13. (a) Compute the 3rd roots of 1.
(b) Compute the 3rd roots of -1.
(c) Compute the 2nd roots of $1 - i$.
(d) Compute the 5th roots of $\cos (\pi/8) + i \sin (\pi/8)$.
(e) Compute the 7th roots of $5[\cos (\pi/3) + i \sin (\pi/3)]$.

Answers

Chapter 1

1. (a) True. (b) False. (c) False.

2. (a) 3. (b) An infinite number. (c) $A \subseteq B$ is true.

3. (a) $V \subseteq W$ is true. (b) (i) False. (ii) True. (iii) True.

4. (a) (i) True. (ii) True. (iii) True. (iv) True.
(b) (i) True. (ii) True. (iii) False. (iv) True.
(c) (i) True. (ii) False. (iii) False. (iv) False.

6. (a) 4. (b) 8. (c) 2^4; 2^5.

10. (a) {7, 8, 11, 13, 4, 2, 17, 9}.
(b) {7, 8, 11, 13, 4, 1, 5, 19}.
(c) {2, 4, 8, 17, 9, 1, 7, 5, 11, 19}.
(d) {8, 4}.
(e) {7, 11}.
(f) $\varnothing$.
(g) {7, 11, 13}.
(h) {2, 17, 9}.
(i) {8, 13, 4}.
(j) {1, 5, 19}.
(k) {2, 4, 8, 17, 9}.
(l) {1, 7, 5, 11, 19}.

24. (a) $\{(1, 2), (2, 2)\}$.
(b) $\{(0, 8), (0, 5), (5, 8), (5, 5)\}$.

25. (a) $\{3, 2\}$ is the domain; $\{2\}$ is the range.
(b) $\{1, 3, 2\}$ is the domain; $\{2, 5, 7\}$ is the range.
(c) $\{2, 7, 5\}$ is the domain; $\{4, 3, 1\}$ is the range.

27. (a) Is a function; not 1-1; the inverse is $\{(2, 3), (2, 2)\}$.
(b) Is not a function; the inverse is $\{(2, 3), (2, 2), (7, 3), (5, 4)\}$.
(c) Is a function; is 1-1; the inverse is $\{(2, 1), (5, 2), (7, 3)\}$.
(d) Is a function; is 1-1; the inverse is $\{(7, 3), (5, 2)\}$.

29. (a) Not reflexive; not symmetric; transitive.
(b) Not reflexive; not symmetric; transitive.
(c) Reflexive; symmetric; transitive.
(d) Not reflexive; not symmetric; transitive.
(e) Reflexive; symmetric; transitive.
(f) Reflexive; symmetric; transitive.

Chapter 2

1. (a) $\{x | x < \frac{13}{3}\}$.
(b) $\{x | x > \frac{27}{2}\}$.
(c) $\{x | x \geq \frac{25}{11}\}$.
(d) $\{x | x > \frac{5}{2}\} \cup \{x | x < 0\}$.
(e) $\{x | 0 < x \leq 2\} \cup \{x | x \leq -\frac{1}{3}\}$.
(f) $\{x | -10 < x < 6\}$.
(g) $\{x | \frac{1}{2} \leq x \leq \frac{17}{6}\}$.
(h) $\{x | x \leq 1\} \cup \{x | x \geq 7\}$.

18. (a) 0.
(b) 2, -2.
(c) 1.
(d) -1, $\frac{3}{7}$.
(e) No solution.
(f) 0.
(g) $\frac{4}{3}$, $-\frac{4}{5}$.
(h) $x = y$.

19. (a) $\{x | x \leq \frac{3}{2}\}$.
(b) $\{x | -\frac{7}{6} < x < \frac{3}{8}\}$.
(c) $\{x | x > 5\} \cup \{x | x < 3\}$.
(d) $\{x | x > 6\} \cup \{x | -8 > x\}$.

20. (a) If S is a non-empty set of real numbers, then the number x is a *lower bound* of the set S if and only if $x \leq s$ for all $s \in S$.
(b) Let S be a non-empty set of real numbers and t be a lower bound for S such that if u is any lower bound of S, then $u \leq t$. Then t is called the *greatest lower bound* of S.
(c) If S is a non-empty set of real numbers, then r is the *largest element* of S if and only if $r \in S$ and $x \leq r$ for all $r \in S$.

21. (a) 100 is an upper bound; -100 is a lower bound.
(b) -10 is a lower bound; there is no upper bound.

(c) 101^2 is an upper bound; -2 is a lower bound.
(d) 2 is an upper bound; -1 is a lower bound.
(e) 2 is an upper bound; -1 is a lower bound.
(f) 2 is an upper bound; -1 is a lower bound.

22. (a) $-\sqrt{2}$ is the greatest lower bound; 0.78 is the least upper bound.
(b) 0 is the greatest lower bound; there is no least upper bound.
(c) 0 is the greatest lower bound; 100^2 is the least upper bound.
(d) 0 is the greatest lower bound; 1 is the least upper bound.
(e) 0 is the greatest lower bound; 1 is the least upper bound.
(f) 0 is the greatest lower bound; 1 is the least upper bound.

27. (a) $\sqrt[3]{2}$ is the least upper bound of the set
$\{y \,|\, y$ is a positive rational number and $y^3 < 2\}$.
(c) $3^{3/5}$ is the least upper bound of the set
$\{y \,|\, y$ is a positive rational number and $y^5 < 3^3\}$.

Chapter 3

9. (a) 1. (b) $\sqrt{130}$. (c) $(\frac{5}{4})\sqrt{17}$. (d) $\sqrt{2\sqrt{2} + (\frac{273}{64})}$.

12. (a) Circle, center at (0, 0), radius of 1.
(b) Not a circle.
(c) Not a circle.
(d) Circle, center at (1, 1), radius of 2.
(e) Not a circle.
(f) Circle, center at $(-8, -5)$, radius of $\sqrt[4]{2}$.
(g) Circle, center at $(-\frac{1}{2}, 1)$, radius of 1.

13. (a) $\{(x, y) \,|\, x^2 + (y - 1)^2 = 1\}$.
(b) $\{(x, y) \,|\, (x - 2)^2 + (y + 4)^2 = \frac{1}{2}\}$.
(c) $\{(a, b) \,|\, (a + 1)^2 + (b + 2)^2 = \frac{9}{64}\}$.
(d) $\{(c, d) \,|\, (c + \frac{8}{9})^2 + (d - 0.6)^2 = 6\}$.

19. (a) $\{(x, y) \,|\, x \geq 1\}$.
(b) $\{(x, y) \,|\, y - x = 1\}$.
(c) $\{(x, y) \,|\, |x| \leq 1$ and $|y| \leq 1\}$.
(d) $\{(x, y) \,|\, y \leq x + 1\} \cap \{(x, y) \,|\, y \geq x - 1\}$.
(e) $\{(x, y) \,|\, x = y\} \cup \{(x, y) \,|\, x = -y\}$.
(f) $\{(x, y) \,|\, y = |x|\}$.
(g) $\{(x, y) \,|\, x = y$ and $x \geq 0\} \cup \{(x, y) \,|\, x = -y$ and $x \geq 0\}$.

(h) $\{(x, y) \mid y \leq -x \text{ and } x \leq 0\} \cap \{(x, y) \mid y \geq x \text{ and } x \leq 0\}$.
(i) $\{(x, y) \mid y \leq -\mathrm{x}\} \cup \{(x, y) \mid y \leq x\}$.
(j) $\{(x, y) \mid x^2 + y^2 = 1\} \cap \{(x, y) \mid x \leq y\} \cap \{(x, y) \mid y \geq -x\}$.

20. (a) Not a function.
(b) Not a function.
(c) A function.
(d) Not a function.
(e) Not a function.
(f) Not a function.
(g) Not a function.
(h) Not a function.

21. For 15. (a) Not a function.
(b) Not a function.
(c) Not a function.
(d) Not a function.
(e) A function.
(f) A function.
(g) Not a function.

For 16. (a) Not a function.
(b) Not a function.
(c) Not a function.
(d) Not a function.

For 17. (a), (b), (c) are functions. (d), (e) are not functions.

23. (a) $f(a) = a^2 + 1$.
(b) $f(x) = x^2 - 5$ for $x \in [-6, -5]$.
(c) $f(c) = \sqrt{c}$.
(d) $f(c) = \sqrt{8 - c}$.

24. (a) 14.
(b) -1.
(c) 0.
(d) 0.
(e) $200t^2 + 35t - 1$.
(f) $15 + 7\sqrt{2}$.
(g) $(8a^2 + 7ab - b^2)/(b^2)$.
(h) $8(a - b)^2 + 7(a - b) - 1$.

25. (a) 0.
(b) 3.
(c) n.

27. (a) $f(g(x)) = 2x - 1$.
(b) $f(g(x)) = 25x^2 - 10x + 2$.
(c) $f(g(x)) = [x^2]$ for $x \in [-2, 2]$.
(d) $f(g(x)) = [1 + 1/x]$ for $x \in [0, 10]$.

Chapter 4

1. (a) Not a polynomial.
(b) A polynomial of degree 2.
(c) Not a polynomial.
(d) The zero polynomial.
(e) A polynomial of degree 9.
(f) Not a polynomial.
(g) Not a polynomial.

4. (i) (a) $y = 0$. (b) Above the line $y = 0$. (c) Low point: $(0, 0)$.
(ii) (a) $y = 0$. (b) Below the line $y = 0$. (c) High point: $(0, 0)$.
(iii) (a) $y = -\frac{1}{4}$. (b) Above the line $y = -\frac{1}{4}$. (c) Low point: $(\frac{1}{2}, -\frac{1}{4})$.

(iv) (a) $y = 0$. (b) Above the line $y = 0$. (c) Low point: $(0, 0)$.

(v) (a) $y = 0$. (b) Above the line $y = 0$. (c) Low point: $(0, 0)$.

(vi) (a) $y = -\frac{59}{12}$. (b) Below the line $y = -\frac{59}{12}$. (c) High point: $(\frac{1}{6}, -\frac{59}{12})$.

(vii) (a) $y = -\frac{1}{4}$. (b) Below the line $y = -\frac{1}{4}$. (c) Low point: $(-\frac{1}{2}, -\frac{1}{4})$.

(viii) (a) $y = -\frac{15}{16}$. (b) Below the line $y = -\frac{15}{16}$. (c) High point: $(\frac{1}{4}, -\frac{15}{16})$.

5. (a) It is not possible for the graph to be nowhere above the line $y = 101$ for any number k.

(b) The graph is never above the line $y = 101$ for each number k in the interval $[-10, 10]$.

6. (i) 0. (ii) 0. (iii) 0, 1. (iv) 0. (v) 0. (vi) None. (vii) $0, -1$. (viii) $(-1 \pm \sqrt{17})/(-4)$.

7. (a) The discriminant is -3; the quadratic has no zeros.

(b) The discriminant is $2(2 - \sqrt{2})$; the zeros are $(-\sqrt{2} \pm \sqrt{2 - \sqrt{2}})/2$.

(c) The discriminant is $\frac{49}{4}$; the zeros are $-\frac{2}{3}, \frac{1}{2}$.

(d) The discriminant is -15; there are no zeros.

8. (a) Q has no zeros in any of the given domains.

(b) (i) In $[-1, 1]$ Q has two zeros: $\frac{2}{3}, -\frac{1}{2}$.

(ii) In the set of rational numbers Q has two zeros.

(iii) Q has no irrational zeros.

(iv) Q has no zeros in $[10, 101]$.

(v) Q has two zeros in the set of real numbers.

(c) Q has no zeros in any of the given domains.

(d) (i) Q has one zero in the interval $[-1, 1]$: $(-\sqrt{2} + \sqrt{2 - \sqrt{2}})/2$.

(ii) Q has no rational zeros.

(iii) Q has two irrational zeros: $(-\sqrt{2} \pm \sqrt{2 - \sqrt{2}})/2$.

(iv) Q has no zeros in the interval $[10, 101]$.

(v) Q has two real zeros.

(e) (i) Q has one zero in the interval $[-1, 1]$: $\dfrac{(10+11\sqrt{2}) - \sqrt{386+246\sqrt{2}}}{2+2\sqrt{2}}$.

(ii) Q has no zeros in the set of rational numbers.

(iii) Q has two irrational zeros.

(iv) Q has one zero in $[10, 101]$: $\dfrac{(10 + 11\sqrt{2}) + \sqrt{386 + 246\sqrt{2}}}{2 + 2\sqrt{2}}$.

(v) Q has two real zeros.

9. 3.

11. $-\frac{1}{2}$.

12. (a) Sum: 1 Product: $\frac{1}{4}$.
(b) Sum: 1 Product: $\frac{1}{4}$.
(c) Sum: $-\sqrt{2}$ Product: $\frac{1}{4}$.
(d) Sum: $-\sqrt{2}$ Product: $\frac{1}{4}$.
(e) Sum: -3 Product: 1
(f) Sum: 3 Product: 1.
(g) Sum: 4 Product: $\frac{1}{4}\sqrt{2}$.
(h) Sum: 4 Product: $\frac{1}{4}\sqrt{2}$.

13. (a) $x^2 + (\sqrt{2} - 1)x - \sqrt{2}$.
(b) $x^2 - 7x - 8$.
(c) $x^2 - 4x + 1$.
(*d*) $16x^2 - 6x - 1$.
(e) $4x^2 - 8\sqrt{5}x + 19$.

15. $\{k \mid k \leq 1 \text{ or } k \geq 4\}$.

18. $m \in [-2, 2]$.

19. $\mathcal{R}(F) = \{c \mid c \geq \frac{1}{4}\}$.

20. (a) $2x^4 - 10x^2 - 7 = (x + a)(x - a)(x^2 - b)$ where $a = \sqrt{\dfrac{5 + \sqrt{39}}{2}}$,

$b = \dfrac{5 - \sqrt{39}}{2}$.

(b) $3x^4 - 29x^2 + 18 = (\sqrt{3}x + \sqrt{2})(\sqrt{3}x - \sqrt{2})(x + 3)(x - 3)$.

(c) $x^4 - 6x^3 + 8x^2 + 3x - 2 = (x - a)(x - b)(x - c)(x - d)$ where
$a = (3 + \sqrt{17})/2$, $b = (3 - \sqrt{17})/2$.
$c = (3 + \sqrt{5})/2$, $d = (3 - \sqrt{5})/2$.

21. $f(1) = 1$, $f(2) = 13$, $f(5) = 253$, $f(-1) = 7$, $f(-3) = -27$, $f(-6) = -363$.

22. $f(3) = 596$.

23. $f(a) = 0$.

24. $m = 3$.

25. $k = 22$, $n = -24$.

26. (a) $x - 2$.
(b) $3x^2 + 2x + 12$.
(c) $x^4 - 3x^3 + 5x^2 - 18x + 54$.
(d) $x^3 - x^2 - 7x + 6$.
(e) $5x^2 + 7x + 21$.
(f) $x^3 - 3x^2 + 7x - 16$.

28. $\dfrac{1}{x(x+1)} = \dfrac{1}{x} - \dfrac{1}{x+1}$.

29. $\dfrac{x}{(x+1)(x-1)} = \dfrac{1/2}{x+1} + \dfrac{1/2}{x-1}$.

30. $\dfrac{4x+1}{2x^2 + 4x - 6} = \dfrac{5}{8(x-1)} + \dfrac{11}{8(x+3)}$.

31. $\dfrac{x^2}{x^2-1} = 1 - \dfrac{1/2}{x+1} + \dfrac{1/2}{x-1}.$

32. $\dfrac{2x+1}{x^3+1} = \dfrac{-1/3}{x+1} + \dfrac{(1/3)x+4/3}{x^2-x+1}.$

33. $\dfrac{x^3-x^2+x-1}{(2x+1)(x^2+1)^2} = \dfrac{-6}{5(2x+1)} + \dfrac{3x+1}{5(x^2+1)}.$

34. (a) $\{x \mid x \le 2 - \frac{1}{2}\sqrt{14}\} \cup \{x \mid x \ge 2 + \frac{1}{2}\sqrt{14}\}.$

(b) $\{x \mid (-3-\sqrt{33})/4 \le x \le (-3+\sqrt{33})/4\}.$

(c) $\varnothing.$

(d) $\{x \mid x < (1 - \sqrt{1+2\sqrt{3}})/\sqrt{2}\} \cup \{x \mid x > (1+\sqrt{1+2\sqrt{3}})/\sqrt{2}\}.$

(e) $\{x \mid 0 \le x \le 1\}.$

(f) $\{x \mid (1-\sqrt{41})/10 < x < (1+\sqrt{41})/10\}.$

34. (g) $\{x \mid x \le a\} \cup \{x \mid x \ge b\}$, where

$$a = \frac{(10+11\sqrt{2}) - \sqrt{386+264\sqrt{2}}}{2(1+\sqrt{2})}.$$

$$b = \frac{(10+11\sqrt{2}) + \sqrt{386+264\sqrt{2}}}{2(1+\sqrt{2})}.$$

36. (a) $\{x \mid -1 < x < 4\}.$

(b) $\{x \mid -5 < x < -1\} \cup \{x \mid x > 4\}.$

(c) $\{x \mid x < -\frac{1}{3}\} \cup \{x \mid \frac{8}{5} < x < \frac{17}{7}\}.$

(d) $\{x \mid x < -2\} \cup \{x \mid 1-\sqrt{5} < x < 2\} \cup \{x \mid 3 < x < 1+\sqrt{5}\}.$

(e) $\{x \mid -\sqrt{\frac{5}{2}} < x < -\frac{1}{2}\sqrt{2}\} \cup \{x \mid \frac{1}{2}\sqrt{2} < x < \sqrt{\frac{5}{2}}\}.$

(f) $\{x \mid x < -2\} \cup \{x \mid x > -1, x \ne 3\}.$

Chapter 5

1. (a) $(1, 0).$
(b) $(1, 0).$
(c) $(\sqrt{\frac{3}{2}}, \frac{1}{2}).$
(d) $(\sqrt{\frac{3}{2}}, -\frac{1}{2}).$
(e) $(\frac{1}{2}\sqrt{2}, \frac{1}{2}\sqrt{2}).$
(f) $(\frac{1}{2}, \frac{1}{2}\sqrt{3}).$
(g) $(0, 1).$
(h) $(0, -1).$
(i) $(0, -1).$
(j) $(-\frac{1}{2}, \frac{1}{2}\sqrt{3}).$
(k) $(-\frac{1}{2}\sqrt{3}, \frac{1}{2}).$
(l) $(-1, 0).$
(m) $(-\frac{1}{2}\sqrt{2}, -\frac{1}{2}\sqrt{2}).$
(n) $(-\frac{1}{2}\sqrt{3}, -\frac{1}{2}).$
(o) $(-\frac{1}{2}, -\frac{1}{2}\sqrt{3}).$
(p) $(\frac{1}{2}, -\frac{1}{2}\sqrt{3}).$
(q) $(\frac{1}{2}\sqrt{3}, -\frac{1}{2}).$
(r) $(0, 1).$
(s) $(-\frac{1}{2}, -\frac{1}{2}\sqrt{3}).$
(t) $(-\frac{1}{2}\sqrt{3}, \frac{1}{2}).$
(u) $(-1, 0).$
(v) $(-\frac{1}{2}\sqrt{2}, \frac{1}{2}\sqrt{2}).$
(w) $(-\frac{1}{2}\sqrt{3}, \frac{1}{2}).$
(x) $(\frac{1}{2}, \frac{1}{2}\sqrt{3}).$

3. (a) $0.$
(b) $\frac{1}{2}.$
(c) $-\frac{1}{2}.$
(d) $-\frac{1}{2}\sqrt{3}.$
(e) $\frac{1}{2}\sqrt{2}.$
(f) $-1.$

17. (a) Amplitude $\frac{1}{3}$; period 2π.
(b) Amplitude 1; period 2.
(c) Amplitude 1; period $2\pi/7$.
(d) Amplitude 2; period 2π.
(e) Amplitude 1; period π.
(f) Amplitude 2; period 2.

25. (a) $\{\pi/6 + 2n\pi \mid n \text{ is an integer}\} \cup \{-\pi/6 + k\pi \mid k \text{ is an odd integer}\}$.
(b) $\{k\pi + 1 \mid k \text{ is an integer}\}$.
(c) $\{\pi/2 + 2n\pi \mid n \text{ is an integer}\}$.
(d) $\{2\pi/3 + 2n\pi \mid n \text{ is an integer}\} \cup \{-2\pi/3 + 2n\pi \mid n \text{ is an integer}\}$.
(e) $\{k\pi \mid k \text{ is an integer}\} \cup \{2\pi/3 + 2k\pi \mid k \text{ is an integer}\} \cup \{-2\pi/3 + 2k\pi \mid k \text{ is an integer}\}$.
(f) $\{\pi/2 + m\pi \mid m \text{ is an integer}\}$.

27. (a) $\{3(4n + 1)\pi/8 \mid n \text{ is an integer}\} \cup \{-3(4n + 1)\pi/4 \mid n \text{ is an integer}\}$.
(b) $\{(4n + 1)\pi/2 \mid n \text{ is an integer}\} \cup \{-(4n + 1)\pi/6 \mid n \text{ is an integer}\}$.
(c) $\{-(4n + 1)\pi/6 \mid n \text{ is an integer}\} \cup \{-(4n + 1)\pi/2 \mid n \text{ is an integer}\}$.
(d) $\{t \mid t = n\pi/6 \text{ or } t = (2n + 1)\pi/2 \text{ where } n \text{ is an integer}\}$.

28. (a) No solution.
(b) If s is any number such that $\sin s = \frac{1}{3}\sqrt{3}$, then the solution set is
$\{2s + 4n\pi \mid n \text{ is an integer}\} \cup \{-2s + 2(2n + 1)\pi \mid n \text{ is an integer}\} \cup \{-2s + 4n\pi \mid n \text{ is an integer}\} \cup \{2s + 2(2n + 1)\pi \mid n \text{ is an integer}\}$.
(c) $\{\pi/2 + n\pi \mid n \text{ is an integer}\}$.
(d) $\{2n\pi \mid n \text{ is an integer}\} \cup \{\pi/2 + 2n\pi \mid n \text{ is an integer}\}$.

29. (a) $360°$.
(b) $0°$.
(c) $22\frac{1}{2}°$.
(d) $330°$.

30. (a) $\pi/45$.
(b) $(0.59) \times (\pi/180)$.
(c) $13\pi/720$.
(d) $(0.32) \times (\pi/180)$.

31. (a) $\sin 30° = \frac{1}{2}$; $\cos 30° = \frac{1}{2}\sqrt{3}$.
(b) $\sin 90° = 1$; $\cos 90° = 0$.
(c) $\sin 135° = \frac{1}{2}\sqrt{2}$; $\cos 135° = -\frac{1}{2}\sqrt{2}$.
(d) $\sin 225° = -\frac{1}{2}\sqrt{2}$; $\cos 225° = -\frac{1}{2}\sqrt{2}$.
(e) $\sin(-45)° = -\frac{1}{2}\sqrt{2}$; $\cos(-45)° = +\frac{1}{2}\sqrt{2}$.
(f) $\tan 180° = 0$; $\sec 180° = -1$.

33. $a = 2\sqrt{2 - \sqrt{3}}$; $\sin B = \sin C = \frac{1}{2}\sqrt{3(2 + \sqrt{3})}$.

Chapter 6

1. (a) A 1-1 function.
(b) Not a 1-1 function.
(c) A 1-1 function.
(d) Not a 1-1 function.

2. (a) Not a 1-1 function.
(b) Not a 1-1 function.
(c) Not a 1-1 function.
(d) Not a 1-1 function.
(e) A 1-1 function.
(f) Not a 1-1 function.

4. (a) $f^{-1}(x) = \frac{1}{2}(7 - x)$.
(b) $f^{-1}(x) = -\sqrt{1 - x^2}$, $x \in [0, 1]$.
(c) $f^{-1}(x) = 1/x$, $x > 0$.
(d) $f^{-1}(x) = 1 - 3/x$, $x < 0$.
(e) $f^{-1}(x) = x/(1 - x)$, $x > 1$.
(f) $f^{-1}(x) = \frac{1}{4}(1 - \sqrt{1 + 4x})^2$, $x \geq 0$.
(g) $f^{-1}(x) = (b - dx)/(cx - a)$.

8. (a) $x = 1$.
(b) $x = 0$.
(c) $x = (\frac{1}{7}) \log_3 2$.
(d) No solutions.
(e) $\sqrt{2}, -\sqrt{2}$.
(f) $\sqrt{\frac{3}{2}}, -\sqrt{\frac{3}{2}}$.
(g) No solutions.

10. (a) $f^{-1}(x) = \log_4 x$.
(b) $g^{-1}(x) = \log_2 x + \log_2 14$.
(c) $h^{-1}(x) = 1/\big(\log_a(x - 1)\big)$
(d) $f^{-1}(x) = 2^x$.
(e) $g^{-1}(x) = \frac{1}{2}\sqrt{2}E_3(x/2)$.
(f) $h^{-1}(x) = (\frac{1}{7})\big(E_a(x) - 2\big)$.

11. (a) $\{x \mid x \leq 0\}$.
(b) The interval $(0, 1)$.
(c) $\{x \mid x \leq \frac{3}{5}\}$.
(d) $\{x \mid x \leq -1\} \cup \{x \mid x \geq 0\}$.
(e) The interval $[\pi/4, 3\pi/4]$.
(f) $\{x \mid x > \frac{1}{3}\}$.
(g) $\{x \mid x > \sqrt{2}\} \cup \{x \mid -\sqrt{2} < x < 0\}$.

12. (a) Arc sin $0 = 0$; Arc cos $0 = \pi/2$; Arc tan $0 = 0$.
(b) Arc sin $1 = \pi/2$; Arc cos $1 = 0$; Arc tan $1 = \pi/4$.
(c) Arc sin $(-1) = -\pi/2$; Arc cos $(-1) = \pi$; Arc tan $(-1) = -\pi/4$.
(d) Arc sin $(\frac{1}{2}\sqrt{2}) = \pi/4$; Arc cos $(-\frac{1}{2}\sqrt{2}) = 3\pi/4$.
(e) Arc sin $(-\frac{1}{2}) = -\pi/6$; Arc cos $\frac{1}{2} = \pi/3$.
(f) Arc sin $(\frac{1}{2}\sqrt{3}) = \pi/3$; Arc cos $(-\frac{1}{2}\sqrt{3}) = 5\pi/6$.

14. (a) $f^{-1}(x) = \sqrt{\cos^2 x + 1}$, $x \in [\text{Arc cos } \sqrt{3}, \pi/2]$.
(b) $f^{-1}(x) = \frac{1}{2}$ Arc sin $(x - 1)$, $x \in [0, 2]$.
(c) $f^{-1}(x) = $ Arc sin $\big(E_a(x) - 2\big)$, $x \in [0, \log_a 3]$ if $a > 1$, $x \in [\log_a 3, 0]$ if $a < 1$.
(d) $f^{-1}(x) = \log_2 \tan x$.

Chapter 7

1. (a) $7 \cdot 1 + 7 \cdot 2 + 7 \cdot 3 + 7 \cdot 4 + 7 \cdot 5$.

(b) $(5 - \frac{1}{2}) + (6 - \frac{1}{2}) + (7 - \frac{1}{2}) + (8 - \frac{1}{2}) + (9 - \frac{1}{2}) + (10 - \frac{1}{2})$.

(c) $a^1 + a^2 + a^3 + a^4 + a^5 + a^6 + a^7 + a^8$.

(d) $7 + 7 + 7 + 7$.

4. (a) 63. (d) $(\frac{40}{27})$.

(b) 31. (e) $1 - 5^{1-n}$.

(c) 7. (f) $(\frac{5}{8})(5^{n-1} - 1)$.

7. (a) 6. (d) 5.

(b) 6720. (e) $m(m-1)(m-2) \cdots (m-n+3)$.

(c) 10. (f) $(t-1)(t-2)(t-3)(t-4) \cdots \cdot 2 \cdot 1$.

8. 16.

9. 30.

10. 29.

11. 210.

12. 1680.

13. There are 16 possible ways if none of the other players has been dealt a 4 or a 5. If he saw his neighbor discard a 5, and none of the other players has been dealt a 4 or 5, then he has 12 ways of filling his inside straight.

14. (a) (i) 1000. (iii) 0010. (v) 1100. (vii) 1001. (ix) 0101. (xi) 1110. (xiii) 0111. (xv) 1111.

(b) (ii) $\{b, c, d\}$. (iv) $\{a, b, c\}$. (vi) $\{a, d\}$. (viii) $\{a\}$. (x) $\{c\}$. (xii) $\{b, c\}$. (xiv) $\varnothing$. (xvi) $\{a, b, d\}$.

16. 24; 11!.

17. (a) $a^3 - 3a^2b + 3ab^2 - b^3$.

(b) $81x^4 - 108x^3 + 54x^2 - 12x + 1$.

(c) $x^6 - 6x^5 + 15x^4 - 20x^3 + 15x^2 - 6x + 1$.

(d) $x^2 + 6x^{5/3}y^{1/3} + 15x^{4/3}y^{2/3} + 20xy + 15x^{2/3}y^{4/3} + 6x^{1/3}y^{5/3} + y^2$.

(e) $32x^{-5} + 40x^{-3} + 20x^{-1} + 5x + 5x^3/8 + x^5/32$.

(f) $a^6 - 3a^4bx + 3a^2b^2x^2 - b^3x^3 + 3a^4x^2 - 6a^2bx^3 + 3b^2x^4 + 3a^2x^4 - 3bx^5 + x^6$.

18. $2a^4 + 36a^2 + 18$.

19. $116\sqrt{2}$.

21. (a) $-6435x^8$. (b) $240d^4/c^6$. (c) 853,125.

Chapter 8

1. (a) $\{(x, y) \mid y = -(\frac{5}{4})x\}$. (c) $\{(x, y) \mid x = \frac{1}{2}\}$. (e) $\{(x, y) \mid y = x + 10\}$.
(g) $\{(x, y) \mid y = -x\}$. (i) $\{(x, y) \mid y = \pi\}$.

3. (a) $\{(x, y) \mid x = -1\}$. (c) $\{(x, y) \mid x + y = \sqrt{2}\}$. (e) $\{(x, y) \mid y = 0\}$.

9. (a) $\{(x, y) \mid y = 4x - 3\}$. (b) $\{(x, y) \mid x - 5y + 4 = 0\}$.

10. (a) $\{(x, y) \mid x + y + 2 = 0\}$. (b) $\{(x, y) \mid 12x + 4y = 29\}$.

12. (a) $6/\sqrt{2}$. (b) $8/\sqrt{5}$.

14. Vertex: (0, 0); directrix: $\{(x, y) \mid x = -\frac{1}{2}\}$; axis: the x-axis; focus: $(\frac{1}{2}, 0)$.

16. Vertex: (0, 1); directrix: $\{(x, y) \mid y = 0\}$; axis: $\{(x, y) \mid x = 0\}$; focus: (0, 2).

18. Vertex: (0, 2); directrix: $\{(x, y) \mid y = \frac{55}{28}\}$; axis: $\{(x, y) \mid x = 0\}$; focus: $(0, \frac{57}{28})$.

21. $\{(x, y) \mid y^2 = -8x\}$.

23. $\{(x, y) \mid (x + 1)^2 = 12(y - 5)\}$.

30. (a) $(-\frac{1}{2}, \frac{3}{5})$. (c) $(-\frac{1}{2}, \frac{28}{5})$. (e) $(\sqrt{2} - \frac{1}{2}, \frac{11}{10})$.

31. (a) $\{(\bar{x}, \bar{y}) \mid 10\bar{x} - 10\bar{y} + 11 = 0\}$. (c) $\{(\bar{x}, \bar{y}) \mid \bar{x} = \bar{y}\}$.
(e) $\{(\bar{x}, \bar{y}) \mid (\bar{y} - \frac{6}{5})^2 = 4(\bar{x} + 1)\}$.

32. (a) $\{(\bar{x}, \bar{y}) \mid \bar{y} = 0\}$; i.e., the $\bar{x}$-axis.
(c) $\{(\bar{x}, \bar{y}) \mid (1 - 2\sqrt{3})\bar{x}^2 + (3 + 2\sqrt{3})\bar{y}^2 + (2\sqrt{3} - 4)\bar{x}\bar{y}2\sqrt{3}\bar{x} - 2\bar{y} = 28\}$.

Chapter *9

1. (a) $(\frac{3}{2}, 9)$. (c) $(-1, 8)$. (e) $-2 - 4i$. (g) $4 + 23i$. (*i*) 3.

2. (a) (1, 0). (c) $\frac{1}{2} + \frac{1}{2}i$. (e) $-\frac{1}{2}i$.

3. (a) $1 + 0i$.
(b) $7 + 2i$.
(c) $2 + 4i$.
(d) $0 + (-1)i$.
(e) $1 + (-\frac{1}{2})i$.
(f) $-(9/595) - (75/595)i$.

4. (a) $-\frac{9}{5} + (\frac{7}{5})i$.
(b) $7 - i$.
(c) $\sqrt{2}i; -\sqrt{2}i$.
(d) $\frac{1}{2}\sqrt{2} - \frac{1}{2}\sqrt{2}i$.

8. (a) $\frac{1}{2}\sqrt{2}(\cos \pi/4 + i \sin \pi/4)$.
(b) $\frac{1}{2}\sqrt{2}(\cos(-\pi/4) + i \sin(-\pi/4))$.
(c) $-7\sqrt{2}(\cos(-\pi/4) + i \sin(-\pi/4))$.
(d) $2(\cos 0 + i \sin 0)$.
(e) $2(\cos \pi/2 + i \sin \pi/2)$.
(f) $0 \cdot (\cos \pi + i \sin \pi)$.

(g) $-4(\cos \pi/3 + i \sin \pi/3)$.

(h) $2(\cos \pi/3 + i \sin \pi/3)$.

(i) $2(\cos(-\pi/6) + i \sin(-\pi/6))$.

9. (b) $-\frac{1}{8}$. (c) -1024. (d) $-512(1 - i)$.

10. (a) $i, -i$. (b) $\sqrt[4]{2}i$. (c) $\sqrt{7}i$. (d) $2i$. (e) $\sqrt{|d|}\,i$.

12. (a) $-\frac{1}{2} \pm \frac{1}{2}\sqrt{3}i$. (c) $-1 \pm i$. (e) $\frac{1}{4} \pm \frac{1}{4}\sqrt{7}i$.

13. (a) $1, \cos(2\pi/3) + i \sin(2\pi/3), \cos(4\pi/3) + i \sin(4\pi/3)$.

(c) $2^{1/4}(\cos(-\pi/8) + i \sin(-\pi/8)), 2^{1/4}(\cos(7\pi/8) + i \sin(7\pi/8))$.

Index

Index